Patterns or Principles
and
Other Essays

By the same author

Les tendances nouvelles de l'ecclésiologie

The Relevance of Physics

Brain, Mind and Computers
(Lecomte du Nouy Prize, 1970)

The Paradox of Olbers' Paradox

The Milky Way: An Elusive Road for Science

*Science and Creation: From Eternal Cycles
to an Oscillating Universe*

*Planets and Planetarians: A History of Theories
of the Origin of Planetary Systems*

The Road of Science and the Ways to God
(Gifford Lectures: University of Edinburgh, 1975 and 1976)

The Origin of Science and the Science of its Origin
(Fremantle Lectures, Oxford, 1977)

*And on This Rock: The Witness of One Land
and Two Covenants*

Cosmos and Creator

Angels, Apes and Men

Uneasy Genius: The Life and Work of Pierre Duhem

Chesterton: A Seer of Science

The Keys of the Kingdom: A Tool's Witness to Truth

Lord Gifford and His Lectures: A Centenary Retrospect

Chance or Reality and Other Essays

(continued on p. [236])

Stanley L. Jaki

Patterns or Principles

and Other Essays

Intercollegiate Studies Institute
Wilmington, Delaware

ISBN: 1-882926-09-9

Library of Congress Cataloguing-in-Publication Data

Jaki, Stanley L.
Patterns or principles and other essays/Stanley L. Jaki

Includes bibliographical references and index.
1. Science and jurisprudence. 2. Physics versus scientism—Cultural aspects.
3. Ecologism. 4. Christianity and science.
5. Brain-mind relationship. 6. M. Foster. 7. E. Gilson.

Library of Congress Catalog Card Number
95-081661

Intercollegiate Studies Institute
P.O. Box 4431
Wilmington, Delaware

Cover design by Glenn Pierce

Printed in the United States of America

CONTENTS

Introduction

Almost half a century has gone by since there appeared in *Foreign Affairs* an article, signed by Mr. X, whose identity was an open secret. In that article George F. Kennan outlined the policy of containment to counter Soviet expansionism. About the overriding need for that policy there could be no doubt. Still, writing that article could not come easily to Kennan. He and other liberals had found nothing strange in Roosevelt's assurances that America could very well live with Uncle Joe. In their perception, democracy was not so much a system of principles as a pattern of social activities. But the very nature of pattern is to be variable. Therefore all those who identified democracy not so much with principles as with patterns of living could readily bring themselves to seeing in communism just another variety of democracy. They were the ones who found it natural to hail revolutionary leaders as innocent agricultural reformers as long as their own pocketbooks and portfolios were not hit directly.

They themselves were, of course, bent on reforming, or rather deforming, whatever legal and social structure still smacked of principles. Today, this process is taking on the character of an apparently runaway process, though under, as one would expect, some atttractive label. The label is culture. It is increasingly recognized that the major facet of the coming century will be a grim confrontation among major cultures. It is even recognized that cultures have something to do with cult, that is, religion. But religion is tolerated only as a variable pattern of behavior and not as a depository of unchangeable truths and principles.

Thus while it is acknowledged that secularism did not prevail over religion, religions are subsumed under the heading of behavioral patterns with no substantive differences among them. Worse, all kinds of patterns of behavior, however unprincipled, are gaining legal recognition. This development goes far deeper than mere politics. Fueling it is a new kind of thinking, which wants to have its supreme justification from science. Science, at least on the face of it, deals only with data, with patterns, with statistical configurations. They all are variable and all can be modified. Not one of them is intrinsically better than any other. Relativism, so that thinking goes, can and ought to rule supreme all across the social spectrum.

It is this frightening trend and its pseudoscientific roots that are dealt with in these essays in a wide variety of perspectives. The evidence they contain ought not to be taken lightly by that overwhelming majority of conservative activists who are not scientifically trained. For the most part they are busy in the political arena and the market place. There it is fully well known that in order to sell one's wares, they must be attractively wrapped. Next to sport and sex, science is such a wrapper, or rather slogans with scientific flavor.

Yet, whatever their innocence of science proper, conservatives live in an age which becomes more and more scientific with every passing year. What is even more significant, this age of ours has already its thinking conditioned by profuse references to science, or rather to an ideology grafted on it.

The most explicitly scientific of those references are the easiest to deal with. Far more slippery are the presuppositions that are scientific only in a broad sense. Of these none is so pervasive as the idea of pattern. It should be seen for what it is, if one is to counter it effectively with principles. For only principles can conserve the kind of patterns that alone are worth living.

S.L.J.

1

Patterns or Principles:
The Pseudoscientific Roots of
Law's Debacle

Those whom history venerates as spokesmen of an age often cannot perceive the full implications of their words. Such a seer was Voltaire as he offered one of his best though rarely quoted bits of advice. He addressed it to those among his fellow *philosophes* who played with *allegro con brio* their tunes of atheism. They did not heed Voltaire's warning that they should keep their music to themselves, lest one day the populace take their cue and bang their instruments against their heads.[1] Something far worse than mere headbanging was to come. The euphoria of the Constitutional Convention quickly yielded to the convulsions of the Terror. The heads of not a few *philosophes* were sliced off with a guillotine driven by a maddening devotion to justice for all, a specious cover-up for law's debacle. It was at that time that a proponent of that total

---

Based on an address to the Thomas More Society of Harvard Law School, November 14, 1991, first published in *The American Journal of Jurisprudence* 38 (1993), pp. 135-57. Reprinted with permission.

justice declared his faith "in the infallibility of the people."[2] *Some* did indeed succeed in setting themselves up as the true and only "people" at the exclusion of many of their fellow citizens. They also expropriated the true interpretation of law to themselves without being really interested in truth itself. Napoleon had to come so that some legal order be restored.

Today a similar debacle may be in store. Law as truth is being handled in a cavalier manner and some "people" seem to count more as people than others do. Nor are the bloody touches of terror absent, although plenty of antiseptic is on hand. With reference to abortion a vast chorus of legal gurus claim justice for all, at the exclusion of the unborn, of course. They are eager to create the impression that the consensus of the people, which they take for truth incarnate, is behind them. They even speak of justice within that transparently dubious perspective that since the consensus is fragmented, no legal barriers should be set up against those chiefly responsible for the fragmentation. Full legal protection is assured for those who broke away from the consensus and want to break it down completely so that their view may be imposed as the new consensus. In doing so, they hasten the coming of law's debacle despite their professed aim to promote justice for all.

To cover inconsistencies in their approaches, the word justice is invariably invoked. That only a mere word, instead of substantive justice, is on hand in such cases, has many illustrations. They often grace the op-ed page of the *The New York Times*. A case in point is the argument, set forth there in September 1991, of Craig R. Dean, a lawyer and executive director of Equal Marriage Rights Fund, that gay marriages be given full legal recognition. Referring to the laws against mixed racial marriages struck down in 1967 by the Supreme Court in *Loving vs Virginia* Dean observed: "Then, as now, those who argued against granting civil rights spoke of morality, social tensions and protection of family values. But, now, as then, the real issue is justice vs. oppression."[3] Mr. Dean left the readers to ponder what he really meant by justice. He, of course, could not mean justice as something objective. In that case, he would have been confronted with objective standards of justice in the form of the question whether an act (or a state of life) is intrinsically good or wrong in a moral sense transcending the question of mere legality.

The moral acceptability of gay marriage, of polygamic liaisons, and of megafamilies can only be argued on a purely subjective ground, namely, that those who wish to embrace such states of life are entitled to their subjective satisfaction. Homosexuality too can be supported only on such subjective grounds and this holds for abortion as well. The legalization of all personal preferences will, however, promote the debacle of law by demoting objective morality. In that debacle we shall witness countless laws locked in a life-and-death struggle from which only lawyers will draw profits, just as merchants of armaments benefit most from wars. The justice to be served will ultimately be a matter of skill with legal technicalities. There the winner will be the one who can afford the skyrocketing costs of hiring the lawyer better renowned for his legal skills than for his upright character.

I am not suggesting that Justice Oliver Wendell Holmes wished this to happen, when in 1918, in the pages of the *Harvard Law Review*, he delivered a broadside against natural law and crowned it with the remark: "I see no reason for attributing to man a significance different in kind from that which belongs to a baboon or a grain of sand."[4] Perhaps Justice Holmes did not see the legal debacle he thereby advocated, although his private correspondence suggests otherwise. In the wake of World War I, Holmes wrote to his lifelong friend, Sir Frederick Pollock, who was drumming up support for the League of Nations as an international force to prevent a similar world conflagration:

> Man at present is a predatory animal. I think the sacredness of human life is a purely municipal ideal of no validity outside the jurisdiction. I believe that force, mitigated so far as may be by good manners, is the *ultima ratio*, and between two groups that want to make inconsistent kinds of world I see no remedy except force. I may add what I no doubt have said often enough, that it seems to me that every society rests on the death of men—as does also the romantic interest of long inhabited lands.[5]

The ring of a rude and crude Darwinism is unmistakable, muffled though it is with an urbane diction. We are indeed at the time of Aldous Huxley's early manhood when he and his equally urbane friends eagerly espoused Darwin's theory as a justification for looking on life as lawlessly meaningless and therefore to be lived according to one's whims:

> For myself as, no doubt, to most of my contemporaries, the philosophy of meaninglessness was essentially an instrument of liberation. The liberation we desired was simultaneously liberation from a certain political and economic system and from a certain system of morality. We objected to the morality because it interfered with our sexual freedom; we objected to the political and economic system because it was unjust. The supporters of these systems claimed that in some way they embodied the meaning (a Christian meaning they insisted) of the world. There was one admirably simple method of confuting these people and at the same time justifying ourselves in our political and erotic revolt: we could deny that the world had any meaning whatsoever.[6]

What is significant in this revealing message is not so much the invocation of Darwinian science, as the fact that Aldous Huxley and his intellectual and academic confrères wanted their liberation while counting on the full and continued protection of the law as something meaningful. Before long the law itself was made meaningless by having been rewritten so that only the Party might remain free in order to deprive all the rest of due process. To accomplish this Darwinism was heavily invoked in Nazi Germany as well as in Soviet Russia and in Maoist China. A hundred years ago captains of industry in the United States eagerly referred to Darwin as the justification of ruthless economic competition aimed at allowing one to go from rags to riches almost overnight.[7] Today in the West the debacle of law is carried out by a piecemeal process, a performance more in tune with Darwin's idea that the shift from one species to another ought to be an imperceptibly slow affair.

Darwinism as an ideology is undoubtedly the chief and most visible of the pseudoscientific roots of law's debacle, roots that are pushing above the ground under our very eyes. For it is not so much as science than as ideology that Darwinism sets the tone of our culture, including its sector of jurisprudence. Not that Darwinism as a science would be a much more wholesome proposition: Darwinist evolutionary theory is full of holes, some of which, though obvious, are regularly covered up by its chief authorities. This was made crystal clear in Niles Eldridge's devastating indictment of his and his fellow paleontologists' posture during the last four or five decades:

> We have preferred a collective tacit acceptance of the story of gradual adaptive change, a story that strengthened and became

even more entrenched as the [neo-Darwinian] synthesis took hold. We paleontologists have said that the history of life supports this interpretation, all the while really knowing it does not.[8]

Quite recently we have witnessed the similar exposure of another pillar of Darwinism, namely, the standard theory about the origin of life, a theory first proposed in the early 1950's by Stanley Miller. Here, however, we still have to wait for something more than the admission that "the uncertainties clouding the origin of life remain formidable."[9] Still to be heard is the confession, preferably a repentant one, about the unconscionable character of assurances that have come from the scientific community since those experiments of Miller. For, clearly, the uncertainties clouding the origin of life can remain formidable only if they always have been such. And if they have been formidable, then they must have always been known by all those who held themselves to be sharp-eyed scientists, or even scientists with less than 20/20 vision.

In reporting about these holes in the texture of Darwinism one runs the risk of being branded not only an anti-evolutionist, a capital offense in itself, but what is worse, a plain obscurantist. One does not become accepted by the scientific community by holding merely that the various forms of life, be they called species or not, are instrumental in the rise of one another. It is branded as unscientific to hold that scientific reasons are insufficient to justify that instrumentality which should appear particularly mysterious against the background of the periodic extinctions of much of the biosphere. Apart from that it remains for Darwinists a perennial puzzle why a purely physical evolution should issue in beings who can reason, and at a metaphysical level, and convince themselves about that instrumentality without seeing it.

Some of these metaphysical supports of evolutionary theory were partially visible in Darwin's *Origin of Species*. They are the uniformity of nature, and the wonderful properties with which matter is endowed. In his last years Darwin resented that, in order to cater to the public, he credited those wonderful properties to the act of the Creator. He did not take seriously the remark of Harvard's Agassiz that to see a species takes more than the eyes of a biologist.[10] Not that Agassiz had strong enough metaphysical eyes for the ground on which alone one can assign some reality to universals, such as plant and animal species. Darwin, however, thought that philosophy, of which he knew precious little, had once and for all disposed of the question of universals. He felt that it was enough to warn now and then that the word chance cannot mean the absence of cause. But it is interesting to note that he fell back on that word whenever he could not ascertain the causes of stunning patterns, processes, and adaptations for which he had marvelously sharp eyes.[11]

Darwin's gravest and most unforgivable failure in reasoning related to the fundamental question and reality of human experience: one's awareness of acting for a purpose and of one's unquenchable search for an ultimate purpose. The failure of Darwin and of all Darwinists to come clean on this point found its best exposure in Princeton in 1929 in a phrase of Whitehead's Vanuxem Lectures: "Those who devote their whole life to the purpose of proving that there is no purpose, constitute an interesting subject for study."[12] I wonder whether anyone ever will find a more appropriate motto to be carved over the entrance of departments of biology or paleontology whether in Princeton, or in Cambridge, or in Woodshole, or anywhere else.

But the same motto might no less appropriately grace the entrances of many a law school as well, though not because in any of them special courses have ever been offered on Darwinist evolution. The latter is the kind of science which everybody seems to understand without the need of hard study. It has ever been a science that quickly formed a climate of opinion to be breathed in by everybody as if no careful tinking was to be done about it. Thus lawyers, law professors, legislators and judges—all too often overburdened—could feel free to fall back on Darwinism without subjecting it to a thorough cross-examination. Hence the fumbling of courts with the demands of creationists that their views be taught side by side with Darwin. The courts sided with Darwin though invariably for the wrong reasons. They failed to see the intellectual holes of Darwinism and much less the fact that those holes can only be made bigger by complementing them with creationism. Had lawyers and judges applied to Darwinism their specialty, which is to sift the evidence through thorough cross examination, they might have made themselves reliable guides on Darwin and Darwinism. This indeed happened when Norman Macbeth, a trial lawyer by profession, paged through his daughter's college textbook on biology and decided to leave no stone unturned. The result was a book, *Darwin Retried*, which would have done credit to any better-grade philosopher and historian of science. The book was published in Boston in 1971 by the publisher, Gambit Incorporated, and one can only wish for the publication of many more such gambits.[13]

In 1971 ecology was still a largely ivory-tower concern and few took seriously those who drew the final implications of Darwinism, namely, that no species is worthier than any other species. Darwin in fact had as a motto the words: "Never say 'higher' or 'lower'!"[14] Not surprisingly, in this respect too he failed to be consistent. A hundred years later in more than one case carried to higher courts, and even to the Supreme Court, the pseudoscience of specieism is the chief support of the unenlightened fight against the rightful interests of *homo sapiens.*

It now remains to recall briefly other pseudo-scientific roots that, though less visible in legal literature, exert a great influence on those who in their strange way of advocating justice are actually inviting law's debacle. Relativity theory should be mentioned first. Contrary to its name, it is the most absolutist of all physical theories ever proposed in the history of physics.[15] Einstein himself agreed, in 1921, with the remark of a friend of his, that relativity should have been called the theory of invariance.[16] One can only speculate about the course of 20th-century culture if prominent physicists had kept reminding the public that there are absolutes in the physical world as well as in that most exact form of science which is physics. By and large physicists failed to do so. A result is the brashness with which advertisers exploit the gross misinterpretations which physicists have allowed. Thus around the centenary of Einstein's birth, *Time* came out with a full-page advertisement of which the upper half was a photo of Einstein's pensive face. Under it was the line in bold-face letters: EVERYTHING IS RELATIVE. To make matters worse this was followed by the declaration: "In the cool, beautiful language of mathematics, Einstein demonstrated that we live in a world of relative values."[17]

I have recalled this partly in order to spark the interest of a law student in writing a paper, perhaps a thesis, on the science of relativity and the relativization of law. The subject has already been researched with respect to literature, psychology, political science, arts, and philosophy.[18] The literature of jurisprudence provides some eye-opening evidence whose systematic study would, I am sure, well pay the effort. Here let me recall but two salient cases, salient also in the sense that the exploitation of relativity theory on behalf of legal relativism blares forth from the very start.

In 1948 H. Kelsen wrote an essay in 1948 on "Absolutism and Relativism in Philosophy and Politics." There he denounced "philosophical absolutism" or "the metaphysical view that there is an absolute reality, i.e., a reality that exists independently of human knowledge." He further argued that "tolerance, minority rights, freedom of speech, and freedom of thought, so characteristic of democracy, have no place within a political system based on the belief in absolute values." That belief, he concluded, "irresistibly leads—and always has led—to a situtation in which the one who assumes to possess the secret of the absolute good claims to have the right to impose his opinion as well as his will upon the others who are in error. And to be in error is, according to this view, to be wrong, and hence punishable."[19]

Four decades later Professor Laurence H. Tribe regaled the legal world with an essay, entitled, "The Curvature of Constitutional Space: What Lawyers Can Learn from Modern Physics."[20] To be sure, he was not unmindful of the possibility that the essay would seem to contradict some earlier papers of his, one of them carrying the title "Seven Deadly Sins of Straining the Constitution through a Pseudo-scientific Sieve."[21] But he protested too much and also on a patently wrong ground. He simply accepted the operationist view of science: "Science is not so much about proving as it is about *im*proving. To look to the natural science for authority—that is for certainty—is to look for what is not there."[22]

There is plenty of certainty in science and physics in particular. Can we not be certain that there are atoms, that the earth is a slightly flattened sphere, and that the moon revolves on its axis? Can we not be certain about the second law of thermodynamics, or about the inverse square law of gravitation? Should Maxwell's laws of electro-dynamics be tested every day anew as if they were not certain? Is there anything uncertain about the natural frequency at which various atoms radiate? Are we the victims of our imagination in thinking that our galaxy resembles a huge spiral? With such questions one could fill almost an encyclopedic volume.

There are, of course, uncertainties in science and of a far more serious nature than Professor Tribe seems to think. And those uncertainties arise largely because quite a few scientists fail to realize that certainty is a philosophical issue in ultimate analysis. Philosophy in turn is more than logic. Logic may impose the inference that if there are undulations, or waves, there has to be something which undulates. But to assert on such a basis the reality of the ether, as was done by classical physicists, illustrates that aspect of logic which is going wrong with confidence. Through that aspect, logic becomes different from philosophy or the love of wisdom. Modern physicists are equally wrong in thinking that just because they could not measure the speed of the earth with respect to the ether, the latter does not exist. Existence, reality, are parameters that cannot be handled by science. Scientists must assume the reality of their instruments before they can consistently use them for the sole purpose of science. This is to investigate the quantitative properties of things whose existence science must assume. Science assumes reality, instead of providing it, while the quantitative properties of that reality are investigated.

Professor Tribe would not have written his article if he had had such a view about the relation of science to reality. For within such a view science has no relevance for the task of improving our understanding of the law. To his credit he spelled out at a fairly early stage two attainments of modern physics that would, allegedly, provide such improvements. One was the tenet of general relativity that the physical universe can only be explained if one assumes that bodies like "stars and planets *change* the space around them—they literally 'warp' it—so that their effet is both complex and interactive." The other came from quantum mechanics according to which "the very process of observation and analysis can fundamentally alter the things being observed, and can change how they will behave thereafter."[23]

The legal wisdom which Professor Tribe tried to distill from these two points was that judges should develop a keen social consciousness. Whether our Supreme Court, whose non-liberal faction has been the regular target of Professor Tribe's barbs, would improve its social sense by delving into modern physics, is a topic that even some Freudian psychologists might be unwilling to explore, whatever their readiness to delve into the most recondite recesses of the ego. Professor Tribe, though not a physicist, has an undergraduate degree in mathematics that would have enabled him to delve into better-grade physics textbooks. But that would not have helped him to find emphasized in them the point that relativity, especially general relativity, is the most absolutist form of physics ever proposed. Suffice it to recall the invariable measure of the speed of light, a measure independent of the motion of source, of the speed of the detectors, and of the reference systems as well.

Authors of physics textbooks do not emphasize this point, which is simply shoved under the rug by leading philosophers of science. They do so because their philosophies, very unscientific, are incompatible with the specter of the absolute, be it a mere physical one. And the point is still to be perceived by the most important of those whom Professor Tribe consulted among his colleagues at Harvard on Einstein.[24] Professor Tribe's perorations about the not-so-absolute absolutes should seem a very sorry affair against at least the science of general relativity, together with its absolute reference system embodied in the expansion of the universe.

No different is the case with Professor Tribe's exploitation of general relativity on behalf of his claims about social context of law as influencing the law itself. He is, of course, not to be blamed overly on that score. One would try in vain to find among the chief interpreters of general relativity those with sufficiently long memory about a strange development of the meaning of space as used by them. First they looked askance at space as the mythical entity filled with the ether. Then they condoned the use of the word as standing for the network of permissible paths of motion, the only reasonable meaning which space can have in general relativity. But before long that network began to be reified together with its "warps" and "bends." In other words, space was equated with the gravitational field as produced by matter. But since that field exists only inasmuch as it is generated by matter, only the kind of logic that legitimizes the trick whereby one lifts oneself by one's bootstraps will entitle one to view that field as having a reaction properly so-called on the matter that generated it in the first place. Warps of space-time should not be taken for the justification of warped thinking where the cart can readily be put before the horse.

As to quantum mechanics, it is inapplicable on the macro- or human level where law is applied. There the difference between the physics of Newton and the physics of Heisenberg is zero for all practical purposes. This is what is meant by the so-called correspondence principle first formulated by Niels Bohr. Contrary to Professor Tribe's claim, Heisenberg's principle may *not* "be applied successfully beyond the micro-level of quantum mechanics."[25]

The application of quantum mechanics by scientific cosmologists, as mentioned by Professor Tribe, would be very much against the perspectives of his legal philosophy and is also beside the point—beside the point because their applications are basically mistaken. They rest on the *non-sequitur*, voiced by Heisenberg as early as 1927, that an interaction that cannot be measured exactly, cannot take place exactly. The *non-sequitur* is the jump from the operational to the ontological— a fateful jump indeed, because if its bearing is extended from the level of alpha-particle emission from radioactive atoms to the universe itself, it enables the physicist to create entire universes out of nothing by his mere *fiat*.[26] It is hardly this imperiousness, and at times plain haughtiness, that Professor Tribe presumably wants our Supreme Court Justices to imbibe from modern physics. It is another matter whether lawyers and some law professors, with a socialist agenda, would not welcome the return of an imperial president who would fill the Supreme Court with subservient justices. It is an old story that professed liberals are apt to outdo dyed-in-the wool conservatives in illiberality and intolerance.

Or should those justices learn from modern physicists to speak from both corners of the mouth? Should they learn to imitate the ambivalence of physicists who take the wave theory of light on Mondays, Wednesdays, and Fridays, whereas they endorse the particle theory on Tuesdays, Thursdays and Saturdays? Then, of course, it would be justifiable to practice one's opposition to nominees to the Supreme Court on two very different grounds: to oppose Bork because his advocacy of positive law would pose a threat to the Bill of Rights and to oppose Thomas because he espouses natural law. But can the Bill of Rights be threatened by the former nominee's legal philosophy if the Bill of Rights cannot be taken for an embodiment of natural law?

Clearly, if the wave-particle duality of light (and matter) is not to foment radical inconsistency during the weekdays, Sunday should be spent in that form of minimal worship which consists in serious philosophical reflection. Unfortunately, eminent physicists have been responsible for the widely shared illusion that common sense can be given extended holidays. As a result they fomented a far-reaching delusion. They did so by presenting the science of quantum mechanics as a justification for their claim that the study of the complementary aspects of physical reality dispenses with the question whether there is a physical reality in the first place. The systematic and studied oversight of this question leads to thinking that reality is not something which has its own laws which are valid regardless of what is thought of those laws at this or that stage of physics. In a more graphic form the delusion implies that one can speak of the two cheeks of one's face, but one can safely forget about the face, and even about the head in which those cheeks are embedded and without which they make no sense. Pseudophilosophy can indeed reach some cheeky heights where abysses wait for the unwary.[27]

A no less abysmal form of that delusion is the belief that one can readily talk from both corners of the mouth and still appear learned if not reasonable. This belief gained much strength from the interpretation which Bohr gave to the motto in his coat-of-arms, *complementaria non sunt contradictoria*. The motto has become a glorified red-herring aimed at distracting from questions of ontology—not, of course, of that ontology which has now for over forty years found a prominent forum at Harvard. I mean the chair of Professor Quine who, in his very words, "persistently held" that "to be is to be the value of a variable."[28] Compared with this fumbling with existence, the ever fumbling Hamlet should appear a philosophical genius as he called "to be or not to be" the question of questions.

Mere reflection on Hamlet's words, or rather on the insight of that great literary man, Shakespeare, who never for a moment tried to appear scientific, can reveal that "being" is not a variable. A variation is on hand when one can freely move from one aspect of the thing or reality under consideration to any other aspect of it as if the two aspects were merely two variations of one aspect. This process is on hand whenever in physics, or in mathematics, for that matter, one speaks of variables. One's freedom there to choose one's variables is practically unlimited. There is no such freedom with respect to being. Non-existence is not a variation on existence. Nor is freedom a variety of enslavement. And certainly, one is not free to come into being. But since life is a gift, one is not morally free to part with it. Only on such grounds can doctors be prosecuted who, in order to satisfy personal wishes, provide means that enable one to die painlessly.

Less needs to be said about another aspect of the Copenhagen interpretation of quantum mechanics. It is the claim, made in the name of Heisenberg's uncertainty principle, that at the very fundamental level of nature, everything is random, that is, uncaused. This claim has taken many victims who should have known better. One of them is that certainly anti-reductionist philosopher-scientist, Michael Polanyi, an authority quoted by Professor Tribe. Polanyi blissfully fell into the trap of equivocation which is the backbone of the inference that an interaction that cannot be measured exactly cannot take place exactly.[29] The equivocation is the heedless advance from the operational to the ontological. Thus we find Polanyi endorse, in his *The Tacit Dimension*, the idea of events that happen without a cause.[30]

How can this affect thinking about jurisprudence? In principle the connection should be obvious to anyone who knows a little Greek and spots a Greek-English word lurking behind the word "uncaused". The word in question is *an-archē* which means lack of cause. The word in English is best known as anarchy. The subtle impact of this on jurisprudence may be best illustrated from a letter which a historian of science, L. Peirce Williams of Cornell, wrote to *The New York Times* at a time when civil disobedience had its sway on our campuses. If, in writing his letter, Professor Williams had thought of the pseudoscientific roots of the attitude he was to criticize, he most likely would have thought only of the misinterpretation of relativity theory and not of quantum theory. Yet the gist of what he wrote had a deeper connection with the latter than with the former. His immediate aim was to defend a colleague of his, Donald Kagan, who criticized the protesters for failing to provide a sound basis for their disobeying the law:

> What Kagan, I think, was arguing, was that there is no 'moral' universe to which citizens can now appeal that provides an adequate basis for disobedience to the law. I find it strange that liberals, who insist upon the ultimate relativism of all moral values, suddenly appeal to a 'higher' morality (which they are careful not to define) when it suits them. All that went out with the Victorians, and we now inhabit a society in which all moral opinions seem equally valid. . . . The point, of course, as Kagan clearly stated, is that we live in a consensual society in which we often have to do things we don't want to do, or even think are wrong, because we have agreed to abide by majority rule. Destroy that argument, and the result is not freedom but anarchy—a condition which the United States seems rapidly approaching.[31]

What is going to happen to a consensual society when its consensus is visibly fragmenting? What is going to happen to that society when its center, to paraphrase Yeats, holds no longer? For the center should

seem to be disappearing in the measure in which credence is given
to an argument offered in connection with the Thomas-Hill hearing.
Orlando Patterson, Professor of Sociology at Harvard, was not the
only one to think that Mr. Thomas lied as he denied having made
sexual advances to Anita Hill. Professor Patterson may even count on
many who in private would agree with his suggestion that lying in
Court should be admissible "on the moral grounds that any admission
[of such advances by Clarence Thomas] would have immediately
incurred a self-destructive and grossly unfair punishment."[32]

Such resolution of the case is surely an invitation to anarchy. For
what is anarchy if not a total breakdown of law? But this was
precisely the point made by Lewis M. Branscombe, Albert Pratt
Public Service Professor at John F. Kennedy School of Government:
"If we are each allowed to lie under oath whenever we feel the
punishment excessive, a total breakdown in social comity is not far
behind. If this behavior is condoned from Supreme Court nominees,
the last vestige of the public's confidence in its democratic institutions will soon be shredded away."[33] Such are courageous words,
though not sufficiently so. For the true issue is not whether Mr.
Thomas had lied or not. The true issue is the facing up to the
question which is the greater of two crimes: the crime itself or the
pseudosophicated argument that the crime is not crime in ultimate
analysis? Or even more concretely, who are the greater criminals?
Those who commit crimes or those who offer specious arguments
that there are neither criminals nor crimes but only symptoms of
sickness and sick people? As long as these questions are not
answered directly and honestly, anarchy will be waiting in the wings.

Intellectual intimations that anarchy is the only stance justifiable
are gaining ever fresh support from highest-level science populariza-
tion written by most eminent scientists. Such is Professor Roger
Penrose's book, *The Emperor's New Mind*, a much-applauded effort
to save the mind from the teeth of physicalism and computer theory.
What Professor Penrose actually does is to turn that mind into the
prey of what he calls a radically probabilistic or quantized form of
physics as the mind's sole explanation. Unfortunately that physics is
so esoteric that even Professor Penrose, winner of the Wolf-Prize in
mathematics, is unable to say anything specific about it.[34]

Let me conclude my survey of the pseudophilosophical roots of
law's debacle with a less esoteric though no less insidious kind of it
which, though already a hundred years old, is still very much alive.

I mean positivism. I do not mean its philosophical form, but as it flourishes in physical science as its interpretation. Positivistic physics is the idea that the physicist's sole task is to collect his data and arrange them into patterns that appear to be most economical in dealing with them. According to that idea the work of the physicist has nothing to do with reality. Therefore he is free to rearrange his data into any form or pattern which he calls laws only for convenience's sake.

The putting of patterns, or mere configurations of data, expressed in quantitative or mathematical forms, on the highest pedestal of science may seem more revealing if one considers the principal way in which physicists nowadays collect and classify their data. The way is statistical. For the statistical method is the very soul of that quantum mechanics which has achieved phenomenal successes in the investigation of the atomic and subatomic world. It can therefore but encourage those, sociologists and psychologists, who for some time relied on the statistical method as the sole means of giving their field the aura of exact science. The advent of desk-top computers further fueled this infatuation with the statistical method. It claimed as one of its early victims a prominent American historian, who argued that unless the voting record of all members of Congress from 1825 until 1859 were fed into a computer we would never understand the real reason for the Civil War.[35]

Clearly, if science is the kind of uncertainty which is statistics, then science, in the name of which everything can be sold and justified nowadays, should seem to favor neither those who hold high natural law nor those who are known as positivists, but the conventionalists. Conventions can best be ascertained by taking opinion polls which are insidiously encroaching on the voting booths. Through opinion polls one can also easily establish whether a new-fangled behavior is being acted out by a statistically significant number of people. Such a number will then serve an agenda for further modification of existing laws, for further decisions to be made by the Supreme Court to satisfy practically everyone's whims and fancy. Such is the road, a pseudo-scientifically coated road, toward law's debacle which is taking patterns, statistically ascertainable patterns of behavior, for so many principles.

We have thus come to the main title of this essay. Though rather abstract, this title contains a word, "pattern," which is a concrete gem in English and not easily translatable into other languages. I learned this when the Italian translator of my books, *God and the Cosmologists* and *The Purpose of it All*, tried to cope with my fondness for that word.[36] As a historian and philosopher of science I have found the word "pattern" very expressive to convey the idea of configurations either in the physical or in the biological realm, all of which indicate that nature is very much limited to a relatively few among a practically infinite number of possibilities.

The richness of the meaning of the word "pattern" is conveyed by looking even at one-volume dictionaries of the English language. In *Webster's II New Riverside University Dictionary* one finds ten different meanings of "pattern." They cover a wide range of human experience or reflection. The first seven meanings are as follows: archetype; an ideal worthy of imitation; a plan, or diagram, or model to be followed in making things; a representative sample; a design, which in turn can be either of artistic or natural, or of accidental origin; a composite of traits of features characteristic of an individual, such as emotional patterns; form or style in an artistic work. The last three meanings are of interest because of their bearing on military, media, and garment technology. Thus the configuration of identically aimed shots on a target is a pattern and so is the ordered flight path of an aircraft. The standardized diagram of a pattern transmitted to test television picture quality is called a pattern and so is the material needed to make a complete garment.

On reading this list I was surprised that no reference was made to possibly the most significant use of the word, in the form of behavioral patterns. My greatest surprise came, however, on seeing the word derived from the middle-English "patron" which came from its old-French equivalent. However, as I have already hinted before, neither in French nor in the other Romance languages, had the word "patron" developed in the direction of what is meant in English by pattern.

The provenance of the word "pattern" from "patron" easily leads us to the second word in the main title of this essay, principles. Principles have something to do with princes, or rulers. In English, a patron can be a customer who thinks he sets the rules of transaction, whereas all too often he is at the mercy of highly developed patterns of sale-tactics. Just think of the expression, custom-tailored. It may mean a suit tailored to individual specification, or simply that it was tailored with a little more care than usual to suit a large number of people.

History has taught us that to be ruled by princes is at best a mixed blessing. But history is rich in evidence that unless people are ruled by principles they are bound to disintegrate. Disintegration is to gather speed if we fail to keep in mind that science delivers only patterns but no principles. Here too history should help. A century and a half ago, when belief in progress was at its intoxicating zenith, Herbert Spencer assured the world that thorough scientific education would automatically eliminate crime.[37] Since then science and scientific education have seen an explosive growth and so has crime.

During the same period of time science has been invoked with ever greater frequency in our courts. All too often the net result is a hung jury and perplexed judges. All too often what happens is something similar to what President Kennedy found after consulting on ABM two chief experts, Jerome Wiesner, his own scientific adviser, and Edward Teller. After finding that the two perfectly contradicted one another, Kennedy quipped: "Now I am absolutely free to do whatever I want to do."[38] The farce threatening the courts by their eager reliance on scientific experts has recently found its best journalistic expression in a full page advertisement in *The New York Times*. It shows a pig with wings over two lines in large type: "In a courtroom anything will fly if a scientist testifies to it."[39]

Such is another aspect of law's debacle. For an antidote against this let me recall the experience of a friend of mine, a former Federal Judge, who once was saddled with an extremely complicated technical case of copyrights violation in TV electronics. Perplexed with the scientific part of the case, he asked me about the meaning of some technical terms. After he had presented his ruling in a lengthy report, which met with applause from every side, we met again. He thanked me for my help, but added: "Ultimately, it became clear to me that only common sense gave me sure guidance in a matter about which technically I could understand very little."[40]

By common sense he meant, of course, not that *ersatz* of it which is common opinion, a commodity as shifting as quicksand in this age of canned information. The common sense he had in mind was precisely that sense which made sense because of its being rooted in principles. That sense is more than that parody of reason which inspired some mad projects of the Enlightenment aiming at full rationality and justice. The madness even implied the scientific reorganization of the Courts. On finding that the chance was 1/150,000 for a mailboat to capsize on its route from Calais to Dover,

Condorcet calculated that miscarriage of justice would occur with the same probability in a court consisting of thirty judges each of which made one wrong decision out of ten. If people were willing to live with the former hazard, so Condorcet argued, they should find the latter acceptable as well.[41] What Condorcet did not calculate was whether judges made wrong decisions only because they were not in full possession of facts and legal precedents or whether they were possessed by some "prejudices" that, being moral in the deepest sense, could be praiseworthy as well as outright fearsome.

Something far more fearful may be in store in this age which readily takes for scientific thinking some bad philosophies grafted on very good science. One may ponder, for instance, the legal consequences if a climate of opinion were to be created by views so far entertained only among prominent scientists and philosophers of science. One example should suffice. It relates to the pseudoscientific evaluation of that very basis of human consciousness which is the experience of the *now*. To make matters worse, one of those who claimed that this experience was fully subjective with no objective value was Albert Einstein.[42] But if such is the case, how can one accuse a criminal for acts committed months or years ago? Is not the permanence of consciousness based on the objectivity of experiencing the actual moment, the *now*, that makes sense of a moral responsibility that transcends space and time? By denying this, one supports that counterfeit moral conscience to which John Henry Newman gave a still unsurpassed portrayal as he defended papal infallibility against its blatant misconstruction by Gladstone, then Prime Minister of Great Britain. Newman presented that counterfeit conscience as the great prerogative which Englishmen claim to themselves. He could have said that the typical modern American too means that by invoking conscience

> he can be his own master in all things, and to profess what he pleases, asking no one's leave, and accounting priest or preacher, speaker or writer, unutterably impertinent, who dares to say a word against his going to perdition, if he like it, in his own way. Conscience has rights because it has duties; but in this age, with a large portion of the public, it is the very right and freedom of conscience to dispense with conscience, to ignore a Lawgiver and Judge, to be independent of unseen obligations. It becomes a license to take up any or no religion, to take this or that and let it go again, to go to church, to go to chapel, to boast of being

above all religions and to be impartial critic of each of them. Conscience is a stern monitor, but in this century it has been superseded by a counterfeit, which the eighteen centuries prior to it never heard of, and could not have mistaken for it, if they had. It is the right of self-will.[43]

Reference to papal infallibility and to conscience ruled by absolute perennial standards would be reason enough to turn to Thomas More, that is, to Saint Thomas More, lawyer and martyr, even if this essay had not originated in an invitation by the Thomas More Society of Harvard Law School. It is therefore only right to formulate my concluding remarks in reference to him. He lived through a historic debacle of law and died as one of its two most prominent victims. The debacle was spawned when Henry VIII, in carrying a positivist theory of law to its full logic, set the will of the sovereign as the ultimate source of law. The debacle might have been obviated if there had been among English leaders of the time a fair number of those whom Thomas More described as society's leaders in his *Utopia*. They were men of cautious thought, because More thought that their being well trained in the sciences had made them cautious in reasoning. Today, More might not necessarily see such a one-to-one correspondence.

Ten or so years before Thomas More had been taken to the Tower, he fully perceived the perils of the positivist theory of law. In late summer 1525, when England was at war with France, More put in this light the King's friendship towards him to William Roper, his son-in-law: "I thank our lord, I find his grace my very good lord indeed, and I believe he doth as singularly favour me as any subject within this realm: howbeit, son Roper, I may tell thee I have no cause to be proud thereof, for if my head would win him a castle in France, it should not fail to go."[44] For all that he kept his course where eternal norms prevailed over all legality. When he knew that he would shortly be sentenced to beheading, he sealed his legal fate by putting perjury in this absolute perspective: "And if this oath of yours, Master Rich, be true, then I pray that I never see God in the face, which I would not say, were it otherwise, to win the whole world."[45]

Ready to be reborn into life eternal More was the true Renaissance man even as a lawyer and public servant. One main witness is that Erasmus who, though he never dared to act in depth, invariably saw deep. On More's magnificently detailed character-portrait, which

Erasmus drew in 1517 in a letter to Hutton,[46] it was possible to improve only by being succinct. This Erasmus did on learning about More's elevation to the chancellorship: "I do not at all congratulate More, nor literature; but I do indeed congratulate England for a better or holier judge could not have been appointed."[47] The other, Robert Whittinton, came up with the immortal phrase that brings to a close his testimony: "More is a man of an angel's wit and singular learning. I know not his fellow. For where is the man of that gentleness, lowliness and affability? And, as time requireth, a man of marvellous mirth and pastimes, and sometime of as sad gravity. A man for all seasons."[48]

More was a good guardian of himself even when his lot was to be out of season in the most ignominious sense. During his trial he took that highest legal ground which his lawyer judges loathed to countenance because strictly moral and spiritual factors ruled there. "You must understand," he admonished them, "that in things touching conscience, every true and good subject is more bound to have respect to his said conscience and to his soul than to any other things in all the world beside." After the death sentence had been passed on him, and only then, did More make an observation on legal positivism which claimed him as its victim. He did so by emphatically denying "that a temporal lord could or ought to be head of the spirituality." In his very last words uttered on the scaffold, he declared himself to be "the King's good servant but God's first."[49] Cranmer, the King's chief tool in More's condemnation, could only confess, when his own execution came, that he had offended the King. Nothing more could be said by the one who followed the positivist interpretation of law. Such was also to be the sad lot of all Communists devoured by Communism itself.

The high ground of legality Thomas More had taken was a conscience rooted in full consciousness about natural law. It was worlds removed from the counterfeit conscience which three hundred years after him another great Englishman, Cardinal Newman, denounced as the chief harbinger of law's debacle in the form of Anglo-Saxon pragmatism. I am sure William James would spiritedly disagree. A hundred years ago he held high pragmatism and agreed with those who spoke of the "puerility" of the Christian dogma of creation.[50] In doing so he must have pitied all those friends and acquaintances of his in the legal profession who learned their trade from William Blackstone's great commentaries on English law. There

Blackstone singled out the metaphysical recognition of the Creator and of the laws imposed by him on creation as the basis of man's pursuit of his own happiness as "this law of nature" which "being co-eval with mankind and dictated by God himself, is . . . superior in obligation to any other. It is binding over all the globe, in all countries, and at all times: no human laws are of any validity, if contrary to this; and such of them as are valid derive all their force, and all their authority, mediately or immediately, from this original."[51] Clearly, Blackstone had in mind something very different from that pursuit of happiness which is the grim resolve to get, regardless of common interest, the largest slice out of the common pie.

William James did not see the day when the victorious democracies sat in judgment in Nuremberg over Nazi implementers of the positivist theory of law and failed to admit that their right to do so rested with the truth of natural law. Not even Senator Robert Taft was ready to go that far in logic as he disputed America's legal right to be part of the Nuremberg trial. But William James, always proud of his logic, should have perceived at least one irony in the proceeding. In his day it was still possible to preach the wisdom of pragmatism or commodism (jurisprudential or other otherwise), and at the same time take full advantage of a still widespread consensus about natural law. Today we have increasingly fewer reasons to avail ourselves of the dubious luxury of that parasitic wisdom. Two decades ago, editorial attacks on natural law still had to acknowledge the need of falling back on "considerable semantic gymnastics to rationalize abortion as anything but taking a human life." Then it was still necessary to recognize that "the process of eroding the old ethic and substituting the new has . . . [merely] begun."[52]

Today this process has advanced very far and revealed some of its unintended consequences. The medical profession is already under siege in a society which, in its selfish pursuit of happiness, lays claim to immunity from all harms, real and imaginary, intended as well as unintended. The medical profession is already bending under the weight of the multiplication of malpractice suits. The legal profession should see some handwriting on the wall as more and more often one hears the question whether there are not just too many lawyers around.

The social turmoil already in the offing will see many innocent victims and some who will rightly suffer the consequences of having preached their parasitic legal wisdom either in the form of a positivist theory of the law or in its conventionalist form. Among the innocent will be those who will find at least some explanation in their belief of natural law which implies that human nature is very apt to act lawlessly. There will be no such spiritual comfort for the upholders of the positivist and conventionalist theories of law. The positivists may at best wistfully look for a strongman who would impose some "positive" order. The conventionalists, if they still care for logic, will have to take the consequences as something convenient even when they greatly inconvenience them. Let us hope that these consequences will not amount to more than some improper use of musical instruments. Such a retribution should seem rather mild for the crime of planting and nurturing the pseudoscientific roots of law's debacle by placing patterns over principles.

[1] On the atheism which some of Voltaire's fellow *philosophes* were busy preaching in the name of science, see my *The Relevance of Physics* (Chicago: University of Chicago Press, 1966), pp. 375-77.

[2] A. Cloots, a revolutionary ideologue from Strasbourg. See, J. H. Billington, *Fire in the Minds of Men: Origins of Revolutionary Faith* (New York: Basic Books, 1980), p. 62.

[3] *The New York Times*, Sept. 28, 1991, p. 19, col. 5.

[4] O. W. Holmes, "Natural Law," *Harvard Law Review*, 40 (1918), p. 252. My first lead to this and half a dozen other quotations from the legal literature came from a batch of articles which Prof. Charles Rice kindly sent me. Among them was his valuable essay, "Some Reasons for a Restoration of Natural Law Jurisprudence," *Wake Forest Law Review* 24 (1989), pp. 539-571.

[5] *Holmes-Pollock Letters: The Correspondence of Mr Justice Holms and Sir Frederick Pollock, 1874-1932* , ed. M. De Wolfe Howe (Cambridge, Mass.: Harvard University Press, 1941), vol. 2, p. 36.

[6] A. Huxley, *Ends and Means: An Inquiry into the Nature of Ideals and into the Methods Employed for Their Realization* (New York: Harper and Brothers, 1937), p. 316.

[7] The best remembered case is, of course, John D. Rockefeller's exhortation that only by cutting many buds can a really large and beautiful rose be produced.

[8] Quoted in R. Augros and G. Stanciu, *The New Biology* (Boston: New Science Library, 1987), p. 175.

[9] Quoted in M. W. Browne's report on recent studies concerning the temperature on the primitive earth and the evolution of life. *The New York Times,* June 18, 1991, p. C10.

[10] "If species do not exist at all, as the supporters of the transmutation theory maintain, how can they vary? And if individuals alone exist, how can the differences which may be observed among them prove the variability of species?" asked Agassiz in the wake of the publication of the *Origin of Species.* See L. Agassiz, "On the Origin of Species," *American Journal of Science and Arts,* 30 (July 1860), p. 143.

[11] This is even true of Ch. V, "Laws of Variation," in *The Origin of Species* where Darwin begins with the remark that the word 'chance' "is a wholly incorrect expression, but it serves to acknowledge plainly our ignorance of the causes of each particular variation." Actually, the heavy realiance of Darwinists on that word greatly helped them in creating the contrary impression.

[12] A. N. Whitehead, *The Function of Reason* (Princeton: Princeton University Press, 1929), p. 12.

[13] The book carried the appropriate subtitle, *An Appeal to Reason.*

[14] See *More Letters of Charles Darwin*, ed. F. Darwin and A. C. Seward (New York: D. Appleton, 1903), vol. 1., p. 114.

[15] See ch. 1, in my *The Absolute beneath the Relative and Other Essays* (Lanham Md.: University of America Press, 1988).

[16] In his letter of September 30, 1921, to E. Zschimmer.

[17] September 24, 1979, p. [65].

[18] For some salient publications, see notes to essay quoted in note 15 above.

[19] *American Political Science Review*, 42 (1948), pp. 906 and 913.

[20] *Harvard Law Review,* 103 (1989), pp. 1-39.

[21] Ibid., p. 2, note 2. Prof. Tribe referred to three other essays of his where he had criticized efforts to reduce human affairs to cost-benefit equations.

[22] Ibid., p. 2.

[23] Ibid., pp. 4-5.

[24] I have in mind Professor Gerard Holton whose well known studies on Einstein's metaphysically realist epistemology do not emphasize the absolutist character of Einstein's relativity.

[25] Ibid., p. 18.

[26] For details, see my *God and the Cosmologists* (Edinburgh: Scottish Academic Press; Washington: Regnery Gateway, 1989), pp. 138 and 257-58.

[27] For details and documentation, see ch. 13, "The Horns of Complementarity," in my Gifford Lectures, *The Road of Science and the Ways to God* (Chicago: University of Chicago Press, 1978).

[28] W. Quine, "Ontology and Ideology Revisited," *The Journal of Philosophy* 80 (September 1983), p. 499.

[29] See my essay, "Determinism and Reality," *Great Ideas Today* (Chicago: Encyclopedia Britannica, 1990), pp. 273-302.

[30] "Quantum mechanics has also established the conception of uncaused causes, subject only to the control by a field of probabilities. The decomposition of a radioactive atom may be an uncaused cause." See ed. Doubleday, Anchor Book, 1967 p. 88-89.

[31] *The New York Times*, Dec. 21, 1983, p. A26.

[32] *The New York Times*, Oct. 20, 1991, p. E15.

[33] *The New York Times,* Oct. 25, 1991, p. A32.

[34] See my review of Penrose's book in *Science and Religion Forum. Reviews* (February 1991), pp. 9-16.

[35] L. Benson, of the University of Pennsylvania, in a History Department Faculty Colloquium, Princeton University, on "Quantification and History," May 11, 1967.

[36] The translator is Luisa-Maria Gozzi, who taught Italian language and literature at Oregon State University, before joining the Faculty of Columbia Unviersity. The two translations have appeared as *Dio e i cosmologi* (Roma: Casa Editrice Vaticana, 1991) and *Lo scopo di tutto* (Milano: Ares, 1994).

[37] H. Spencer, *Social Statics, or the Conditions Essential to Human Happiness Specified and the First of them Developed* (London: Chapman, 1851), pp. 64-65.

[38] The story, if memory serves me right, is quoted in Anne H. Cahn's thesis, "Eggheads and Warheads," MIT 1971.

[39] *The New York Times*, July 16, 1991, p. D20.

[40] I refer to Judge Arthur S. Lane and to his report, "Radio Corporation of America v. Philco Corporation," *Federal Supplement* 275 (1967), pp. 172-230.

[41] For details, see my *The Relevance of Physics*, p. 376.

[42] In a conversation with R. Carnap. See the latter's "Intellectual Autobiography" in P. A. Schilpp (ed.), *The Philosophy of Rudolf Carnap* (La Salle, IL.: The Library of Living Philosophers, 1963), pp. 37-38.

[43] J. H. Newman, *Letter addressed to His Grace The Duke of Norfolk on Occasion of Mr. Gladstone's Recent Expostulation*, in *Certain Difficulties Felt by Anglicans. . .* (London: Longmans, Green and Co., 1891), vol. 2, p. 258.

[44] W. Roper, *The Life of Sir Thomas More*, with notes, and an appendix of letter, ed. S. W. Singer (Chiswik: C. Whittingham, 1822), pp. 21-22.

[45] Ibid., p. 82.

[46] "No one was ever more ambitious of being admitted into a Court, than he was anxious to escape it. . . . Difficult questions are often arising, which require a grave and prudent judge; and these questions are resolved by More in such a way, that both sides are satisfied. And yet no one has ever induced

him to accept a present. What a blessing it would be for the world, if magistrates like More were everywhere put in office by sovereigns!" *The Epistles of Erasmus*, translated with a commentary by F. M. Nichols (London: Longmans, Green and Co., 1918), vol. 3, p. 397.

[47] Quoted in T. E. Bridgett, *The Life and Writings of Blessed Thomas More* (3d ed.; London: Burns and Oates, 1904), p. 225.

[48] Whittinton's statement is from his *Vulgaria*, published in 1522. Quoted in R. W. Chambers, *Thomas More* (London: Jonathan Cape, 1935), p. 177.

[49] Chambers, *Thomas More*, pp. 336-37 and 349.

[50] W. James, *A Pluralistic Universe* (New York: Longmans, Green and Co., 1909), p. 29.

[51] W. Blackstone, *Commentaries on the Laws of England* (facsimile of the first edition of 1765-1769; Chicago: University of Chicago Press, 1979), vol. 1, p. 41.

[52] Editorial, "New Ethic for Medicine and Society," *California Medicine* 67 (Sept. 1970), pp. 67-68.

2

Ecology or Ecologism?

From ecology to ecologism

Ecology, so reads a short definition of it, "deals with organisms in an environment and with the processes that link organism and place."[1] Taken in itself the definition presents a branch of science, one of its many branches or specialties. As such it may appear to be of interest only to those specializing in it. Actually, ecology is of very broad interest. A proof of this can be found in the context of that very same definition. There we are told that

> ecology as such cannot be studied, only organisms, earth, air, and sea can be studied. It is not a discipline: there is no body of thought and technique which framesan ecology of man. It must be therefore a scope or a way of seeing. Such a perspective on the human situation is very old and has been part of philosophy and art for thousands of years. It badly needs attention and revival. Man is in the world and his ecology is the nature of that *inness*.[2]

First published in *Man and his Environment. Tropical Forests and the Conservation of Species* (Vatican City State: Pontifical Academy of Sciences, 1994), pp. 271-93. Reprinted with permission.

Within that context ecology is far more than a branch of science. It is rather a philosophy, a Weltanschauung, an ideology, and possibly a mystique of sorts.

To say the least, the difference between that short definition and its context represents a shift in methodological perspective. The shift took place within a mere decade, the 1960s. Before it, the word ecology stood for a scholarly specialization. No ideology was visible when in the late 1860s there appeared in Germany the word *Oekologie* to denote the study of man's habitat, or *oikos* (home, house) taken in a broad sense.[3] Through translations of some of E. Haeckel's works ecology became part of the English lexicography, first in the forms oecology and Oekology.[4] Ecological thinking could, of course, assert itself without that word. The latter was just being born when the first major steps were taken in the USA to protect the forests, the chief topic of this conference. I have in mind the legislative impact made by the publication in 1864 of Perkins Marsh's book, *Man and Nature; or Physical Geography Modified by Human Action.*[5]

Two generations later, in 1937 to be specific, it could, however, still pass for a stylish hyperbole when the literary critic, Kenneth Burke, warned that "there is one little fellow named Ecology, and in time we shall pay him more attention."[6]   No reader of the article "Ecology" in the 1936 edition of the *Encyclopedia Britannica* would have concluded that Burke's warning should be taken seriously.[7] Twenty years later ecology was presented in the *Encyclopedia Britannica* under four headings, of which "Human Ecology" was but one. The separate discussions given to "Animal Ecology," "Plant Ecology," and "Population Ecology" clearly meant that Ecology as such was still to make a dent on scholarly, let alone on public consciousness.[8]

Much sooner than the authors of those four articles might have suspected, ecology began to loom large as a single science. Moreover, that science could no longer be confined to the ivory towers of the academia. Already in 1962 the naturalist Marsten Bates described ecology as possibly "the most important of the sciences from the viewpoint of long-term human survival." One wonders whether ten years later he would still have complained that ecology is among those sciences which are "least understood by the general public."[9] By the early 1970s self-styled experts on ecology were legion and promoted it as the most sacred and vital cause ever befallen to mankind. For a justification of this nothing more was needed than to agree with a pioneer crusading ecologist's declaration that "the first law of ecology is that everything is connected to everything else."[10] The law could mean nothing less than that ecology ruled all the other sciences.

This methodological shift, that raised ecology from a particular science to the rank of universal science, was so complete as to become a possible boomerang to ecology itself. Already in 1972 ecology appeared to one of its cultivators as "the most perishable item to come along in years." The same ecologist also assured those concerned for the future of ecology that a new program had been devised "to invent a new name for ecology," so that it may be kept alive "after it's been talked to death."[11]

By the early 1970s the vision of a not too distant universal death kept exercising not a few ecologists. Some of them readily became prophets of an impending ecological doomsday. In 1969 at a symposium in the Brookhaven Laboratories one participant suggested that the human race has, maybe, thirty-five years left.[12] A few years earlier the anticipated rise of the world population by 2000 to about 7 billion was taken for such a disturbance of the eco-system that as a result "we will have had it."[13] In fact a population expert specified 1972 as the point of no return.[14] The 1960s also witnessed the warning about a wholesale "ecocatastrophe."[15]

The pallor cast by all this could hardly be alleviated by assigning to mankind another two hundred years. This hardly encouraging "generosity" came in 1970 from Martin Litton, director of the Sierra Club, a powerful environmental organization in the United States, who warned:

> We are prospecting for the very last of our resources and using up the non-renewable things many times faster than we are finding new ones. We've already run out of earth, and nothing we can do will keep humankind in existence for as long as another two centuries.[16]

In the same year the silent threat posed to mankind by the slow rise of global temperature was described with a reference to a well-known experiment with frogs placed in water whose temperature is raised very slowly but steadily. They die without a whimper, with no sense of their impending demise.[17]

Whatever the validity of these forecasts about an ecological doomsday in the offing, some specifically dire predictions turned out to be wide off the mark. The book *Famine 1975!*, written in 1967, contained the prediction that India "cannot be saved" no matter how much grain is shipped to her.[18] By 1975 India produced enough grain to support its still fast growing population. Most recently, a ten-year-long study, costing half a billion dollars to American taxpayers, yielded the result that, in the words of its director, James R. Mahoney, whatever problems remain "the sky is not falling."[19] Contrary to the prediction, made around 1980, that within a decade acid rain would increase by tenfold the acidity of thousands of lakes in the United States, the increase would be at most five-fold over 20 to 50 years and in far fewer lakes.[20]

Ecology is better kept free of the hysterics of some "ecofreaks," another neologism produced by zealous interest in the environment. Long before ecology had become a fad for many, vast areas were reclaimed for forests. A much larger number of people, both in absolute and relative terms, are today far better fed, clothed, and housed than in Malthus' time. Average life-expectancy more than doubled since the early 19th century and is still rising. Contrary to a much publicized play, the present course of the world from the viewpoint of ecology is not an unqualified heading into a not-so-distant future where everybody would soon give the last gasp for air and slump to the ground.[21]

There are, of course, grave ecological problems that are well known and there may be others still unknown, perils potentially no less serious than the data indicating the depletion of the ozone layer. Global warming may be an already irreversible fact, although at present it is not even known for sure whether there has been such a warming for the past twenty years or so, the first of such periods to be investigated in a direct and systematic manner. Industrial pollution of rivers and oceans has in some places come close to a crisis point. Last, but not least, plant and especially animal species are being literally decimated by the encroachment of technology.

A greater threat may be posed by the fact that for the past thirty or so years the total area of arable land has decreased annually by a land-area comparable to the size of Belgium. Equally serious is the threat posed by automobiles as their number approaches half a billion. Whether we like it or not, they are the strongest and most dangerous man-made competitors for Lebensraum.

Obviously much is to be done if the globe is to remain as habitable as it is now. Even greater is the task if the globe is to be made more habitable for a world-population which is to become twice as large as it is now before it would stop growing, if at all. Mankind's gratitude should indeed be enormous to pioneer ecologists who until recently have been more resented than appreciated. All too often their message has been found subversive. They themselves did not recoil from putting the label subversive on their message.[22]

Ecological catastrophes can only be forestalled by subverting widely accepted lifestyles in the affluent world. The warning that "the joyride is over"[23] is of necessity a subversive message though in a constructive sense. Surgical operation is needed all too often if survival is to be secured. But ecology has in recent years been taking a turn whereby it can subvert its very objective. In fact, it is in specifying the broader objectives of ecology that some ecologists, who cared to ponder its basic aim, which is very different from its particular targets, began to sound as an uncertain if not plainly dubious trumpet. In doing so they merely paid the price for carelessness with methodology.

This outcome is not in itself equivalent to a shift of attention from the particular objectives of a particular method of a specific science to its possibly broadest objectives, although not independent of it. In itself the shift means a confrontation with objectives which are difficult, and at times plainly impossible to evaluate in quantitative terms. It should be enough to think of the difference between the evaluation of the means needed for the cleaning up of a river and the evaluation of means necessary for assuring as long a survival to the human race as possible. Another such difference is the one between saving an endangered species and the stabilization of the entire global ecosystem.

Through these differences one encounters more than problems that are difficult to handle quantitatively or technically. In connection with the broad or universal objectives of ecology one becomes involved in the far greater difficulties posed by a highly controversial policy and by a no less controversial ideology. The policy mostly relates to population control through artificial contraception, abortion, eugenics, and euthanasia. The ideology which supports this policy is based on the claim that man is the product of purely natural forces, and indeed a purely chance product of them. If this ideology is valid, it then follows that man can have no claim to special status in nature. He is just one of the 5 or possibly 20 million animal species now living, to all of which the same right to survival being granted. Not a few writers on ecology, who purportedly begin with the program of saving man's environment, quickly run their logic to the point where environment takes absolute priority over man. Then instead of ecology one is faced with sheer ecologism.

This shift in methodology is advocated in increasing frequency and with the co-operation of prestigious academic presses. The shift represents more than an apparently purely theoretical problem the like of which had occurred before. For even these shifts proved to be more than theoretical. A case in point is the inconsistency of Aristotle who, contrary to his own methodological precepts, erected biology into a universal pattern for all the empirical sciences. More than purely theoretical was the result as it led to the putting, for almost 2000 years, the study of motion, and therefore physics itself, into a conceptual straitjacket. Culturally no less disastrous was the extension of mechanistic physics into a mechanistic ideology endowed with universal validity. A pioneer figure in the creation of quantum mechanics, W. Heitler, traced to that mechanistic ideology the tragedies unleashed by two World Wars.[24] No less serious tragedies may be hatched by the turning of ecology into ecologism.

The shift, verbal and ideological, from physics to physicalism and from science to scientism may provide an informative parallel with the shift from ecology to ecologism. When physicalism and scientism began to be spoken of they were much more theoretical constructs than programs for action. Still the threat they posed, if implemented, to human culture could easily be gauged. It should be enough to think of the implications, say, of the proposition—all errors of man are errors of physics—on which Condorcet based his plan for the reorganization of public education in France.[25]

As to scientism, it first appeared also in France a century or so later, in 1910 to be specific.[26] Those were the times that resounded with the claims that the scientific method was the exclusive source of all valid statements. Logical positivists subscribed to scientism with their basic claim that any proposition that could not be expressed in the terms of exact science was purely subjective. Unlike logical positivists who, with the excepion of Neurath, well known for his Marxist sympathies, were not activists, ecologists all too often are. Activism is never missing from the perspective of those ecologists, and their number is increasing, who champion ecologism. The latter may be defined as the view that the environment taken in its global sense is the supreme value to which all other value judgments and courses of action are to be subordinated.

Man, a unique species

An integral part of this view is the claim that man is merely one of the very large number of species, all equally valuable and with the same rights if there are any rights at all. This view has crystallized in the ecological literature in various forms. In general there is the idealization, at times plain idolization, of primitive life. The Pueblo Indians, one author states, "got out hunting in an attitude of humility" and ask the deer with a song "to be willing to die for them."[27] Another author offers the generalization, sweeping both geographically as well as psychologicaly: "every tribe in Africa has a ritual of politeness . . . and a ritual of affection, of respect, of authority, of hospitality . . . to express what words are too small to utter,—not the trifles of the soul, but its immensities."[28] Still another quotes a Wintu Indian woman who contrasted her tribe's care for every pebble with the white man's use of explosives that scatter stones and rocks everywhere.[29]

Already in the early 1950s Walter Prescott Webb, the famed interpreter of modern history as the completion of the conquest of the Frontier, could seem to celebrate the good old primitive days as he asked two questions and replied by offering a sharply drawn alternative:

> If you could hold in your right hand the earth in miniature as it was in 1500 or 1600 and in your left hand the earth as it is now, which earth would you consider richer in resources? Or preferable as a base for of future operations? On the first earth you would have the Great Frontier, the natural forests, the clear streams, the virgin soils, and the precious metals intact. On the second earth you would have stumps, foul streams, eroded soils, and outside of Kentucky a depleted store of precious metals.[30]

A few weeks ago, a report in *The New York Times* praised some primitive Amazonian Indians for doing agriculture without polluting the environment.[31] None of these writers ponder whether they would be here at all to make ecological studies if mankind had kept to primitive methods of production. Much less do they spell out specific courses of action to be taken if modern technical civilization were to return to a bucolic past.

Another manifestation of this ecologistic view is the advocacy of animal rights that goes together with the claim that all species are equally valuable.[32] It is possible to detect some Romantic overtones in the very fact that this re-valuation extends mainly to mammals, birds, and some fish, but not to insects. Such ecologism demands, and in some cases obtains, the unconditional yielding of man.

As a result, strange things can happen or be proposed. Thus a Federal Panel has recently recommended that up to 2.5 million acres of national forest in the Northwest States be off limits to logging. A reason relates to the impact of logging on the spotted owl which requires extensive old-growth habitat.[33] In late March a court order blocked the start of construction of the world's most powerful land-based telescope on Mount Graham in southeast Arizona, because it is the only known habitat for a species of red squirrels of which only about 180 or so are believed to exist.[34] In early April some ecologists called for the protection of coyotes that appeared in the neighborhood of suburban areas north of New York City, although their night-time howling penatrates through the bedroom windows. While this may be a matter of smile, the return of laughing gulls in the vicinity of John F. Kennedy airport is hardly a laughing matter. Major airplane crashes are in store if no quick action can be taken for the gulls' prompt removal, and with drastic means, if necessary.[35]

The mentality of powerful groups that are able to impose delaying legal actions reveals more than intense nature loving. Their members all too often harbor ideological justification such as the one formulated by A. Naess in the early 1970s.[36] According to him there are two kinds of ecologies, shallow and deep. The differences between the two he formulated in a set of parallel propositions. Some of them are purely pragmatic and debatable, such as that "people will not tolerate a broad decrease in their standard of living" and that "people should be ready to accept a reduction in the standard of living in overdeveloped countries." According to another parallel of this type "pollution should be decreased if it threatens ecological equilibrium" and that "decrease of pollution has a priority over economic growth."

Other contrasts between shallow and deep ecologies as drawn up by Naess are distinctly philosophical and ideological. Shallow is in his eyes the ecological view that "natural diversity is valuable as a resource for us, whereas he sees depth in the principle that "natural diversity has its own (intrinsic) value." He characterizes as shallow the claim that "it is nonsense to talk about value except as value for mankind," and presents as deep the view that "equating value with value for humans reveals a racial prejudice." Some other deep principles, as set forth by Naess, sound rather provocative in their generality: "We have no right to destroy the natural features of this planet" and "nature does not belong to man." The ultimate logic of ecologism fully reveals itself in the following deep principle which implies abysmal depths for man: "Nature is worth defending, whatever the fate of humans."

In sum ecologism logically leads to denying to man a special position within the multitude of animal and plant species. While few ecologists voice such extreme views, the ecological literature all too often reveals a systematic slighting of human characteristics indicative of man's very special status. An example of this is provided by a series of essays toward an ecology of man, carrying the general title, *The Subversive Science*. It includes an essay from an anthropological journal dealing, under the title, "The Human Revolution," mainly with the evolution of language. There, whatever there may have been "revolutionary" in the evolution of man is turned into a most unrevolutionary process which advances through trivial stages such as follows: "Hundreds of generations of chattering, first in a call system, then in a pre-language, increases the innervation of the vocal tract, and enriches the cortical representation of that region. The stage is set for the development of the kind of articulatory motions familiar today."[37]

This account of the emergence of language, this most revolutionary aspect of man, should seem suspect already by its heavy reliance on hundreds of generations of chit-chat and pre-language about which nobody knows anything. Most reprehensible is the author's silence about great perplexities felt by some leading students of language and linguistics in spite of their avowedly materialistic notion of man. Thus, in view of the extreme complexity of the logical structure of any known language, Noah Chomsky of MIT held it impossible that language could have arisen without a neuronal pre-wiring in the brain, a sequence inadmissible in the Darwinian evolutionary perspective.[38] It is the hardly unintentional silence about such difficulties that makes certain books on ecology really subversive.

Language, although we take it for granted, is a most astounding marvel which has stubbornly resisted all attempts to pigeonhole it in reductionist categories. Moreover, it is not the only such marvel unique to the human species. This is not the place to go into a detailed appraisal of such marvels that reveal man to be the only tool-making animal, and equally alone with his ability to make symbols. These symbols can be of the highest degree of abstraction, such as the idea of zero or nothing. Man-made symbols are also of immense variety as displayed in pictures, words and their graphic transposition, or phonetic writing. Man alone can count in a way in which enumeration leads to branches of mathematics and geometry that have little to do with empirical considerations. Moreover, very special individual men are needed for the production of artistic masterpieces. This is the point of a remark of Einstein that General Relativity, which he considered as his most particular contribution to science, would have been eventually formulated even if he had not existed at all, but that without a Beethoven the Ninth Symphony would have never been composed.[39] Einstein also gave an incisive reminder about the basis of individual human consciousness which is the experience of the *now*. It remains, so he noted in a conversation with Carnap, forever outside the nets of that exact science which, let it be noted, always deals with the generic and the non-individual.[40]

Last but not least, man is the only species in the entire ecosystem that can behave un-ecologically. If this point is mentioned by ecologists it is done in two, hardly constructive, ways. One of them is to note this point in the writings of those who defend the exploitation of nature, and to turn it against them. Such is the gist of the remark: "One never gets far from intimations of man's exemption from ecological rules and his superiority over beasts. In this there are no claimants more strident than the admirers of corporate human acitvities who insist that people must not be interfered with."[41] The other way is to bury man's uniqueness under a heap of dubious rhetoric:

> *Homo sapiens*, that creature mad beyond the craziest of hares, lunatic beyond all lemmings, may go to the end of the road with no impulse more logical than to discover what lies there. . . . Which in the end will bend the ultimately defeated knee, we or our world? . . . One cannot say. The tragedy and the magnificence of *Homo sapiens* together rise from the same smoky truth that we alone among animal species refuse to acknowledge natural law.[42]

Obviously, the natural law meant in the context is not any of the laws of physical nature as investigated by the exact sciences. Rather the law, since it can be refused or disobeyed, has to be the kind of natural law which is a moral law. And if it is truly a law, universally binding, and not merely some social convention or a biological utility, then free will too, which is the basis of moral responsibility, will appear as an ontological reality. Here a brief reference should suffice to evoke the sorry predicament of efforts to dilute free will into crude or sophisticated forms of determinism. About all of them is valid Henri Poincaré's concise observation: "C'est librement qu'on est déterministe."[43]

It is this freedom of man which forms the ultimate dividing line between ecology and ecologism. It is man's free will, together with his ecological responsibility, which is at stake whenever man is taken for just another species. The only logical alternative to this is to take the position of might makes right. This is what the American biologist, G. Hardin, did as he warned his fellow-Americans, in an editorial in *Science*, that

> every day we are a smaller minority. We are increasing at only 1 percent per year; the rest of the world increases twice as fast. By the year 2000, one person in 24 will be an American; in 100 years, only one in 46. The projected figures assume that the present trends will continue. . . . If the world is one great commons, in which all food is shared equally, then we are lost. Those who breed faster will replace the rest. . . . In the absence of breeding controls a policy "one mouth, one meal" ultimately produces one totally miserable world. . . . In less than a perfect world, the allocation of rights based on territory must be defended if a ruinous breeding race is to be avoided. It is unlikely that civilization and dignity can survive everywhere; but better in a few places than in none. Fortunate minorities must act as trustees of a civilization that is threatened by uninformed good intentions.[44]

The least one can say about such defense of fortunate minorities, be they confined to America or to the Western World in general, is that it is "barbarism,"[45] and in reality far worse.

At any rate, even if one takes free will seriously and chooses ecology instead of ecologism, there still remain some major problems or hurdles. Let it be assumed that those ecologists are right who locate the chief source of environmental pollution in what is essentially a technical and marketing process. According to them there are three major polluting factors: population, affluence, and intensive technological productivity. Analysis of the respective contributions of these three factors reveals a most surprising picture.

Contrary to what one may expect, it is not the population as such or its rate of increase during the last four or five decades which is the foremost pollutant. In fact, taken together with the affluence or luxury factor, it is a mere fifth of the total. Four-fifths of the total are due to the explosive post-World War II use of automobiles, including trucks of all sorts. In the United States this led to the decline of the ecologically far less pollutant railroad transport by almost a factor of four-fifths. Worse, more and more powerful cars were demanded, both by the industry and the public. Car-making companies adopted the slogan, "mini cars mean mini profits," whereas the public wanted joyrides in bigger though not necessarily better cars. Such cars demanded the drastic increase of the compression ratio in the cylinder, and consequently a much higher operating temperature.[46]

The fact already mentioned above that today there is one automobile for every ten human beings, half a billion to five billion, should in itself indicate the correctness of this analysis and the magnitude of the problem it poses. By magnitude much more is meant than a numerical or quantitative one. The problem is ultimately a problem for the human will, or rather good will. It is a problem that cannot be evaded with a recourse to technology. In a deeper sense than one may suspect, there is no technological fix to the environmental crisis, precisely because the crisis is ultimately the free doing of man.

This is not to suggest that science and technology will not be of enormous support. Hardly a week passes without important news about scientific advances with encouraging ecological significance. During the last two months alone word has come about a breakthrough in improving the quality of rice,[47] about bamboo made to flower in laboratories,[48] and about gas burners, which, without burning with flame, convert light into electricity.[49] Wider use of solar energy and of bio-batteries is now not so much a question of technology as of human resolve.

On the more distant horizon is the fusion energy which I mention not as an ultimate panacea to all energy needs but as a lesson in scientific or technological history. There almost all advances imply the going through some ecologically questionable phases such as atomic fission. The lesson throws light on what should be the basic consideration in ecology. In more than one sense, and whether we like it or not, this world of ours, or this globe of ours, is not and cannot be a Paradise. It never looked like a Paradise except in some fortunate islands and even there only when tornados, hurricanes, monsoons, and tidal waves were at a safe distance.

That this earth of ours will not be a Paradise is in part due to man's free will which has all too often gone astray. To think that it will not continue to do so, is sheer naiveté. No less naive would it be to bank on that long-discredited Confucian precept that "when things are investigated, then true knowledge is achieved, when true knowledge is achieved, then the will becomes sincere."[50] This precept did not work through China's very long history, riddled with internal warfare. The same precept did not work when taken up by the ideologues of the Enlightenment. Its great 20th century try-out, the Marxist experiment, has failed under our very eyes. The *glasnost* of the last few years revealed, though with some slowness, more than enough of the ecological disaster spreading all across the Soviet Union.

Religious and scientific dynamics
If the instruction of the mind is not enough, only the will, the heart, remains to be considered. But more is needed than remarks, however inspiring such as the one of Einstein that "it is easier to denature plutonium than it is to denature the evil spirit of man."[51] About the same time, around 1950, Bertrand Russell made a statement that in view of his well known scoffing at Christian ethics, should have sent shock waves around the intellectual world:

> The root of the matter is a very simple and old-fashioned thing, a thing so simple that I am almost ashamed to mention it, for fear of the derisive smile with which wise cynics will greet my words. The thing I mean—please forgive me for mentioning it, is love, Christian love or compassion. If you feel this, you have a motive force for existence, a guide in action, a reason for courage, an imperative necessity for intellectual honesty.[52]

This may lead us to a brief consideration of a statement of the late Lynn White Jr, probably the most often quoted single statement throughout the vast ecological literature: "Christianity bears a huge burden of guilt . . . . We shall continue to have a worsening ecologic crisis until we reject the Christian axiom that nature has no reason save to serve man."[53]

It is rather sad that such a charge should come from a prominent historian of technology. As the son of a Protestant minister, White should have at least known that according to Christian faith the primary purpose of nature is to reveal the glory of God. For this reason alone man, Christian man in particular, could not feel entitled to take willful advantages of nature. Could a Christian man not feel compunction of heart for turning forests into wastelands while repeating the Psalms about trees shouting to God for joy? Some very large-scale and irreversible deforestations took place in distinctly non-Christian milieux.

As a historian of technology White, and those many who echoed his charge, should have considered a fact that can be known without any expertise in the history of technology. Until the advent of the steam engine, of railroads, of electric motors, and of internal combustion engines, man had been very much on the defensive vis-à-vis nature. Man's most necessary, and partly ruthless, conquest of nature began at a time, the early 19th century, which is also the beginning of the heavy de-Christianization of the Western World. Some, relatively few, 19th-century captains of industry, were practicing, perhaps badly practicing, Christians. Many more were Christians but in name, and an increasingly large number of industry captains were and are not Christians at all.

At any rate, it is curious that in hardly a single context where White's preposterous charge is repeated is credit given to Christians for the most decisive breakthrough toward modern physical science. The breakthrough consisted in the formulation of the idea of inertial and accelerated motion in the 14th-century Sorbonne and in a distinctly theological context.[54] The evidence presented by Pierre Duhem in vast and erudite works almost a century ago, is still to penetrate academic consciousness.[55] To appreciate that breakthrough one must consider the invariable failure of the best scientific minds in all great ancient cultures, including the Greeks and the Arabs,[56] to come up with even a remotely correct intimation of inertial motion.

If Christians, or Catholics in particular, share a responsibility for the ecological crisis it is only by not speaking up early and loudly enough. Here too the perceived loudness may be very different from its real strength. Only history will put in true light the frequent and strong warnings about the misuses of technology by Pius XII, whose pontificate coincided with those 10 or 15 years when technology, as was noted before, took on an explosive growth.[57] Decades earlier, let alone a century earlier, when unemployment was time and again at crisis levels, it would have been counterproductive to request a slowdown of production and of the exploitation of natural resources.

If today such requests are more feasible, it is because the exponential post-War growth in scientific know-how provided the tools for a shift from a heavily polluting to a mildly-polluting technology. As long as the law of entropy remains valid, there never will be a non-polluting technology. It is also a fact that this growth of scientific know-how did not generate a comparable growth of moral resolve to make proper use of those new tools. It did not because that method is impotent to do so. It can at best, with exact and concrete evaluation of the threat to ecology, put some fear in mankind, though not necessarily the most productive of such fears, the fear of the Lord.

This is not the place to elaborate on the lion's share of the role which, in the ecological program, will have to be taken by self-sacrifice and genuine altruism, so akin to Christian love. If there is any solution to the ecological crisis it will consist in the moral development of the technologically developed nations. It will be a task whose magnitude may be mesmerizing. We need to marshal spiritual resources or else we must settle for the fatalistic note, recorded by Herodotus, which a Persian officer struck on foreseeing the decimation of many of his countrymen on the battlefield near Thebes. To the question, why don't you warn them, he replied: "Many of us Persians know all this, but we follow in the bondage of Necessity. This is the bitterest pain to human beings: to know much and to control nothing."[58] Ecology has already taught us a great deal, but it has remained rather cagey as to what or who will provide the control. A Big Brother, on whom some misguided ecologists are counting,[59] is waiting in the wings if the sense of true brotherhood does not prevail over a sense of hopelessness.

A modern literary echo of what Herodotus recorded is Melville's *Moby Dick*, the story of Captain Ahab's maddening pursuit of the great white whale. "Now, in his heart, Ahab had some glimpse of this, namely: all my means are sane, my motive and my object mad."[60] Earlier, William Blake, who cried over the landscape destroyed by smokestacks and by the slavery practiced within what he called "Satanic mills," noted the hopelessness of the human predicament in which "you never know what is enough until you have more than enough."[61]

Most but not all methods and tools of science and technology are undoubtedly sane. To have a full mastery of what those tools can do is indispensable for solving the ecological problem. Only science, not poetry, can establish the fact whether there is a steady rise in global temperature, whether the ozone layer is really breaking up, whether the Amazon rain forest can or cannot be replaced by a different flora and fauna. In the dynamics of ecological responsibility nothing can supplant the role which scientific know-how can and should play.

Science as such cannot provide the criteria that would indicate in each and every case that one or another tool produced by it is intrinsically insane. In fact the man of science may, by the dynamics of curiosity, feel himself pushed to go ahead with a project and consider only afterwards the measure of its sanity. The psychology of this dynamics has its perhaps most poignant expression in some words of Oppenheimer. They formed his rather defiant reply to the question why there had not been a thorough discussion about the desirability of the atomic bomb before it was made:

> It is my judgment in these things that when you see something that is *technically sweet*, you go ahead and do it and you argue about what to do about it only after you have had your technical success. That is the way it was with the atomic bomb. I do not think anybody opposed making it; there were some debates about what to do with it after it was made.[62]

The very opposite fault may assert itself in in the religious dynamics concerning ecological responsibility. It is the essence of that dynamics to see things *sub specie aeternitatis* and energize thereby man's good will. That dynamics can alone provide those eternal truths about which empirical science can say nothing. That dynamics alone, in terms of its method, is justified to speak about the difference between the *is* and the *should*. Unfortunately, it is a dynamics which, because of its concern with unchangeable truths and norms, can turn into an advocacy of a more or less static posture. In other words, it may see too much sweetness in the *status quo,* though this may be a cover-up for lack of courage to face up to ever pressing new situations.

As an illustration let me recall a more than sixty-year old story, connected with the Meeting of the British Association for the Advancement of Science in Leeds in 1927. On September 4, a Sunday, quite a few of the hundreds of participants took the train to the nearby small town of Ripon to attend the Sunday service customary with the Meetings of the Association. The sermon preached by the Bishop of Ripon made the headlines in *The Times* (London) as well as in *The New York Times.* No wonder. He asked for nothing less than for a moratorium on scientific work for ten years. The Bishop's reasons should be given in his own words:

> After all we could get on very happily if aviation, wireless, television, and the like advanced no further than at present, disappointing as it would be for those whose life work has lain in such fields. Dare I even suggest, at the risk of being lynched by some of my hearers, that the sum of human happiness outside scientific circles would not necessarily be reduced if for ten years every physical and chemical laboratory were closed and the patient and resourceful energy displayed in them transferred to recovering the lost art of getting on together and finding the formula for making both ends meet in the scale of human life. Much, of course, we should lose by this universal scientific holiday. We should possibly miss new forms of comfort and convenience, new means of making more money for the few at the cost of less work for the many, and a right curiosity on many points would go unsatisfied for a time. But human happiness would not necessarily suffer.[63]

In the same evening, at a gala dinner, Sir Oliver Lodge, then the great old man of British science, spoke animatedly about the dynamics of science. Scientists, he said, would in no way slow down, let alone to stop, their research, theoretical and experimental, into the secrets of Nature.

Whether one likes it or not, that research will go on relentlessly and at an accelerated rate. Moreover, science offers no assurance that its findings will always be put to proper ends and in sane proportion. At times the progress may appear a headlong rush of a runaway locomotive where the only observers are in the caboose and look merrily backward. Clearly, there will be much need for that ingredient of Christian love which is self-discipline. By insisting on

it, in various ways, the Church will keep providing an essential help
to the cause of ecology. This should be particularly clear from a most
important fact, though one hardly ever discussed by defenders of the
environment. The fact is that the more radical is an ecological
proposition, the greater is the dislocation, and at times the plain
elimination of jobs which such a proposition demands. It hardly
credits, to mention a most recent case, the defenders of the pine
barrens in Suffolk County, Long Island, that they are making no
estimate of the loss of wages if construction of new houses there
would come to a halt. At the same time they demand three billion
dollars from local taxpayers to evaluate the ecological situation.[64]

It is particularly timely to ponder such and similar facts only a
year away from the centenary of Leo XIII's Encyclical *Rerum
novarum* on the condition of working men, one of the greatest papal
encyclicals of modern times. Of course, the workers' conditions and
the means of improving them were discussed in that encyclical with
references to a broader context. Such were Leo XIII's statements,
made with an eye on Genesis 1, that the earth was created for the
sake of man and that he has the command to people and subdue it.
Some ecologists may find those references irritating even when,
owing to new circumstances produced by a runaway technology, they
have recently been coupled with a call for restraint in using the
earth's resources. But what many ecologists, and certainly all
advocates of ecologism would find in that Encyclical very irritating
is a warning there about Utopianism. "No effort, no artifice," Leo
XIII warned, "will ever succeed in banishing from human life the ills
and troubles which beset it."

The profound truth of this warning, which should be so clear
against the background of the last hundred years, should seem to be
applicable to the broader aims of ecology. The latter is bound to turn
into ecologism if no respect is paid to the truth of the phrase that
follows in that Encyclical: "If there be any who pretend differ-
ently—who hold out to a hard-pressed people the boon of freedom
from pain and trouble, an undisturbed repose, and constant enjoy-
ment—they delude the people, impose upon them, and their deceitful
promises will one day bring forth evils worse than the present."
Ecologists can choose no better motto than Leo XIII's next phrase:
"Nothing is more useful than to look upon the world as it really
is."[65] Living by this motto will encourage them in their indispens-

able warnings about the real condition of the ecosystem and will keep
their work at a safe distance from the unrealities of ecologism.

[1] P. Shepard, "Introduction: Ecology and Man—a Viewpoint," in P. Shepard
and D. McKinley, eds., *The Subversive Science: Essays toward an Ecology
of Man* (Boston: Houghton Mifflin Co., 1969), p. 1. Ecology deals "with the
relation of organisms or groups of organisms to their environment,"
according to E. P. Odum, *Fundamentals of Ecology* (2d ed.; Philadelphia:
W. B. Saunders, 1959), p. 4. The definition proposed by S. J. Gould—"ecology is the study of organic diversity" (*Ever since Darwin: Reflections in
Natural History* [New York: W. W. Norton, 1979], p. 119)—is obviously so
wide as to negate the very function of a definition.
[2] Ibid.
[3] D. N. Slusser and G. H. Slusser, in their *Technology: The God that Failed*
(Philadelphia: The Westminster Press, 1971, p. 9.), The Slussers credit a
certain W. Reiter for coining the word. Interestingly, a certain Matth. Reiter
is listed as the author of *Zur Sytematik und Oekologie der zwei-
geschlechtlichen Rhabotiden* (Berlin: W. Junk, 1928), a monograph (92pp
with double pagination) written in the Zoological Institut of the University
of Innsbruck (Bd. III, Heft 4). He may be a younger relative, perhaps the
son of the one cited by the Slussers. In the literature (for instance, Gould,
Ever since Darwin p. 119) Haeckel is usually given as the originator of the
word.
[4] See *Dictionary of the English Language* (2d ed.; Oxford: Clarendon Press,
1989), vol. V, p. 58, col 1. In an indirect evidence of lack of widespread
interest in ecology, no effort is made in the first edition (1933, Supplement,
vol. XIII, p. 319, col. 3) to trace the early history of the use the word. The
second edition contains reference to such derivates as "ecofreak" and
"ecocidal."
[5] Its impact was attested by its republication in 1965 by Harvard University
Press at a time when further major steps were taken by the US government
to protect forests and rivers.
[6] Quoted in M. E. Adelstein and J. G. Pival, eds., *Ecocide and Population*
(New York: St. Martin's Press, 1972), p. 2. In the section, "The New
Malthusian Principle," of his book *Attitudes towards History* (New York:
The New Republic, 1937), K. Burke used in a matter-of-fact style the
expressions, "ecologically minded" and "ecological balance" (vol. 2, p. 191).
No less interestingly, he also pointed out that the elimination of agricultural
waste by the use of chemical fertilizers increased the chemical waste or
pollution (p. 190). Burke wrote in a Marxist perspective.

[7] And all the more so as the article (see Vol. VII, cols. 915-24) dealt entirely with animal ecology, and ended with a reference to plant ecology to be discussed in a general article on Plants.

[8] Human ecology was treated in a mere two columns (ibid., cols. 922-24).

[9] Quoted in Adelstein, *Ecocide and Population*, p. 2.

[10] B. Commoner, *The Closing Circle: Nature, Man and Technology* (New York: Alfred A. Knopf, 1971), p. 29.

[11] Quoted in Adelstein, *Ecocide and Population* p. 103. "Common usage," wrote S. J. Gould in the late 1970s (*Ever since Darwin*, p. 119) "now threatens to make 'ecology' a label for anything good that happens far from cities or anything that does not have synthetic chemicals in it."

[12] According to J. B. Cobb, *Is It Too Late? A Theology of Ecology* (Beverly Hills, Calif.: Bruce, 1972), p. 13. This statement is not contained in *Diversity and Stability of Ecological Systems* (Brookhaven Symposia in Biology 22, May 26-28, 1969; Upton N.Y.: Brookhaven National Laboratory, 1969).

[13] An admittedly "wild estimate" by B. Commoner, reported in Adelstein, *Ecocide and Population*, pp. 104-05.

[14] "The battle to feed all of humanity is over," so declared Paul E. Ehrlich, a population biologist, in his *The Population Bomb* (New York: Ballantine, 1971, p. xi). He also cancelled his long-term life-insurance. In an interview in *Look* April 21, 1970) he stated that "when you reach a point where you realize further efforts will be futile, you may just as well look after yourself and your friends and enjoy what little time you have left. That point for me is 1972."

[15] P. R. Ehrlich, "Eco-catastrophe!" in G. De Bell (ed.), *The Environmental Handbook* (New York: Ballantine Books, 1970), pp. 161-76. He also predicted the irreversible deterioration of the oceans by the late 1970s.

[16] Quoted in *Time*, Feb. 2, 1970.

[17] An analogy used by R. Register in *Los Angeles Times*, February 8, 1970, p. 12.

[18] W. Paddock and P. Paddock, *Famine, 1975! America's Decision: Who Will Survive?* (Boston: Little Brown, 1967).

[19] He did so in an address to a gathering of some 700 scientists from over 30 countries in Hilton Head S.C. Quoted in W. K. Stevens, "Worst Fears on Acid Rain Unrealized," *The New York Times*, Feb. 20, 1990, p. C1.

[20] Ibid. p. C11.

[21] In T. McNally's " 'Last Gaps'—A New Play of Tomorrow," each of the brief scenes begins at 11:59 and ends a mintue later. See report in *The New York Times*, Oct. 26, 1968, pp. D1 and D15.

[22] First by P. B. Sears, "Ecology—a Subversive Subject," *BioScience* 14(7) 11 July, 1964. See title of book quoted in note 1 above.

[23] An expression of Dr. W. Pollard, director of the Oak Ridge Associated Universities.

[24] W. Heitler, "The Departure from Classical Thought in Modern Physics," in P. A. Schilpp (ed.), *Albert Einstein: Philosopher-Scientist* (Evanston, Il.: Library of Living Philosophers, 1949), p. 196.

[25] "Toutes les erreurs en politique, en morale, ont pour leur base des erreurs philosophiques, qui elles-mêmes sont liées à des erreurs physiques." *Esquisse d'un Tableau historique des progrès de l'esprit humain*, in *Œuvres de Condorcet* (Paris: Firmin Didot, 1847), vol. VI, p. 223. Condorcet merely echoed Baron d'Holbach's claim that "toutes les erreurs de l'homme sont des erreurs en physique." *Système de la nature* (London, 1777), p. 19.

[26] The word was first used in that sense in 1910 by J. Maritain to denote the abuse made of science in materialistic philosophies. See my article, "Maritain and Science," reprinted in my *Chance or Reality and Other Essays* (Lanham Md.: University Press of America, 1986), pp. 41-62. See there note 34 on the failure of French lexicographers to recognize Maritain's priority. Although in English the first use of "scientism" goes back to the 1870s, it did not begin to be used in the sense in which Maritain had used it until after World War I. This happened mainly through the influence of George Bernard Shaw's Preface to his play *Back to Methuselah* which described the "iconography and hagiology of Scientism" as being "as copious as they are mostly squalid." See *Dictionary of the English Language* (2d ed.; Oxford, 1989), vol. XIV, p. 651).

[27] G. Snyder, "The Wilderness and the Non-Verbal," *The Center Magazine*, 3(4) (July, 1970), pp. 70-71.

[28] A statement of W. C. Willoughby (1857-1938), Professor of Missions, Kennedy School of Missions, in his book *The Soul of the Bantu* (Garden City: Doubleday, Doran, 1928), eagerly seized upon by J. Collier, "Fulness of Life through Leisure," in Shepard, *The Subversive Science*, p. 422. Obviously, he deemed it preferable not to quote the book's subtitle: *A Sympathetic Study of the Magico-religious Practices and Beliefs of the Bantu Tribes of Africa.*

[29] Reported in T. Roszak, *The Making of a Counter Culture* (Doubleday Anchor Book, 1969), p. 245.

[30] W. P. Webb, *The Great Frontier* (Boston: Houghton Mifflin. 1952), p. 292.

[31] W. K. Stevens, "Research in 'Virgin' Amazon Uncovers Complex Farming," *The New York Times*, April 3, 1990, p. C1.

[32] A fair number of books and articles supportive of the equality of all species is cited and discussed in *Why Preserve Natural Variety?* (Princeton, N.J.: Princeton University Press, 1989) by Bryan G. Norton, who has for some time been vigorously advocating the same position.

[33] T. Egan, "Struggles over the Ancient Trees Shift to British Columbia," *The New York Times*, April 15, 1990, p. E1.

[34] Reported in *The New York Post*, March 28, 1990, p. 16.

[35] J. P. Fried, "As Laughing Gulls Flourish, Airport Officials Fret," *The New York Times*, May 1, 1990, pp. B1-2. In the news summary (p. A2) the hatching of a drama is condensed into the statement: "The laughing gull is coming back to the New York area—to the delight of naturalists and the dismay of officials at Kennedy International Airport who say the growing numbers of the birds pose a hazard to planes." It is largely ignored in the report that, owing to the pressure of environmentalist groups, those officials cannot take prompt actions that alone could prevent major airline disasters.

[36] A. Naess, "The Shallow and the Deep, Long-range Ecology Movement," *Inquiry* 16 (1973), 95-100. See also his "The Deep Ecological Movement: Some Philosophical Aspects," *Philosophical Inquiry* 8 (1986), pp. 10-29.

[37] P. Shepard, *The Subversive Science*, pp. 13-41. The essay was written by C. F. Hockett and R. Ascher. For quotation see p. 31.

[38] N. Chomsky, *Aspects of the Theory of Syntax* (Cambridge, Ma.: M.I.T Press, 1965), p. 58. Fifteen years later Chomsky stated: "It's about as likely that an ape will prove to have a language ability as that there is an island somewhere with a species of flightless birds waiting for human beings to teach them to fly." Quoted in *Time*, March 10, 1980, p. 57.

[39] As reported by A. Moszkowski, *Einstein the Searcher: His Work Explained from Dialogues with Einstein*, tr. H. L. Brose (London: Methuen, 1921), p. 99, a report somewhat embellished later by G. Sarton, *The Study of the History of Science* (Cambridge: Harvard University Press, 1936), p. 51.

[40] R. Carnap, "Intellectual Autobiography," in *The Philosophy of Rudolf Carnap*, ed. P. A. Schilpp (La Salle, Il.: Open Court, 1963), pp. 37-38.

[41] D. McKinley, "The New Mythology of 'Man in Nature'," in *Perspectives in Biology and Medicine* 7(1) (Autumn 1964), p. 93.

[42] R. Ardrey, *The Social Contract* (New York: Athenenum, 1970), p. 46.

[43] H. Poincaré, "Sur la valeur objective des théories physiques," *Revue de métaphsyique et de morale* 10 (1902), p. 288.

[44] G. Hardin did so in a guest editorial, "The Survival of Nations and Civilization," in *Science* 172 (June 25,1971), p. 1297.

[45] An expression of B. Commoner, *The Closing Circle*, p. 296.

[46] As set forth in not too technical terms by B. Commoner, ibid., pp. 165-69.

[47] See the report, "Bioengeneering Points to Better Rice Plant," by W. K. Stevens in *The New York Times* (Feb. 6, 1990, p. C1) with the caption: "Breakthroughs in genetic engineering may make a new green revolution possible for the high percentage of the world's population that depends on rice."

[48] See the front-page report, "Bamboo Coaxed to Flower in Lab; Global Impact on the Crop is Seen," by N. Angier in *The New York Times*, March 22, 1990, p. A1.

[49] See report, "Better Ways to Make Electricity," by M. L. Wald in *The New York Times*, April 11, 1990, p. D9.

[50] Tahsueh, Liki, chap. XLII, in *The Wisdom of Confucius, ed. and tr. with notes by Lin Ytang (New York: Modern Library, 1938)*, p. 140.

[51] From an interview with M. Amrine, *The New York Times Magazine*, June 23, 1946, p. 44.

[52] B. Russell, *The Impact of Science on Society* (New York: Columbia University Press, 1951), p. 59.

[53] L. White, Jr. "The Historical Roots of Our Ecological Crisis," *Science*, 155 (March 10, 1967), pp. 1203-07. For quotation, see pp. 1206 and 1207. In the same address White strictured "orthodox Christian arrogance toward nature" and urged for its replacement with a new panpsychic religious view which he saw embodied in Saint Francis of Assisi and the primitive Franciscans. Further, White praised the "cosmic humility" of the Incarnation as starting in a manger and ending on the cross, while wholly ignoring such an "arrogant" act of the same Christ as his command that made an entire swine heard rush over a cliff into self-destruction. While White deplored Christian insensitivity toward "sacred groves," prominent in pagan cults, he failed to mention Christ's cursing of the fig tree which He let wither in order to demonstrate moral truth. For an incisive critique of White's paper see R. V. Young Jr., "Christianity and Ecology," *National Review*, December 20, 1974, 1454ff.

[54] The context was the Christian dogma of creation out of nothing and in time. For details, see my *The Savior of Science* (Washington D.C.: Regnery Gateway; Edinburgh: Scottish Academic Press, 1989), pp. 66-80. Hungarian translation (Budapest: Ecclesia, 1990); Italian translation (Roma: Libreria Editrice Vaticana, 1990); Polish translation (Wroclaw: Wydawnictwo twe, 1994). A French translation is forthcoming.

[55] As amply discussed in my *Uneasy Genius: the Life and Work of Pierre Duhem* (Dordrecht: Martinus Nijhoff, 1984).

[56] See for a detailed discussion, chapters 1-6 and 8 in my *Science and Creation: From Eternal Cycles to an Oscillating Universe* (2d rev. ed.; Edinburgh: Scottish Academic Press, 1986; Lanham Md.: University Press of America, 1990).

[57] A rich selection of Pius XII's statement on technology was compiled by L. J. Hagerty, *Pius XII and Technology* (Milwaukee: Bruce Publishing Company, 1962). See pp. 181 and 186.

[58] *The History. Herodotus*, translated by D. Grene (Chicago: University of Chicago Press, 1987), p. 618 (Bk 9. ch. 16).

[59] Thus M. Ketchel, professor of physiology at Tufts Medical School, approved of the eventual putting of fertility controlling chemicals into the water supply; G. Hardin, biologist at the University of California, denounced voluntary birth control as "insanity"; D. Aiken, an astrophysicist, took the view that "the government has to step in and tamper with religious and personal convictions." Comparatively mild is the call of P. Ehrlich, of Stanford University, in his *The Population Bomb* (New York: Ballantine, 1968, p. 8), for population control "by compulsion if voluntary methods fail."

[60] H. Melville, *Moby Dick* (New York: Modern Library, 1926), p. 185.

[61] "The Marriage of Heaven and Hell," in *The Complete Writings of William Blake*, ed. G. Keynes (London: Oxford University Press, 1960), p. 152.

[62] *In the Matter of J. Robert Oppenheimer* (Washington, DC: U.S. Government Printing Office, 1954), p. 81.

[63] *The Times* (London), Sept. 5, 1927, p. 15, col. 2.

[64] Sarah Lyall, "Pine Barrens Lawsuit Halts L. I. Builders," *The New York Times*, May 8, 1990, p. B1.

[65] These quotations are from section 18 of that Encyclical.

3

Socrates
or the Baby and the Bathwater

Jesus and Socrates

That every book is autobiographical is the substance of a longer observation in Samuel Butler's *The Way of All Flesh*, a spiritual biography in spite of its title.[1] The remark has some applicability even to the four canonical biographies of the Word made Flesh. The young man who in Mark's Gospel lets his nightgown be grabbed by Jesus' captors and runs away naked is very likely Mark himself. Had Luke not been a physician, he might not have paid special attention to the miraculous healings performed by Jesus.

That Jesus aimed above all at a moral healing of man and taught it most effectively by His own death has always been the principal reason for drawing a parallel between him and Socrates. Nothing extols more justly the greatness of Socrates than Kierkegaard's apparent slighting of him: "If God had not come himself, all the relations would have remained on the Socratic level."[2]

First published in *Faith and Reason* 16 (1990), pp. 63-79. Reprinted with permission.

For the level was very high, and certainly so intellectually. Each of the great Greek philosophical schools—the Platonists, the Aristotelians, the Epicurean atomists, and the Stoics, to all of whom Western thought owes so much—took Socrates for inspiration. There were, of course, other war heroes like Socrates, there were other men of wisdom, there were others who died bravely though perhaps not with the same calm as he did. But no one from classical antiquity is remembered as having matched Socrates' resolve to avoid, as if it were "the poisonous bite of a Tarantula,"[3] the vice of homosexuality in which the classical world saw the noblest form of love.

On this point no ancient or modern critic charged Xenophon, whose writings on Socrates constitute one of the two chief surviving sources, for having injected himself into Socrates' story. But in many other respects Xenophon was very much "autobiographical," a reason why his writings on Socrates have been much less commented upon than is the case with the other chief source, Plato's four dialogues known as *Euthyphro, Apology, Crito,* and *Phaedo.* Yet even these have not been immune to the charge that they are more the record of Plato's ideas than of Socrates.

Undoubtedly it was Socrates who drank the hemlock and not Plato, doubtful as one may be about the motivations which Plato ascribes to Socrates for that heroic act. The variety of motivations ascribed to Socrates in the remote and recent past may seem to constitute a further proof of the validity of Butler's remark. It should be enough to take the very different views offered on Socrates by three such different thinkers and personalities as Stone, Popper, and Guardini. Yet they are at one in missing something most decisive in the thinking of Socrates in reference to his death, the very point to be explored in this essay because of its great cultural significance.

A Marxist Socrates

As to the recent American bestseller, *The Trial of Socrates*, its thesis may appear a foregone conclusion if one recalls that its author earned his living for much of his life as the editor of *I. F. Stone's Weekly*, a muckraking leftist New York journal. At the very start of his book Stone voices his hope about the eventual realization of a social system in which Marx and Jefferson would be the two leading lights.

Plato has always been high on the list of compulsory readings for Marxists. Plato's ideal state as described in the *Republic* and the *Laws* could easily appear as an anticipation of regimented Marxist society. Since it is regimented, it has also to be elitist, a point which Marxists try in vain to gloss over. But for Stone, Socrates is not only an elitist but also a most skillful elitist who goads the working democracy of Athens into condemning him to death for exercising the basic right of democracy which is free speech: "Socrates looks more like a picador enraging a bull than a defendant trying to mollify the jury."[4]

Marxist writers have always loved working in democracies that worked. Obviously, it is in their best interest to discredit anyone who either by his arguments or by his outstanding comportment exposes their double standards which is to take full advantage of a working democracy while doing their best to undermine it. Not one of them likes to recognize boomerangs in those very weapons that were supposed to serve as foolproof instruments for bringing about the ultimate triumph of the proletariat. Champions of *perestroika* must have nightmares on realizing that today they are beaten with their most vaunted strategy or technique.

Have not those champions been taught that the tools of production determine the outcome of history? Are they not at last seeing that Marxism is being beaten by the new physics and the semiconductor technology built on it? Is it not evident that the technology in question can be developed and kept explosively productive only through the free flow of information, the very last thing compatible with a closed society?

But these are precisely the points not seen by Stone, a political ideologue and a stranger to science and technology. Consequently, Stone makes the preposterous claim that Socrates chose death because he was tired of life.[5] Stone deliberately slights what Socrates really looked for and the principal argument he afforded on behalf of that outlook. The latter has an eery relevance for this scientific age, which Stone and other humanists, Marxists as well as Christians, still have to discover. But this is to anticipate.

A Popperian Socrates

It may seem more puzzling that the argument in question was completely missed by Popper whom many in our times take for the definitive philosopher of science. The points of definitive validity which, according to Popper, are made by Socrates can readily be gathered from Popper's *The Open Society and Its Enemies*. Among the points are the principle of falsifiability and Socrates' commitment to teaching "that the spirit of science is criticism."[6] But if Socrates was so Popperian and so intent on science, the extent of his knowledge of the science of his time must have been considerable.

Popper's failure to raise the question about that extent and probe into it should seem baffling for several reasons. One is that Popper admits only one philosophy, namely the one which has science for its sole object. Another reason is that Socrates was very much concerned about science. In fact science was Socrates' supreme concern in his supreme hour. To ignore that concern of Socrates should seem all the more serious if one is to grant at least a modicum of truth to a remark of Xenophon suggesting the very opposite. According to Xenophon Socrates recommended to his followers the study of astronomy only insofar as it provided useful information for everyday life. "To continue the study of astronomy so far as to distinguish the bodies which do not move in the same circle with the heaven, the planets, and the irregular stars, and to weary ourselves in inquiring into their distances from the earth, the periods of their revolutions, and the causes of all these things, was what he greatly discountenanced."[7]

Popper's failure to consider Socrates' real concern about science may suggest that perhaps Popper's own chief concern is not so much the criticism of science but criticism for the sake of criticism. Such a criticism can serve as a sophisticated foil against facing up to points of fundamental validity. It should be no secret to anyone familiar with *The Logic of Scientific Discovery* that whenever Popper faces up to criticism as a means for establishing a truth to which all must bow, he sidesteps the issue. He does not want to cast a vote on behalf of that closed society which sets limits, in the name of universally valid truths and norms, to the individual's unbridled pursuit of his own individualism.

Popper holds high individualism as he identifies Socrates' foremost leading principle as the conviction that "it is better to be a victim of injustice than to inflict it upon others." Then Popper adds: "I think it is this last doctrine which can help us best to understand the core of his teaching, his creed of individualism, his belief in the human individual as an end in himself."[8]

Of course, Popper does not mean by this anything similar to the Christian conviction about the sacredness of the individual. At any rate, Popper holds that Socrates' death was the ultimate proof of his sincerity. "He showed that a man could die, not only for fate and fame and other grand things of this kind, but also for the freedom of critical thought," if not for the principle of falsification, one would be tempted to add. Popper injects into the story of Socrates's death his own thinking about democracy as an "open society." In fact he injects himself into that story so deeply as to see only his thoughts in the most decisive turn of that story, which comes when Socrates is given the opportunity to escape. According to Popper, had Socrates seized that opportunity "and become an exile, everybody would have thought him an opponent of democracy. So he stayed and stated his reasons."[9]

In recounting those reasons Popper is not at all eager to dwell on the overriding perspective and preoccupation of Socrates: the individual soul's eternal responsibility. The latter meant for Socrates either an eternal peace of mind, or a never ceasing remorse of conscience. Moreover, Socrates was ready to probe fully the materialist (and therefore Popperian) objection to the soul's immortality. The essence of the objection, in Socrates' very words, was a particular interpretation of "the subject of the causes of generation and decay,"[10] a subject undoubtedly scientific. And possibly because Socrates made even more unscientific whatever was scientific in the contemporary understanding of that subject, Popper had to pass over the matter, lest he make appear ridiculous his presentation of Socrates as a champion of the scientific spirit.

An Idealist Socrates

Romano Guardini, another important modern interpreter of Socrates' trial and death, certainly cannot be suspected of being uneasy about the question of the immortality of the soul. With his book, *The Death of Socrates*, he hoped to lead a modern world, but especially his adopted country, Germany, devastated and decimated by World War II, to the vision of something in man that survives death. Guardini tried to achieve this most noble aim by reconstructing as closely as possible Socrates' state of mind in the process of taking one step after another toward his being condemned to death and the implementation of his death sentence. Guardini proceeds most meticulously. He offered, with many quotations, a step by step analysis of *Euthyphro,* of the *Apology,* of *Crito,* and of *Phaedo,* all with subheadings, lest anything be missed by the reader as the interpretation develops. Guardini's reader will, however, miss the crucial point by being endlessly reminded of the Platonic essence or *eidos.*

In *Euthyphro* Socrates allows Euthyphro suspect that he, Socrates, is not in quest of a particular form of piety but of its essence. It is the question of essence which for Guardini is, and rightly so, the basic idea in those four dialogues. It reappears in Socrates' three defense speeches, recorded in the *Apology*, in reference to truth and to the duty to speak truthfully in harmony with that divine voice that speaks through man's conscience. Even more so does the idea of essence take the center stage in *Crito*, especially when Socrates declines the offer to make use of the opportunity to escape. His reason is that the act of escaping would contradict his very essence which is manifested in his life-long commitment to solving ethical problems.

It is here that the immortality of that essence or soul comes into sharpest focus, a point that dominates *Phaedo* throughout. It does so both through the objections of Cebes and Simmias to the immortality of the soul and through Socrates' replies. Socrates first tries to prove the soul's immortality from the principle of the generation of opposites. Socrates' friends remain unimpressed by his reference to the Egyptian practice of embalming the body as suggestive of the soul's immortality. He makes no better impression on them by referring to the mind's ability to recall ideal, that is, essential forms or absolute forms of things which cannot be seen by bodily eyes.

Socrates himself realizes that a far better argument is needed. That it will be such is signalled by Guardini through the subheading, "The answer to Cebes and the decisive argument."[11] To call that argument "decisive" certainly fits the existentialist setting in which Socrates presents it. The setting reveals him to be at a decisive stage of his life, indeed at a point where he turns from youth into man, in more than one sense.

Socrates recalls that as a young man he had a passionate desire for the wisdom which he hoped to find in the study of physical science. But he obviously needed a shock, a sudden disillusion, if he was to extricate himself from the trap in which his infatuation with physical science had landed him. The blow came from his hearing somebody read aloud a book, called *Mind*, by Anaxagoras, the latest and most impressive among pre-Socratic *physikoi*. Young Socrates eagerly listened in the hope that finally he would hear of a physics which explains processes with a reference to a mind which always acts for a purpose and therefore accounts in the deepest possible sense for the question why this and that happens. "If we wish to discover the cause of the generation or destruction or existence of a thing we must discover how it is *best* for that thing to exist, or to act, or to be acted on" (italics added).[12]

But as he was sitting on the bed in the cell in which he was soon to drink the hemlock, he recalled that he had had "all his splendid hopes dashed." To illustrate the haplessness he had felt as a young man, he assured his friends that on the basis of the enlightenment provided by physics he would have long ago escaped: "For, by the dog of Egypt, I think that these muscles and bones would long have been in Megara or Boeotia, prompted by their opinion of what is best, if I had not thought it better and more honourable to submit myself to whatever penalty the state inflicts, rather than escape by flight."[13]

After quoting these lines from *Phaedo*, Guardini offers his comment: Socrates went to the philosophers of nature with fundamental philosophical questions about the existence of things and their origin. In listing those questions Guardini does not mention the one about the purpose of things or about their being for their very best. Socrates had to find, Guardini states, that those philosophers understood by their looking for the arrangement of things by reason or the Mind "the reference of empirical phenomena to ultimate, metaphysically conceived constituents, such as water, air, fire, and so forth." In Guardini's reconstruction those philosophers "practised, therefore, a kind of mythological physics—and Socrates got no answer to his questions."[14] He had to realize, Guardini continues, that questions about beings and their nature "cannot be deduced from any analysis of their component parts." He is in the prison because "he has come to see clearly the ethical *eidos* which contains both the imperative, that which ought to be, and the "best" for himself, that is, the meaningful."[15]

The rest of Guardini's comment is an elaboration on the *eidos* or the Platonic substance which as such has to be immortal. It is a comment that signally fails to do justice to the fact that Socrates did not want merely to restate his belief in the immortality of the soul with a reference, however dramatic, to his youthful experience, but wanted to give, in Guardini's very words, a "decisive argument."

The decisive argument

That Guardini was to miss that decisive argument was foreshadowed by his failure to quote from *Phaedo* a crucial passage of over twenty lines that precedes Socrates' reference to his dashed hopes. The passage is introduced by Socrates' remark, already quoted, that Anaxagoras' reference to Mind as the guiding principle of Nature could only mean that a true physics of Nature should find everything in Nature arranged for the best. The passage makes it clear that Socrates found most valuable a physics in which the principal concern is not, for instance, whether the earth is spherical and in the center of the universe, but whether both features are *best* for the earth. Socrates recalled that he also wanted to learn from Anaxagoras why was it best for the sun, the moon, and the stars to do their revolutions as they did. He was disappointed all the more so because he felt to be shortchanged by Anaxagoras on the all important point of what the role of mind, or understanding, was ultimately about: "I never thought that, when he said that things are ordered by Mind, he would introduce any reason for their being as they are, except that they are best so."[16]

Socrates (or Plato) utterly failed to realize that his identification of understanding as a means of registering purpose and, consequently, as a decisive proof of the immortality of the individual soul, was to undermine the credibility of his argumentation. It was also to steer, by the same stroke, discourse about nature into a bottomless morass. The latter is usually the product of equivocations or of misplaced analogies, in this case the heedless application of the same word "best" to inanimate and animate, and in fact, to spiritual acts. And since Guardini did not have for his expertise that discourse, or science, and much less its history, he failed to note Socrates' failure and the enormous threat it posed to culture. Yet Guardini's own German cultural ambience should have alerted him to that threat. Was it not the German idealists—Fichte, Schelling, and Hegel—who tried to replace Newtonian physics with a physics of purposes in which not a single paragraph was free of absurdities?[17]

In offering his "decisive" argument Socrates performed a most un-Socratic, that is, unwise turn, a turn with fateful consequences for Greek as well as early Western intellectual history. What that "decisive" argument lead to has been taken very lightly by almost all readers of *Phaedo* except some very attentive ones. Of course, the reader must be especially attentive, which is not an easy task for most readers of Platonic dialogues, full of repetitions and conversationalist platitudes. Their attention may already be flagging by the time they reach the point in *Phaedo* where Socrates suddenly changes tactics.

Instead of developing in full his "decisive" argument, forshadowed in his questions about what was best for the earth, the sun and other bodies, he begs for licence to shift to another argument, which he calls "the second string to my bow."[18] He merely plucks again an old string as he waxes prolific on the idea of an absolute that alone explains any class of existents insofar as they embody such general properties as beauty, quantity, good, and so forth.

Plato's occasional sophistry, if not wishful thinking, is nowhere more visible in the entire *Phaedo* than in his portrayal of Cebes' surrender to a proof of the immortality of the soul which he had already rejected. Plato's only excuse may lie in the fact that he had written *Phaedo* a decade or two before he wrote *Timaeus*. There he speaks of the universe as an animated being acting for its own good which he leaves unspecified. Yet in the pages which in *Phaedo* immediately precede Socrates' preparation for death, Plato puts in Socrates' mouth a myth in which one can recognize that *good* about which Socrates had just claimed that he could not find out either from others or from himself.

The myth is about the interior of the earth, full of streams and cavities, so many passage ways and abodes for the souls according to their good or bad record.[19] In other words, the only good that can be meaningfully known about the earth or physical reality in general is, according to Socrates, a markedly spiritual or, rather, biological or organismic metaphor. The only question that should be asked about physical reality relates to its suggesting, and in a rather primitive manner, the eternal good of the soul or its eternal punishment. It was that perspective that in Socrates' eyes justified decisively his belief in the immortality of the soul and made him ready to drink the hemlock. A classic case of an anti-reductionist trying to achieve his aim by endorsing a different kind of reductionism.

Antiscientific failure of nerve
Socrates drank the poison without losing composure even for a moment, an undoubtedly heroic act. Yet the reasoning underlying that act included a failure of nerve with respect to the investigation of physical reality. The impact which Socrates made on classical antiquity and beyond always carried with it that failure, or an absence of what William James memorably called "tough minded" mentality. All major intellectual trends of post-Socratic antiquity are an example.

The most obvious case is that of the Epicureans. For all their fondness for atomism, they initiated no systematic search into the constitution of matter or a consistent discourse about an atomistically constituted universe. They did not because of their fear that thereby they would deprive existence of purpose. The Stoics let the universe be subject to periodic conflagrations while they bravely tried to find purpose in cosmic ashes. The Platonists, especially their brand initiated by Plotinus, tried to find purpose in a process which suggested the very opposite: They as a man shied away from the physical universe as an object of inquiry with any purpose. Plotinus was in particular praised by his biographer, Porphyry, for cultivating only the theoretical parts of the sciences.

Even the Aristotelians, whose leader so resolutely pointed at the terrestrial ground as the starting point of all knowledge, failed to break out of the perspective set by Socrates. With Aristotle too the primary questions about purpose could only be saved if all is supposed to be permeated with purpose. Such is the basis of Aristotle's doctrine of natural places and natural motions, a doctrine that put the study of physics into a straitjacket for almost two millennia.[20] It was no accident that Aristotle discussed the free fall of bodies in terms of their nature or propensities. Worse, he gave a quantitative touch to that intellectually perverse enterprise of his. A body, so Aristotle claims in *On the Heavens*, which has twice as much mass as another body, will fall twice as fast toward the center of the earth, its natural place owing to its twice larger nature or propensity.[21]

Aristotle's reasoning was perverse not only because it flew in the face of everyday evidence, but also because it revealed some perversity in man's nature. The perversity consists in man's inability to show intellectual humility in the face of the fact that man's knowledge of reality has various aspects that conceptually cannot be reduced to one another. Why, one may ask, did Socrates fail to oppose Anaxagoras with a *distinguo*: the mechanistic (quantitative) features of things and processes were one thing, an exclusively mechanistic philosophy of existence another. Could Socrates not have espoused the former while rejecting the latter?

The baby and the bathwater
The question is the one about the baby and bathwater. Was it necessary to throw out the baby, or the quantitative study of matter,

just because that study was immersed in a dirty bathwater which, in this case, was not even of the baby's own making? Should it not have been obvious to separate the two and save the quantitatively exact study of matter as a most valuable enterprise?

Had Socrates and his many admirers perceived this, intellectual as well as political history would have been very different. As to the former, thinking about scientific method might not have become restricted to the principle of "saving the phenomena" which barred the consideration of real physical causes. For that restriction the lop-sided Socratic program of "saving the purpose" bears a heavy responsibility.

As to political history, it should be enough to consider the following question: What if the colonizing urge of the Greeks had gone hand in hand with expertise in the science of motion, or specifically in the science of ballistics? About the latter even an Archimedes had only some practical rules and, what is most important, he loathed being involved in constructing machines. The statics of floating bodies he developed meant no breakthrough toward that science which becomes true to itself only by dealing successfully with that physical world all of whose parts are constantly in motion.

The Babe behind the baby
That there lay a moral failure behind the Greeks' inability to give birth to science, which is either the science of motion or hardly science at all, is amply brought out by scientific history. The first of Newton's three laws of motion was formulated in a medieval theological context, which, let us not forget it, is always a context of divine grace aimed at healing man's various failings, of which one of them is the failure to see the obvious and all too often to resist it. It is against this background that one should see Buridan's epoch-making commentaries on Aristotle's *On the Heavens*, itself a most systematic celebration of the eternity and divinity of the cosmos and a relentless unfolding of some stupefying "scientific" consequences of that cosmic vision.

In rejecting Aristotle's claim about the eternity of the universe, Buridan was sustained by a long Christian tradition about the creation of the universe out of nothing and in time. Buridan, however, went one step further than the theologians by also asking the question about the *how* of the beginning of all motion. Duhem's great pioneering studies, now almost a century old, of Buridan's feat and its impact on Copernicus, Descartes, and Galileo, and indirectly on Newton, cannot be reviewed here in detail.[22] Let it merely be noted that Buridan's belief in creation out of nothing and in time was a Christian belief, a belief rooted in the Babe of Bethlehem.[23]

As a Christian, Buridan believed in that Babe as the only begotten son of God. In and through that belief Buridan had a powerful safeguard against the temptation of taking the universe for a begetting, that is, for an emanation from the divine principle. That temptation of pantheism, to which all pagans of classical antiquity fell a ready prey, ruined their religion as well as their science. To that temptation Jewish and Muslim scholars put up a far from convincing opposition.

It should therefore be easy to understand that in these modern or post-Christian times, so heavily infected with pantheism, one witnesses the Socratic "turn" both in its original form and also in its reverse. In its original form it is resurrected by the proliferation of cosmic gnosticism which is all too often the ideology behind sundry efforts to save the earth from ecological threats. In its reverse the Socratic turn is at work in the infatuation with quantitative patterns which in our times all too often serves as an excuse for ignoring considerations about purpose and values. Patterns, invariably quantitative or statistical, serve as justification for outright contempt for values, especially for ones hallowed by Christian moral tradition.

Indeed, post-Christian modern man finds it practically impossible to recognize the respective rights of quantitative considerations as well as of genuine value judgments. Engrossed with patterns, which he takes for substitutes for values, modern man throws out the baby of pure values, a baby invisible in the dirty water of scientistic reductionism. Modern man's predicament has been aggravated by many wrong cures which unwittingly point to the only effective remedy: It consists in a surrender to that Babe who as the Master from Nazareth challenged reductionism at its very core. He did so by pointing out the respect due to both sides of the tax coin or of any real coin for that matter. In doing so He set the pattern for a turn to which mankind, if it is to save its very purpose, must constantly return, and especially in this age which is not only the age of science but which, with every passing year, becomes even more scientific.

[1] "Every man's work, whether it be literature or music or pictures or architecture or anything else, is always a portrait of himself, and the more he tries to conceal himself, the more clearly will his character appear in spite of him." Quoted from the Signet edition, New York, New American Library. 1960, p. 60.

[2] S. Kierkegaard, *Philosophical Fragments,* tr. D. F. Swenson (Princeton: Princeton University Press, 1946), p. 44.

[3] See Xenophon, *Memorabilia,* 3, 12. Everyman's Library edition, p. 22.

[4] I. F. Stone, *The Trial of Socrates* (1988; New York: Doubleday, 1989), p. 186.

[5] Even Plato, Stone remarks, does not take seriously Socrates' mysticism in which death appears as a "doorway to unblurred vision" (ibid. p. 196).

[6] K. R. Popper. *The Open Society and Its Enemies* (1945; Princeton: Princeton University Press, 1971), vol. 1, p. 185.

[7] Xenophon, *Memorabilia,* 7, 4. Everyman's Library edition, p. 147.

[8] Popper, *The Open Society and Its Enemies,* vol. 1, p. 190.

[9] Ibid., p. 194.

[10] *Phaedo,* XLV. This and the subsequent quotations are from the translation by F. J. Church, in the Library of Liberal Arts (Indianapolis: Bobbs-Merrill, 1951).

[11] R. Guardini, *The Death of Socrates,* tr. B. Wrighton (New York: Sheed & Ward, 1948), p. 142.

[12] *Phaedo,* XLVI.

[13] Ibid., XLVII.

[14] Guardini, *The Death of Socrates,* p. 148.

[15] Ibid., p. 149.

[16] *Phaedo,* XLVI.

[17] For details, see ch. 8 "The Illusions of Idealism," in my Gifford Lectures, *The Road of Science and the Ways to God* (Chicago: University of Chicago Press, 1978).

[18] *Phaedo,* XLVII.

[19] Ibid., LVII.

[20] For details, see ch. 1 in my *The Relevance of Physics* (Chicago: University of Chicago Press, 1966).

[21] *On the Heavens,* 273b.

[22] See ch. 10 in my *Uneasy Genius: The Life and Work of Pierre Duhem* (Dordrecht: Martinus Nijhoff, 1984).

[23] For further discussion, see my *The Savior of Science* (Washington: Regnery-Gateway, 1988).

4

Medieval Creativity
in Science and Technology

The word "medieval" is a derivative of *medium aevum* (Middle Ages), a term unknown to the medievals. Had anyone among their contemporaries tried to fasten that term upon them, they would have strongly protested. From the closing decades of the twelfth century, the latest possible point to mark the beginning of the High Middle Ages (a late nineteenth-century term), the medievals were very conscious of being in the forefront of progress, which is the very opposite of being caught somewhere in the middle between the old and the new. The idea of a progressive history was, in fact, formulated in the medieval School of Chartres.[1]

Those in that school and other twelfth-century scholars in the Latin West knew all too well the immense measure of their debts to ancient Greece and Rome. John of Salisbury, first a teacher in the School of Chartres and then bishop of Chartres, spoke of ancient Greece and Rome as a giant's two shoulders. It was only by standing on those shoulders, John of Salisbury warned, that he

First published in *Technology in the Western Political Tradition*, ed. M. R. Zinman *et al* (Ithaca, N.Y.: Cornell University Press, 1993), pp. 46-68. Reprinted with permission.

and his contemporaries saw farther than their remote predecessors.[2] For all his genuine modesty, John of Salisbury did not mean to disparage thereby his and his colleagues' conviction of seeing very much farther than the ancients.

And see they did many novel things, either by achieving them or by boldly conjuring them up as so many marvelous characteristics of a perhaps not too distant future. Toward the middle of the fourteenth century, which may mark the end of the High Middle Ages, the medievals coined the word "modern" and applied it to themselves. The word certainly contained the meaning of being modish, but this is precisely what progress is all too often. Even today, to progress is to come up with ever new modes, manners, fashions, and novelties—so many marks of an unrelenting readiness to innovate and invent.

The most monumental evidence of medieval inventiveness relates to architecture. The newly introduced buttresses and pointed arches allowed Gothic cathedrals to soar to daringly new heights. No less innovative were the techniques, many of them unknown today, that produced the enchanting hues in the Cathedral of Chartres and in many other medieval places of worship. Without taking a clue from the few traces of bright color remaining on Greek sculpture, the frieze of the Parthenon, for example, medievals displayed the same exuberance in painting the interior walls of many of their cathedrals.

Medievals were no less notably inventive in music, social organization, philosophy, and, last but not least, technology and science. Awareness of all this had for some time been close to the vanishing point when the expression *medium aevum* made its first appearance in the closing decades of the seventeenth century and inspired the coinage of words such as "Mittelalter," "Moyen-Age," and "Middle Ages." Chief responsibility for this resides with the immensely popular textbooks on history by Christoph Keller, a German educator.[3] As one living in the latter half of what Alfred North Whitehead called the century of genius, Keller had no choice but to see a mere transitional period in what stretched between classical and modern times. The latter began, according to Keller, with the Reformation of faith and the Baconian instauration of knowledge. The Renaissance as a distinct age was yet to be invented by Jacob Burckhardt around 1850.

By then the word "medieval" had for some time been also a term of abuse and has remained so to the present time, a fact still to be recognized by makers of English dictionaries.[4] In actual use the word is all too often synonymous with such unflattering adjectives as "regressive," "obscurantist," and "barbarian." As a term of abuse or contempt, it shows up in the most unwarranted contexts. Undoubtedly, for the public relations man of a State-owned automobile factory in a Communist regime in 1990 it was catastrophic to find that on the day after New Year's none of the 1,500 workers showed up for the morning shift. It may, however, be doubted that this fact justified the official in question to look at the abandoned production lines and sigh: "It's like a medieval plague."[5] He should instead have spoken of "counter-revolution," the plague most feared and resisted in Marxist realms, but he no longer had this privilege. His workers simply extended their celebration of New Year's Day beyond the legal limit by sensing a "medieval" straw in the wind. The still partly Communist regime in Prague had, by giving amnesty to all political prisoners, resorted to the typically "medieval" gesture of forgiving in the uncanny expectation that within a few months they themselves might need a similar gesture, and in an ample measure at that.

But to return to the middle of the nineteenth century. By then the period known as Romanticism had run its course after having restored an appreciation for Gothic architecture, which had been held in contempt for many centuries. Auguste Comte, the father of positivism, even made it fashionable to speak appreciatively of medieval social organization. In the second half of the nineteenth century something more began to be seen in Scholastic philosophy than a slavish imitation of old phrases and a bent for logic chopping. Still later, by the mid-twentieth century, leading American universities vied with one another in setting up chairs and courses in medieval philosophy. No less eagerly they began to find a place in their libraries for books and periodicals on this formerly suspect subject.

But even then it was not yet academically respectable to speak of medieval inventiveness in science and technology. It was one thing to decry as dinosauric a book on the history of astronomy in which the medieval period was represented by three or four literally empty pages.[6] It was another, and a rather risky affair, to speak of medieval science with a touch of genuine admiration. This was all the more curious because by the 1930s and 1940s a massive scholarly evidence about science in the Middle Ages had for some time been available. Even when, from the 1960s on, it could appear unscholarly to ignore medieval science, appreciative references to it were often qualified with remarks that amounted to the art of damning with faint praise.

If the word "damning" is taken in its erstwhile theological connotation, the clue to this curious performance easily comes into focus. "Medieval" and "Middle Ages" became terms of abuse during the Enlightenment, an age that saw its chief task as replacing the darkness of faith with the light of reason. The faith was, of course, Christianity with its insistence not only on a personal Creator but also on a supernatural revelation. That insistence found its most notable social embodiment in medieval Latin Christianity. As to reason, the chief connotation given to it by the champions of the Enlightenment related to Newtonian science. In England Alexander Pope declared that once God "let Newton be, all was light." In France Voltaire's career as the chief of *philosophes* started with his popularizations of Newton's physics, about which he knew no more than popular accounts. In Germany Kant wrote in the preface to the second edition of the *Critique of Pure Reason* that "when Galileo caused balls to roll down an inclined plane, . . . a light broke upon all students of nature."[7]

In writing the *Critique* Kant meant to spread that light in the deepest possible sense. He believed he was offering the only valid and rationally respectable form of metaphysics that, unlike traditional or Scholastic metaphysics, had man instead of God as the ultimate source of reason. Moreover, the anti-theistic arguments of the *Critique* had, according to Kant, that very final validity that in his eyes was the hallmark of Newtonian physics.

Kant had but a smattering of knowledge of Newton's physics.[8] Were this to be widely perceived, broadly shared doubts might arise about the reliability of Kant's attack on the cosmological argument, which is man's principal intellectual avenue to the recognition of God. More likely, modern Western man will find ever fresh pretexts to safeguard the absolute autonomy bequeathed to him by the Enlightenment. The latter is but a continuation of the Renaissance which began with a conscious reaching back to the pantheism and all too often crude paganism of classical antiquity.

We are still in that Renaissance, and its end is far from being in view. That Western man is today a Renaissance man is conveyed by his boasting of now living in a post-Christian age. The deity of this age is science, in which modern Western man finds the chief guarantee of his conviction of being his own absolute master and accountable to nothing higher. No wonder that modern Western man resists few things more violently than the claim, however scholarly, that the Latin medieval centuries, so synonymous with medieval Christianity, were distinctly and, in fact, creatively innovative in technology and science. This and nothing else is the true explanation for a reluctance, now almost a century old, to accept without major reservations Pierre Duhem's most scholarly unfolding of massive evidence about science in the Middle Ages.[9]

Duhem and a few other Catholic historians of science undoubt-edly saw in medieval science a credit to Catholic faith. Duhem himself viewed science in the Middle Ages as a proof of Christ's promise that those who seek first the Kingdom of Heaven will reap benefits on earth as well.[10] Duhem would have been the last to assert that they would be the sole recipients of such benefits. As a great logician, he would readily have seen through the apparent evenhandedness of the statement: "To deny or minimize the culturally desirable products of Christianity because one may consider Chris-tianity to be a fabric of illusions, is as subjective as to argue that Christianity is true because some of its effects seem salutary."[11]

Coming as it does from the late Lynn White, Jr., a prominent historian of medieval technology, the statement should seem most unbalanced for a historical reason. It relates not to the Age of Faith but to the Age of Reason or to modern times in general. Ever since Voltaire, Christians, or Catholics in particular, learned to live with the cultural shibboleth that their faith and science are mutually exclusive realms. Even today, three-quarters of a century after Duhem, they do not seem overly eager to make much of his findings. Yet they could learn nothing less than that they are under a make-believe siege based on their and their antagonists' ignorance about what has taken place in the history of science. But only the dullest Catholic intellectual would fail to sense the plight of modern unbelievers confronted with some facts of medieval science. Those who staked their unbelief or agnosticism on the rationalistic account of the roots of science will hardly learn to live with their scholarly uprooting.

So much for the broader ideological stakes behind the topic of this essay—stakes that ought to be spelled out at the very outset as a service to intellectual honesty. Such honesty may prompt some readers to admit, at least to themselves, that their boasting about not having a religion may be a mere camouflage for their avid espousal of the religion known as secularism. At any rate, it should be clear that one can no more appraise the Middle Ages in general, or its science in particular, while disregarding the Catholic creed, than one can understand the formation of the United States without studying the Federalist Papers or understand England apart from the Magna Carta. This is even true about medieval inventiveness in technology, a field apparently unrelated to theology. But the theological roots of medieval science will appear crucially decisive with respect to the most significant scientific breakthrough in the history of science, which was achieved during the High Middle Ages. It was, as will be seen, a breakthrough to the very possibility of science insofar as it deals with this very physical world, a world of things in motion.

In view of the secularist tone of most discourse about science, it becomes almost obligatory to offer a word of apology whenever those medieval centuries are claimed to be progressive in the scientific and technological sense in which progress is almost exclusively understood nowadays. The editor of *Smithsonian* magazine seemed to be very much on the defensive when introducing an article by Lynn White, Jr., with the caption: "Middle Ages weren't 'dark' since invention found expression in architecture, mills, roads—and ideas bearing fruit in the 20th century."[12] Most likely the editor rather than White was responsible for the title of his essay, "Medieval Europe Foresaw Planes, Cars, Submarines."

This is certainly a catchy title but hardly a promising catch. For if only visionary cars, planes, and submarines can be caught in the net of the student of medieval technology, the efforts are largely wasted. Yet the catch should seem very tangible and exciting if White was right in stating almost at the outset: "While nothing of ancient Greek or Roman engineering perished along the road, the attitudes, motivations and most of the basic skills of modern technology before the electronics revolution originated not in Mediterranean antiquity but during the 'barbarian' Middle Ages."[13]

White was not alone in making his startling statement. In 1976 the MIT Press published Arnold Pacey's study on the ideas and idealism in the development of technology, which contains a long chapter with the title, "A Century of Invention: 1250-1350."[14] Those hundred years are certainly a part of the High Middle Ages. Moreover, in Pacey's book only that chapter has the word "invention" in its title, although eight centuries prior to 1900 are covered in its eight chapters. Clearly, the High Middle Ages had to be particularly inventive in matters technological.

The 1970s also saw the publication of *Turning Points in Western Technology* by D. S. L. Cardwell, who specifies four stages in the development of technology. The last stage began in the late nineteenth century with the establishment of research laboratories. This was preceded by the Industrial Revolution, which in turn owed much to the second stage, or the publicity given to mechanical arts by Bacon and other seventeenth-century empiricists. Cardwell locates the first stage in the Middle Ages and refers to the stationary character of Greco-Roman technology. Furthermore, he describes the advance over classical antiquity made by medieval engineers as something amounting to a mutation. Overused as this word may be among academics today, it should at least alert them to the magnitude of the change:

> Such, in fact, was the precocity, diversity and importance of medieval technics that one is inclined to believe that a *mutation*, philosophical or spiritual, had occurred, so that medieval civilisation was sharply and basically different from all those that had preceded it. The technics of the period were precocious in that they often ran far ahead of the very limited scientific knowledge available. They were diverse in the vast range of activities they were concerned with and they were important, not merely by virtue of their cumulative effects on the economic development of society but also because several medieval inventions decisively and fundamentally changed man's outlook on the world. Very few subsequent inventions had the same universal significance in this respect as did the weight-driven clock and the printing press. Modern society is still basically conditioned by these two medieval inventions.[15] (Emphasis added).

Such glowing appraisals of medieval technology represent a new point of view, perhaps a budding consensus. It certainly contrasts with the view that had set the standard until the 1950s. A memorable instance of that view can be found in a five-volume history of technology produced with the collaboration of many specialists under the editorship of Charles Singer, a leading historian of science half a century ago. In the epilogue to the second volume dealing with medieval technology Singer presented the Middle Ages as the end of a very long preparatory period, possibly even less than a transition.

The chief characteristic of that period, according to Singer, was the flow of technological know-how from the East to the West. Only when the Middle Ages ended, Singer wrote, "had the east almost ceased to give techniques and ideas to the west and ever since has been receiving them." According to Singer, this strange reversal should prompt two reactions. First, one has to marvel at the astonishingly effective accumulation of technological skill even in the absence of scientific guidance. Second, one has to be deeply impressed by what he called a "sharp contrast."[16] It consisted in the difference between a technological development that for many thousands of years did not depend on the guidance of science and a postmedieval development in which dependence on science has been essential for technology.

Clearly, one is in the presence of two very contrasting appraisals. In the one, voiced by Singer, the Middle Ages are at best a recipient; in the other, voiced by White and others, the medieval centuries are a creative starting point to which our modern times, so technological and scientific, are heavily indebted. The two viewpoints differ even in the counting of medieval centuries. Did the Middle Ages begin around 400 and end shortly after 1300? In this view, which is essentially that of Singer, the Middle Ages consist of seven centuries of stagnation followed by two centuries, the twelfth and thirteenth, of some dynamism, tempered if not hampered by the flowering of Scholasticism. Or did the Middle Ages begin with Charlemagne, about 800 and end about 1450, or just before the great majority of Plato's writings became known in the West?

The latter view may be preferable for two reasons. One is that in this case the end of the Middle Ages is closely followed by the beginning of the Renaissance in its deepest aspect, best revealed by the humanists' enthusiastic response to the sudden availability of most of Plato's works.[17] Underlying that enthusiasm was a conscious reassertion of the ideals of Greco-Roman humanism, a humanism very different from the medieval concept of man's nature and purpose. Also, if one begins the Middle Ages with the Carolingian renaissance of learning, one is spared seeing cultural unity in the four centuries postdating the onset of the formal demise of the Roman Empire in 410. Those four hundred years were an epoch of disintegration, upheavals, fragmentation, and instability—so many evidences not so much of a culture as of a transitional period between cultures. To be sure, the church was there as the only stable point, but its culture-making ability still had to make itself felt. The latter is a question not only of faith but of sociological conditions as well.

The chronological definition of the Middle Ages as an epoch from 800 to 1450 provides a logical ground for the historian insofar as the work of evaluation has to be concerned with comparison. Since such a comparison is usually a reference to the preceding culture, the evaluation of the Middle Ages has to be done with an eye on the Roman Empire.

During both the Middle Ages and Roman times material and organizational needs were keenly felt. The Roman Empire had periods of famine, as did the Middle Ages. Both heavily depended on agriculture and relied on manual labor. One was largely served by slaves, the other by serfs. Although the Christian serfs received more humane treatment than did the Roman slaves, the physical conditions of their lives were not much different. At any rate, the pagan Roman landowner had the same interest in a good harvest as did the medieval feudal lord. Why is it then that a major improvement of the plow had to wait for the Middle Ages? Unlike the traditional Roman plow, the medieval plow had, in addition to a vertical knife, a horizontal shear to slice under the sod and a moldboard to turn it over.[18]

Material needs, of course, must have played a part in that very important technological invention, but why then did those needs fail to spur the inventiveness of the Romans of old? They and the Greeks and other ancient nations that made much use of horses in warfare failed to exploit an elementary fact about the horse's anatomy. If a horse is made to pull something by means of a strap around its neck, it not only does so ineffectively but also risks being exposed to strangulation. However, the weight-pulling effectiveness of the horse can be increased fourfold with a breast harness, a medieval invention, as is the nailed horseshoe and the harnessing of horses in front of one another.[19] Their use for plowing the fields is first depicted on the Bayeux tapestry, more famous for showing Halley's comet.

Those medieval inventions made an agricultural revolution. Together with the introduction of three-field crop rotation, they almost doubled the harvest. While many of the physical conditions of medieval serfs remained much the same as those of Roman slaves, they ate much better. A further proof of this is the much wider use of watermills in the Middle Ages compared with Roman times. In England, for instance, a late eleventh-century count of three thousand villages registered almost twice as many watermills, a situation not untypical of other parts of Latin Christendom.

Watermills were needed for more than the grinding of grain. Fullers found a revolutionary use for them, proof of the fact that the clothes worn by medieval people were of better quality than those of their Roman forebears. (Those clothes also had buttons and pockets, two small but most useful advances achieved in the art of dressmaking during the Middle Ages). The use of watermills by fullers is tellingly evidenced in the description of the Abbey of Clairvaux, given about 1180 by a Cistercian monk.[20] The desciption is an encomium to machinery insofar as it relieves man of hard labor.

In the description of the abbey the visitor approaching it along the river first sees two hills, a vineyard and an orchard respectively, between which nestles the abbey itself. On the near side of the orchard the visitor finds a fishery, made possible by damming the river. From there the river is channeled into the abbey, but in such a way that in case of flood its surplus water would flow around the abbey along an auxiliary canal. From here on, let the anonymous monk take over:

> Once the river is let inside the abbey through a sluice, it first rushes against the flour mill, where it is very solicitous and occupies itself in many tasks, both in grinding the grain and in separating the flour from the bran. . . . But the river is far from being through with its work. It is invited by the fullers who labor next to the flour mills and who rightly demand that just as the river was busy in the mills so that the brethren may be fed, it should also assist the fullers so that the brethren may also be clothed. The river does not decline any work the fullers demand from it. By alternately raising and lowering the heavy stumps, or pestles, or if you wish hammers, or wooden legs (because this name better fits the fullers' jumping style of action), the river relieves them of their really heavy work. Or, if one may inject into a serious topic a remark in a light vein, the river takes upon itself the fullers' punishment for their sins. O God, in your goodness you provide so much respite to your poor servants lest they be overtaken by much sadness! How much relief do you administer to penitents from their sins, lest they feel oppressed by the hardship of their work! The backs of how many horses would be broken and how many men's arms greatly exhausted by a labor from which this river gratuitously dispenses us and without which no clothing, no food would be prepared! The river therefore shares our life while demanding nothing in a way of recompense for its work, which it performs under the blazing sun,

except that it may freely leave after it has diligently done its work. It has turned so many big wheels in rapid rotation that it emits froth so that it looks tamed and increasingly so as it moves on.

Instead of following the further course of the river through the numerous other workshops, such as the tannery and laundry, which are also enthusiastically described by that anonymous monk, let us return to his reference to the fullers' up-and-down legwork, now performed by trip-hammers. As well as describing the river's turning "so many big wheels in rapid rotation," he attests to the use of one of the foremost medieval technological inventions, the cam. It does nothing less than transform rotary motion into linear thrust, and vice versa. The medieval introduction of mechanical saws, not mentioned by the monk, is another example of the use of cams.

When in 1444 Bessarion, the future cardinal, arrived in Italy from the Peloponnesus, one of the things that struck him in particular was the widespread use of mechanical saws. He quickly urged his countrymen to send young mechanics to Italy to learn about this and other labor-saving machinery.[21] Here is a long-ignored witness to the technological superiority of Western over Eastern Christendom, a superiority also true with respect to the Muslim world.[22]

By the time of Bessarion's visit, trip-hammers had been in use for over four centuries in Latin Christendom, making possible not only the increased production of felt from raw cloth but also the more effective breaking up of various mineral rocks. One of the results was a truly transparent glass that made possible the invention of eyeglasses about 1280. This feat is still widely attributed to the Renaissance, although documentary evidence has been readily available in scholarly journals for more than half a century. Clearly, one is entitled to ask the question, "How is it that the importance of the late thirteenth-century Italian invention of spectacles has not been more generally appreciated?"[23] Academics, often bespectacled, would hardly disagree about the crucial cultural importance of eyeglasses. Then why are many of them disinclined to recognize the medieval provenance of that discovery? Perhaps because they would then be forced to note the specter of Christian theology and react to it with King Lear's words: "That way lies madness."

Modern Western academics are certainly reluctant to spread the word that medieval trip-hammers were responsible for the making of paper in large quantities. They are even less ready to consider that the greater availability of paper, as distinct from the scarce and very expensive parchment, made it natural to think about paper as a means for the wider distribution of written texts. Herein may lie the source of the medieval invention of printing. First came the extensive use of block printing, in itself a borrowing from the East, and then the introduction of movable type. Whether the idea of movable type came to the medievals from the East is a moot question.[24] At any rate, unlike the medieval Chinese and Koreans, the Christian Latin medievals made the most of printing from the early 1400s on. The Gutenberg Bibles would seem to be as impossible an achievement on a first try as would a Boing 707 for the Wright brothers's first flight or a Mustang for Henry Ford's first car. Gutenberg's contribution to the art of printing may not, in fact, have exceeded "a successful method for printing initial letters in color." This statement, however startling, is now a half century old and comes from Pierce Butler's *Origin of Printing in Europe.* Although published in 1940 by the University of Chicago Press, the book failed to make a dent in cultural consciousness despite its revolutionary message.[25]

Scholarly research notwithstanding, the invention of printing, which may have been an indirect outgrowth of the medievals' interest in watermills, is still largely credited to Gutenberg and the Renaissance. Not so completely ignored is the medievals' inventiveness in constructing windmills. They appeared everywhere in Europe during the latter part of the twelfth century, with a horizontal axis that had been unknown in the East. Furthermore, the vertical plane of the rotation of the blades was slightly tilted in order to obtain a better torque. This invention, too, was in part motivated by material needs, but other motivations must have been present. Otherwise it is difficult to explain the neglect of windmills in the Far East, especially in areas with strong winds, such as Tibet. There they largely drove prayer wheels. Since the medievals also prayed, and certainly their monks did, the ideology underlying their prayers must have had ingredients not possessed by the prayers of Buddhist monks.

Again, if practical need is the mother of all inventions, one is hard put to account for the primitiveness of Roman road building. To keep together their vast Empire, the Romans certainly needed good and easily reparable roads. They invariably used massive stone slabs, but water readily seeped between the big slabs and destroyed their alignment. Although the medievals found that it was better to leave the open roads unpaved, they were the first to cover city roads with square stones.

Mere material need is hardly the explanation for the stunning architectural innovations of the Middle Ages. To be sure, something practical had to be done to the old Roman-style of buildings whose flat, timber-supported, wood-paneled roofs and open fireplaces made them so many fire hazards. One remedy was to construct mantel-type fireplaces with chimneys; another was the replacement of those flat roofs with masonry vaulting. The Gothic-style church represented a saving in stones because the pointed arches did not require the support of walls as thick as those needed for the cylindrical roof of a Romanesque church. No material need can be seen for the raising of Gothic churches to ever greater heights, a feat made possible by the invention of side buttresses. The additionally felt need may have been a satisfaction of vainglory, but was such a need not rather an occasional deformation of genuine spiritual longing? While the predominantly horizontal lines of Greco-Roman temples symbolized a nature-bound religious perspective, Gothic spires symbolized the upward reach of a distinctly supernatural vision.

Again, it would be very difficult to specify the material need that motivated efforts to which Robert the Englishman referred in 1271. According to him "clockmakers are trying to make a wheel that will move exactly as the equinoctial circle."[26] What he meant was that various craftsmen were trying to invent a mechanism that made possible a weight-driven clock making a full turn every twenty-four hours. The pivotal part of such a mechanism was a double-feedback device whereby the gravitational pull of a weight was made to act at regular intervals, preferably measured in seconds or half-seconds.

The periodic rewinding of such a clock, to say nothing of its construction and maintenance, could at first be just as cumbersome as the periodic refilling of water clocks and the turning over of sand clocks. Also, the steady pull of weight-driven clocks was too weak to be useful for industrial purposes. Nor could the need for such a clock relate to better timekeeping. Available sand clocks and water clocks were exact to within a couple of minutes over a period of several hours. Greater precision in marking time was hardly needed in view of the slowness and unreliability of transportation. There is little substance to Lewis Mumford's often quoted statement that the invention of weight-driven clocks was motivated by an anticipation of the modern strictly regulated daily work schedule.[27]

The medievals were, of course, ready to turn their mechanical clocks to practical uses. This is shown by the oldest reference to mechanical clocks, a regulation issued in Sarum (Salisbury) that forbade the purchasing or selling of "flesh, fish or other victuals before the clock of the Cathedral had struck one."[28] More important is the possible identity of that clock as the one in the left nave of Salisbury Cathedral, the oldest of early mechanical clocks extant, dating from 1386. Being a fairly elaborate mechanism, it suggests that cathedral clocks were numerous from the mid-fourteenth century on. The same period marks also the beginning of frequent references to the planetary system, or the system of the world, as a clockwork mechanism. As they celebrated the universe as a clockwork, Newton and Voltaire perhaps unknowingly repeated an expression that, though Greco-Roman in origin, first achieved popularity in the Middle Ages.

Much less did Newton suspect that a most notable medieval reference to the universe as a clockwork occurred in a context that contained, in substance at least, his first law of motion. While Newton knew that Descartes certainly preceded him in stating that first law, the law of inertial motion, he wished posterity to remember him as its discoverer. To assure this, he spent precious time in his old age erasing from his notebooks references to Descartes. Not that Descartes was more ready to give credit to others, let alone to medievals. Though familiar with Scholastic thought as it was discussed in Jesuit schools around 1600, Descartes kept silent about his own indebtedness to the medieval tradition on an all-important point, the idea of inertial motion in the form of the theory of impetus.

The impetus theory was widely discussed in books written by teachers at such principal seats of late sixteenth-century Scholastic learning as the universities of Salamanca and Coimbra and the Collegio Romano. Earlier, and most important, Copernicus used the impetus theory in his *De revolutionibus* to answer objections created by the twofold motion of the earth.[29] Copernicus did not name his sources, nor did he claim originality. In all likelihood he had learned about the impetus theory while a student at the University of Cracow. Its library has several manuscript copies of Buridan's and Oresme's commentaries on Aristotle's *On the Heavens* in which they set forth their theory of impetus between 1330 and 1380. Their commentaries were widely copied and carried to all major universities of Europe. By the time Copernicus came on the scene about 1500, the impetus theory had been a widely shared idea for a century or so, though not yet through printed books. As a student, Copernicus learned about the impetus theory from codices or from plain oral tradition.

Copernicus was a student at the time the practice of publishing turned from the reprinting of medieval manuscripts, often selected at random, to the printing of original texts. Manuscripts, among them Buridan's and Oresme's commentaries, which were not printed until the early years of the sixteenth century, suddenly fell into a total oblivion. They began to be thrown out or to gather dust in many places, including such prestigious ones as the Bibliothèque Royale of Paris (which later became the Bibliothèque Nationale).

Voltaire, who could not have given higher praise to the age of Newton, might have refrained from taking jabs at the Middle Ages had he suspected that Newton's first law was in substance anticipated in the medieval Sorbonne. Early twentieth-century and strongly Voltairian France gasped in disbelief when, between 1905 and 1913, Pierre Duhem unearthed the startling evidence.[30] It included the fact that both Buridan and Oresme based their impetus theory on the very foundation of the Christian creed, or the creation out of nothing and in time. Both were teachers in a Sorbonne that was a bastion of Catholic orthodoxy.

The capital texts of Buridan and Oresme are fully available in English in Marshall Clagett's *The Science of Mechanics in the Middle Ages*[31] and in Edward Grant's *Sourcebook on Medieval Science.*[32] But the comments offered by them do not emphasize two most important points. One relates to Buridan's substantial anticipation of Newton's first law. Of course, Newton and Descartes had in mind a rectilinear inertial motion, while for Buridan (and for Copernicus and Galileo) the inertial motion of the planets and stars was still circular. Hence the insistence of Alexandre Koyré that the origin of modern physics, which is in a sense the origin of the idea of inertial motion, should be located not in the Middle Ages but in the seventeenth-century scientific revolution.[33] But is Buridan's notion of inertia as Aristotelian as Koyré wanted us to believe? Are Koyré's *Galilean Studies* a convincing refutation of Duhem's principal claims?[34]

The answers to these questions depend on an in-depth look at what lies beneath Aristotle's thinking about motion. For him motion always implies, in one way or another, that the moved body should remain in contact with the mover. The way can, of course, be almost "spiritual" such as the perennial desire of the celestial sphere to be moved by the Prime Mover. The latter, let it be recalled, is most likely a still "higher" celestial sphere, perhaps the empyrean heaven, but certainly not a Creator.

Less "spiritual," and indeed subtly physical or "ethereal," is the continuous contact whereby, according to Aristotle, the motion of the sphere of the fixed stars is transmitted to the planets. In discussing the cause of fully physical motions that take place below the moon's orbit, Aristotle reported the idea of *antiperistasis,* according to which a projectile keeps moving because the air that it separates closes in behind it and pushes the projectile forward.

What could Aristotle's reasons have been, one may ask, for not criticizing this rather absurd idea? It is here that an in-depth look is needed, and one that is unabashedly theological. Aristotle reasoned, of course, within the terms of a pantheistic religion for which all motions in the universe must not only be interconnected but be so in a very special manner: Everything had to be in contact with everything else, with no real beginning anywhere. Therefore the notion of *antiperistasis* had to appear to Aristotle as something germane to his general idea of motion as having its source in the continuous contact of the moved with the mover. This idea rested ultimately on his belief that the universe was uncreated and forever in motion.

It was precisely in this distinctly theological point that lay Buridan's break with Aristotle. For Buridan, the medieval Christian, the world was created in time, as explicitly defined at Lateran IV in 1215. In other words, for him the past history of the universe, or of motion for that matter, was strictly finite. Moreover, unlike Aristotle's Prime Mover, the Creator had to be essentially distinct from the universe. As a result, the created universe had to have an autonomy, an autonomy not necessary but contingent on the Creator's choice. It is by that choice that the Creator gave reality to one out of an infinite number of possible universes. Consequently, the celestial sphere and the planets move, according to Buridan, not through a quasi-physical contact with the Creator, who in that case would degenerate into Aristotle's Prime Mover, but rather through an impetus (quantity of motion or momentum) conferred on them in the very moment of creation. Buridan adds the all-important point that the celestial bodies retain their impetus undiminished because their motion takes place in a frictionless region of the universe.

So much on behalf of Buridan's substantial anticipation of Newton's first law of motion. It would seem to contradict Koyré and his many disciples and followers. For them the great breakthrough to modern science is the shift from circular to linear inertia. Rather, the really substantial shift was the one from motion through perennial continuous contact to a motion through an initial impetus imparted in an instant. If the latter shift had not taken place, the shift from circular to linear inertia would have remained inconceivable. In other words, insofar as science is a quantitative study of things in motion and the first law of Newton is the basis of his other laws, one may indeed speak of of the substantially medieval origin of modern science.

Moreover, that medieval origin is also of Christian origin in view of the impact on Buridan's thinking of the Christian dogma of creation out of nothing and in time, the second point not emphasized by Clagett and Grant. Buridan was part of a vast intellectual milieu that consciously relied on that dogma. This was an indispensable condition for the subsequent popularity of the impetus theory in the Christian medieval West. The importance of this point can best be appraised with an eye on medieval Jewish and Muslim milieus.

Surprising as it may seem, the doctrine of creation out of nothing and in time was much less emphasized in Jewish than in Christian ambience. For instance, in all of the many references to creation by Philo of Alexandria, only one constitutes an unambigous endorsement of creation out of nothing.[35] Then as today, liberal Jewish intellectuals displayed a curious sympathy for what is best described as Spinozean pantheism.[36] Within orthodox Judaism it became a trend to avoid questions that are not explicitly posed in the Hebrew Bible.[37] There one would look in vain for an explicit statement of creation out of nothing.

Orthodox Muslim thinkers, such as al-Ashari and al-Ghazzali, turned the voluntarist presentation of God in the Koran into an early form of occasionalism. They frowned on the idea of natural law as a constraint on Allah's ability to do whatever He wants to do. Today's Muslim fundamentalism may indeed be a last-ditch stand against the encroachment of natural law on Muslim thinking through the industrialization of Muslim lands.[38] Not a few intellectuals in Muslim countries are now drifting into a pantheistic stance just as readily as Avicenna and Averroes espoused Aristotelian necessitarianism. In both cases a resort to concealment also proved to be necessary.

The effectiveness with which pantheism has always been resisted within Christianity has much to do with the dogma of Incarnation, a tenet wholly alien to Jewish and Muslim thinking. The dogma of Incarnation, or the doctrine about the *monogenes* or *only begotten* Son who is Christ, could not fail to serve as a strong barrier against pantheism.[39] Within the Greco-Roman form of pantheism, the universe was the "monogenes" or "only begotten" emanation from a divine principle not really different from the universe itself. John's references to Christ as the "only begotten" therefore constituted an enormous semantic and doctrinal break with classical antiquity. Historians of science still have to discover that break as the means to a better understanding of the medieval origin of science.

That break was ultimately responsible for another aspect of the medieval stirrings of modern science. Because belief in the Word-made-flesh became a widely shared climate of thought in the Middle Ages, effective resistance could be made against Cathars and kindred sects. It passes nowadays for scholarship to present Cathars as innocent victims of a power-hungry intolerant Church.[40] The scholarship in question is very shortsighted with respect to the fate and fortunes of science. The medieval stirrings in science would have been nipped in the bud if the hatred for matter cultivated by Cathars and related groups had set the pattern for medieval culture. The same scholarship is also inconsistent because its implicit praise of the Cathar's hostility to matter is delivered from the pedestal of modern material comfort that science makes possible.

Science may become its own boomerang through modern man's worship of, if not of matter, at least of material goods. But in order to come into existence, modern science presupposed a positive attitude toward matter, the very attitude that could not be provided by the Cathars, or even by classical antiquity. There mechanical arts were at best tolerated by those in the know, not only the humanist brand but also their scientific counterparts, such as Archimedes, to mention only a leading figure.[41]

Mechanical arts were, however, cultivated in a spirit of euphoria through the better part of the Middle Ages. Witness the celebration of progress in the writings produced in the School of Chartres, the speculations about machines that fly, about machines that are driven by men pedaling inside them—speculations in which Friar Roger Bacon was not alone, though certainly best remembered.[42] Those speculations rose to such heights as to inspire designs of parachutes.

About 1010, Eilmer, a monk of Malmesbury Abbey, flew, with a glider, over six hundred feet, an event well remembered for almost three hundred years.[43]

Euphoria about material progress found a most colorful expression in medieval cathedrals. Today the plethora of statues and stone decorations in those cathedrals have their exuberance muted by a uniformly grayish shade. Relatively little remains of the original stained-glass windows aflame in inimitable colors. Those windows were matched (the Sainte Chapelle in Paris is the only major surviving example), by the no less colorful painting of columns, arches, and wall spaces.

Nature was fully inside those buildings dedicated to the supernatural. Nature was even celebrated there though never worshiped. A restrained wonder and respect for nature was the only attitude compatible with the doctrine of its having been made by the hands of the Creator. The same doctrine also gave people confidence that as the God-appointed stewards of nature they had to subdue, control, and investigate it. Irresponsible attitudes toward nature have crept in to the extent that people turned away from the beacon of that doctrine.[44]

Medieval man was, from the natural viewpoint, a motley creature in whose veins ran a wide variety of blood. That this racial mixture produced a particularly creative human being remains forever a vague speculative idea. A quite specific connection seems evident, however, between at least some principal aspects of the technological and scientific inventiveness of those who lived in that age and the faith they commonly shared.

If today mankind is in need of an invention, it is of a nontechnical nature. Late twentieth-century man is in need of reinventing a moral strength whereby he can control scientific inventions that nowadays feed upon one another in an almost runaway process. Moral strength, however, can come only from a morality based on knowing the difference between good and evil. Moral strength cannot come from a view of morality within which almost all craving for instant gratification is readily condoned. Furthermore, a morality based on knowing the difference between good and evil also includes knowledge of an all-important point: the knowledge that knowing the good will not necessarily bring about its being done. To forget this is the great fallacy of modern education, increasingly degenerating into mere instruction.

The medievals were no angels but at least they did not wish to abandon that high level to which their Christian faith had raised their vistas. On that level they held fast to knowing the difference between good and evil, even if all too often they fell far short of doing the good. Nothing is more important for their late twentieth-century counterparts, tied to science hand and foot, than to rescue themselves from the lowlands of moral relativism. They, and especially those in America, will not overcome the closing of their minds if a brief recall of places of learning, where an antidote to that relativism is still offered, is all they are willing to take for a remedy.[45] And if they find distasteful the digesting of that remedy, Aristotelian and Scholastic philosophy, they may still take a careful look at the Middle Ages. In Western history that was the first and thus far the last major epoch in which broadly shared respect was paid to the fundamental difference between ends and means.

Means, however spectacular technologically, do not justify the end. Rather they call for an end or a goal that can be morally justified. The survival of our vaunted scientific culture depends on that consideration, so unmistakably medieval. If we do not wish to help turn this most scientific age of ours into the most barbaric of all ages, we had better stop using the term "medieval" as synonymous with obscurantist. In doing so, we may make our mental eyes more sensitive to that light which comes from the Middle Ages. It is a light whose spectrum reveals creativity and inventiveness even with respect to science and technology. It does so because as a light it wanted only to participate in the light of true religion. The latter, if true, must have for its primary source the doctrine, nay the very dogma, of the creation of all in the beginning. Aided by that dogma, people of the Middle Ages made the all-important beginning toward science and technology as we know both in our modern times.

---

[1] See M.-D. Chenu, *Nature. Man, and Society in the Twelfth Century: Essays on New Theological Perspectives in the Latin West*, with an introduction by Etienne Gilson; selected, ed., and tr. by J. Taylor and L. K. Little (Chicago: University of Chicago Press, 1968), pp. 166-67. See also R. W. Southern, "Aspects of the European Tradition of Historical Writing. 2. Hugo of St. Victor and the Idea of Historical Development," *Transactions of the Royal Historical Society* 21 (1971), pp. 159-79.

² *The Metalogicon of John of Salisbury: A Twelfth-Century Defense of the Verbal and Logical Arts of the Trivium*, tr. with introduction and notes by D. D. McGarry (Berkeley: University of California Press, 1955), p. 167.

³ See G. Gordon, *"Medium aevum and the Middle Age"* (Oxford: Clarendon Press, 1925), pp. 4-28. (S. P. E. Tract No. XIX).

⁴ The omission is certainly glaring in the multivolume *Oxford Dictionary of the English Language* (1933), its Supplement volumes, and massively increased 2nd ed. (1989).

⁵ Quoted in *New York Times*, January 4, 1990, p. A15.

⁶ H. S. Williams, *The Great Astronomers* (New York: Newton, 1932), pp. 97-99.

⁷ *Immanuel Kant's Critique of Pure Reason*, tr. by N. K. Smith (New York: St Martin's Press, 1965), p. 20.

⁸ No serious grasp of Newton's physics can be detected in the writings of M. Knutzen who, according to a still well-entrenched academic cliché, is supposed to have introduced the young Kant into that physics in private instruction. See my introduction to my translation with notes of Immanuel Kant, *Universal Natural History and Theory of the Heavens* (Edinburgh: Scottish Academic Press, 1981), pp. 28-29.

⁹ For details, see chap. 10, "The Historian," in my *Uneasy Genius: The Life and Work of Pierre Duhem* (Dordrecht: Martinus Nijhoff, 1984).

¹⁰ See his letter of May 21, 1911, to P. Bulliot, translated in full into English in my *Scientist and Catholic: Pierre Duhem* (Front Royal, Va.: Christendom Press, 1991), pp. 235-40, from Hélène Pierre-Duhem, *Un savant français: Pierre Duhem* (Paris: Plon, 1936), pp. 158-69.

¹¹ Lynn White, Jr., "What Accelerated Technological Progress in the Western Middle Ages," in A. C. Crombie, *Scientific Change: Historical Studies in the Intellectual, Social, and Technical Conditions for Scientific Discovery and Technical Invention from Antiquity to the Present. Symposium on the History of Science. University of Oxford, 9-15 July 1961* (New York: Basic Books, 1963), p. 291.

¹² *Smithsonian*, October 1978, pp. 114-23.

¹³ Ibid., p. 115. This is a point also emphasized by White in his essay quoted in note 11 (p. 273), and previously in his "Technology and Invention in the Middle Ages," *Speculum* 15 (1940), p. 150.

¹⁴ Arnold Pacey, *The Maze of Ingenuity: Ideas and Idealism in the Development of Technology* (1974; repr. Cambridge, Mass.: MIT Press, 1976).

¹⁵ D. S. L. Cardwell, *Turning Points in Western Technology* (New York: Science History Publications, 1972), pp. 211-12.

¹⁶ *A History of Technology*, ed. Charles Singer et al., vol. 2. *The Mediterranean Civilizations and the Middle Ages* (New York: Oxford University Press, 1956), p. 774.

[17] The immediate effect was that Ficino was instructed by his princely patron in Florence to give priority to the translation of Plato's works into Latin. Efforts followed to give intellectual respectability to the idea of eternal recurrence, the quintessence of classical paganism and, for Christians, its most unacceptable aspect. For details, see chaps. 8 and 11 of my *Science and Creation: From Eternal Cycles to an Oscillating Universe* (1974; 2d enlarged ed., Edinburgh: Scottish Academic Press, 1986; repr. Lanham, Md.: University Press of America, 1990).

[18] See White, "Technology and Invention in the Middle Ages," pp. 153-54.

[19] Ibid.

[20] My translation is from the Latin text, "Descriptio positionis seu situationis monasterii Clarae-vallensis," in J.-P. Migne, ed., *Patrologiae cursus completus. Series latina* (Paris: J.-P. Migne, 1844-1864), vol. 185, cols. 569-74.

[21] For quotations from Bessarion's letter, see A. G. Keller, "A Byzantine Admirer of 'Western' Progress: Cardinal Bessarion," *Cambridge Historical Review* 11 (1954-55), 343-48.

[22] As can easily be seen from a perusal especially of chap. 6 in the fourteenth-century Muslim cultural historian Ibn Khaldoun's much praised *Muqqadimah* (that is, the preface and Bk. I of his *Universal History*). That chapter is available almost in full in the one-volume abridgment published by N. J. Dawood (Princeton University Press, 1969) from F. Rosenthal's three-volume translation. For further discussion, see my essay "The Physics of Impetus and the Impetus of the Koran" (1984), reprinted in *The Absolute beneath the Relative and Other Essays* (Lanham, Md: University Press of America, 1988), pp. 140-52.

[23] A question of Lynn White, in his "Technology and Invention in the Middle Ages," pp. 142-43.

[24] See ibid., p. 146, for bibliography and discussion.

[25] Pierce Butler, *The Origin of Printing in Europe* (Chicago: University of Chicago Press, 1940), p. 143. Butler further decries Gutenberg's fame as the inventor of printing as "the purest example of folklore ever developed in modern times." This folklore was given further wide currency in D. J. Boorstin, *The Discoverers* (New York: Random House, 1983), a book which, though written by a former director of the Library of Congress with an army of research assistants at his disposal, embodies an almost thematic blindness about the technological and scientific inventiveness of the Middle Ages, while presenting the medievals as being blind prisoners of Christian dogma.

[26] The first to publish that statement was Lynn Thorndike, "The Invention of the Mechanical Clock," *Speculum* 16 (1941), 242-43.

[27] Lewis Mumford, *Technics and Civilization* (New York: Harcourt, Brace and World, 1934), pp. 13-14.

[28] C. F. C. Beeson, *English Church Clocks, 1250-1850* (London: Antiquarian Horological Society, 1971), p. 16.

[29] A point widely publicized in chap. 1. "The Conservatism of Copernicus" in H. Butterfield, *The Origins of Modern Science 1300-1800* (1949; new ed. 1957; New York: Macmillan, 1960).

[30] For details and documentation, see my *Uneasy Genius,* which contains a full list of Duhem's publications. The disbelief turned into resistance. Volumes 6-10 of Duhem's *Le Système du monde* were published only with a delay of almost forty years and only through the heroic persistence of his daughter and only child, Hélène. This shocking academic scandal is told in full, on the basis of previously unavailable epistolary evidence, in my *Reluctant Heroine: The Life and Work of Hélène Duhem* (Edinburgh: Scottish Academic Press; Front Royal, Va.: Christendom Press, 1992).

[31] *The Science of Mechanics in the Middle Ages* (Madison: University of Wisconsin Press, 1961), chap. 8.

[32] *Sourcebook on Medieval Science* (Cambridge: Harvard University Press, 1974), pp. 275-80.

[33] Most extensively in his *La révolution astrononomique* (Paris: Hermann, 1971).

[34] Originally published in three fascicles between 1937 and 1939. Had those three studies been graced with a name index when published as a single volume (Paris: Hermann, 1966), the far more frequent appearance there of Duhem's name than of any other, would have immediately revealed Koyré's chief intention.

[35] As rightly pointed out by F. V. Cournin, "Philo Judaeus and the Concept of Creation," *New Scholasticism* 15 (1941), 46-58.

[36] A recent example is Yirmiahu Yovel's *Spinoza and Other Heretics* (Princeton, N.J.: Princeton University Press, 1989), which received wide publicity in the United States through Flora Lewis's article, "Israel and Relevance," *New York Times*, December 27, 1989, p. A23.

[37] See my *Savior of Science* (Washington, D.C.: Regnery-Gateway, 1988), p. 70.

[38] See my essay, "The Physics of Impetus and the Impetus of the Koran," mentioned in note 22 above.

[39] It also prompted the first unambigous and emphatic statements, in Athanasius's defense of the Logos's divinity, that a universe created by the Father through such a Logos had to be fully logical, that is, rational. For details, see my *Savior of Science*, pp. 75-79.

[40] Thus, for instance, Jean Blum, *Les Cathares: Mystères et initiation* (Paris: Le Léopard d'Or, 1985). Anne Brenon, *Le vrai visage du catharisme* (Portet-sur-Garonne: Editions, Loubatières, 1988).

[41] See Plutarch's "Life of Marcellus," in *Plutarch: The Lives of the Noble Grecians and Romans*, trans. John Dryden and rev. A. H. Clough (New

York: The Modern Library, n. d.), p. 378. Plutarch also recalls that Plato once reprimanded an astronomer who resorted to compass and ruler to solve a problem in geometry (ibid., p. 376).

[42] In his *De secretis operibus* (chap. 4) Bacon foretells the construction of ships and wagons that move with incredible speed, as well as of submarines and flying machines.

[43] Lynn White Jr., "Eilmer of Malmesbury, an Eleventh-Century Aviator: A Case Study of Technological Innovation, Its Context and Tradition," *Technology and Culture* 2 (1961), 97-111.

[44] A point wholly ignored in the article of Lynn White Jr., "The Historical Roots of Our Ecologic Crisis," *Science* 155 (1967), 1203-7, which has become a principal cudgel in the hands of some ecologists eager to blame Christianity for the ecological crisis. See my essay, "Ecology or Ecologism?" reprinted here as ch. 3.

[45] I have in mind, of course, A. D. Bloom, *The Closing of the American Mind* (New York: Simon & Schuster, 1987).

5

Telltale Remarks
and a Tale Untold

Insofar   as telltale remarks are dropped inadvertently, they are surprising in Michael Foster's three essays that are mainly under consideration in this volume and certainly in this essay. They appeared in *Mind*, an Edinburgh quarterly review of psychology and philosophy, between the end of 1934 and the beginning of 1936. The first dealt with "The Christian Doctrine of Creation and the Rise of Modern Natural Science."[1] The second and third were devoted to "Christian Theology and Modern Natural Science," under two respective subheadings: "Paganism and Rationalism in Greek Philosophy" and "Differences between Modern and Ancient Rationalism."[2] Whatever the other characteristics of those essays, their author meant to be explicit and even blunt at times from start to end. In the third page of the first essay Foster registered the fact that the opposition between pagan Greek philosophy and Christian revelation was as old as Christianity itself and that "the progressive assimilation of Christian dogma by the philosophical understanding was the spring of the whole medieval philosophy." This is why Foster could add in the same breath that "Scholasticism is much more than a re-edition of Aristotle," that it represented a plus, and "if one were to ask the

First published in *Creation, Nature, and Political Order in the Philosophy of Michael Foster (1903-1959)*, ed. C. Wybrow (Lewiston, N.Y.: The Edwin Mellen Press, 1992), pp. 269-96. Reprinted with permission.

question from what source this *plus* is derived, there can be only one answer: it is clearly and obviously derived from Christian revelation."[3]

In saying this Foster said nothing new. By the early 1930s a distinguished array of scholars had recovered the true picture of Scholastic philosophy from the vicious crust foisted on it by Renaissance humanists, Cartesian apriorists, British empiricists, and last but not least by the intellectual shocktroops of the Enlightenment and positivism. To Foster all that recovery of the true physiognomy of Scholasticism seemed to be news. Such was the telltale aspect of the note in which he praised E. Gilson's just published book, *The Spirit of Medieval Philosophy,* as a "particularly lucid exposition of the overriding importance of the presence of that *plus* in medieval philosophy." But Foster was also eager to distance himself from Gilson: "My whole article is a protest against Gilson's further assumption, that we must look to a resurrection of Scholasticism for a continuation of this great task, and against his implied judgment that the work of classical modern philosophers represents a declension from the path upon which medieval philosopy set out."[4]

Towards the end of his third essay Foster summed up his views on the conception of nature which underlay, at times consciously and at times subconsciously, the thinking of 17th- and 18th-century scientists and philosophers as they formulated modern science and its methodology. According to Foster, "This conception of nature and theory of knowledge correspond very closely to Kant's . . . . Kant himself arrived at this philosophy of nature by reflection on the methods of modern natural science."[5]

Between these two very explicit statements there lay about seventy pages—at times repetitious, at times poor in documentation. The meagerness of documentation should seem particularly jarring in connection with the first article, which deals with a distinctly historical topic. Documentation is very uneven in the second and third essays. However, Foster did not miss an opportunity to recall his main points. By modern science he meant the one corresponding to classical physics, which he subdivided into a nascent and a fully grown phase, the latter having Newton for its principal articulator. Foster took Descartes for the initiator of the former phase. Similar was Foster's division of modern philosophy into two phases of which the second he found exemplified in Locke, Hume, and Kant. Concerning the earlier phase, he spoke in some detail of Descartes, Bacon, Hobbes, and Spinoza.

Foster felt that he could readily assume a consensus about the chief features of modern science as well as of modern philosophy, as he understood both. Working on the basis of such a consensus has the dubious advantage that one may feel justified in dispensing with a careful documentation of its reliability. Beneath that advantage may lie a pitfall, namely, that the consensus is based more on a wishful reconstruction of the thought of earlier philosophers and scientists than on painstaking studies of their writings.

Undoubtedly, it is true that Descartes greatly impressed his and the succeeding generation of scientists and philosophers with his claim that search for final causes has no place in science. It is also true that modern science (Newtonian science, or rather Newtonian physicists) looked mainly for mechanistic interconnections in nature. Actually, what they did (and this all-important point wholly escaped Foster) was to assume that interactions could, in theory, be measured with full accuracy and this they took for an evidence of causal interaction. They (though not Descartes, *pace* Foster) also looked in empirical science for proof of this or that particular scientific conclusion. It could also seem obvious that such a methodology of science differed greatly from that of ancient Greek science. It was, however, not nearly as reliable to claim as Foster did that the methodology of ancient Greek science was equivalent to Aristotle's logic and that therefore it was not really important to have a detailed knowledge of Greek science to talk about its very nature and principal features.[6] Here, one is faced with one of Foster's telltale remarks that shows him more a heedless constructor of history in terms of some generic, if not preconceived categories, than a careful reconstructor of history "wie es eigentlich gewesen,"[7] a remark which Foster must have often heard in German scholarly circles.

In general, it was safe to argue, as Foster did, that the Christian doctrine of creation implied a notion of the universe which, because such a universe had to be contingent, called for an empirical investigation if the latter was to become genuinely rational. Foster remained curiously unspecific as to what he meant by "contingent," a word which carries with it two very different meanings in English and a great many important nuances in its philosophical use.[8] Foster also failed to consider that whatever the contingency of the universe, it had to be fully consistent in space and time in order to be useful for science. But as he missed these points, Foster made a most valuable observation though leaving it in a generic form: Neither the empiricist, nor the rationalist philosophers could account in terms of their philosophical presuppositions for the principle that there had to be an empirical investigation if there was to be an understanding of nature which is rational, that is, free of quasi-mystical speculations about finalities and purposes. In view of this, Foster should have included the words 'though unconsciously' and italicized it in the most often quoted phrase of his three essays: "The modern investigators of nature were the first to take seriously [*though unconsciously*] *in their science* the Christian doctrine that nature is created."[9]

Foster meant to convey exactly the opposite. In the pages preceding that quotation he credited the Reformation and Reformed theology with a breakthrough in the understanding of the Christian dogma of creation. Less important, though very misleading, could seem his insistence that the Reformation liberated Christian faith from its monastic enclosures and brought it in contact with the world at large. Foster could not be excused for ignoring that no less a non-Christian than Auguste Comte had already set forth the fallacy of that view about medieval Christianity (Catholicism). Foster may have been invincibly blind in making his second less important claim. It consisted in opposing the "interiorised" Christianity of the Reformation with an "externally imposed" obedience to higher norms as characteristic of Catholicism, especially of medieval Catholicism. Half a century after Foster's articles, and a quarter of a century of intense ecumenism, it is still a widespread belief among Protestants that nothing genuinely "interiorized" can be contained in the Roman Catholic belief that only the continuity of hierachy does justice to Christ's words to the Twelve: "Whatever you declare bound on earth will be declared bound in Heaven . . . ." Here, however, it is not Foster's Protestantism which is the target of criticism, but the narrowing of historical and philosophical perspectives and information which it imposed on him.

The most important facet in this respect relates to what he saw as a crucial contribution of the Reformation to the Christian doctrine of creation. Here again Foster was inconsistent. He generously admitted that the fight of Christianity against classical Greek (Aristotelian) paganism was as old as Christianity itself and that the battle-lines were drawn with particular clarity during the Golden Age of Scholasticism. Had Foster followed up Gilson's masterful reconstruction of the great Scholastics' teaching on God's complete freedom to create or not to create, or to create this world or any other world, he might have thought twice about crediting the Reformers so much on this point. He should have known that the Reformers had inherited a great deal of Scholasticism, though, unfortunately, its nominalist or Ockhamist kind. There God's freedom was so overemphasized as to make hollow the idea of the laws of nature and thereby of science.[10] Apart from this, the distinction between God's absolute and ordained power can be destructive of God's very unity. It wholly escaped Foster that had the Reformers derived their knowledge of Scholastic theology and philosophy from sources better than Ockham and other nominalists, the Reformers might not have turned that distinction into a shibboleth, which they repeated endlessly but never examined closely.

The most a Protestant historian of the early stages of modern science can do with that shibboleth is to locate it, as R. Hooykaas did,[11] in the writings of insignificant journeymen of science from the 17th century. The shibboleth cannot be found in the writings of the great 17th-century scientists, such as Descartes, Galileo, Kepler, Horrocks, Huygens, and last but not least Newton. Their scientific work followed lines very different from those imagined by Foster, who said precious little about them. He was, however, prolific on Francis Bacon without realizing that Newton carefully avoided invoking the one who wrote about science as if he had been its Lord Chancellor.[12] Only the tinkerers, whose number was large in the nascent Royal Society, were swearing by Lord Verulam's guidelines in science.

At any rate, it is doubtful that Descartes' methodology of science allowed for God's freedom. The latter was a topic which Descartes tried to sidestep as much as possible.[13] As to Galileo and Kepler, they seemed to entertain the illusion that God could create the world only along their own geometrical preferences. Newton could not see philosophically as far as to perceive the elementary contradiction in his speculation about God's freedom to create universes where the law of gravitation would be very different from the one he had discovered.[14] Such universes simply could not form that totality which a genuine Universe has to be. The absolute freedom of God, as heedlessly speculated upon, could easily undermine that very notion of the Universe without which science would remain a mere tinkering. Moreover, insofar as these great scientists believed that God freely created the universe, they simply followed a very long Christian tradition that had been robust for many centuries prior to the Reformation.

Foster did not as much as suspect the *a priori* elements in the thinking of Descartes, Galileo, Kepler, and Newton. No better was Foster's appraisal of Immanuel Kant, whose sole contribution was to put a dubious philosophical seal on that apriorism by claiming that Euclidean three-dimensional geometry was a category which the mind necessarily imposed on outside reality. Here too the author of the *Critique of Pure Reason* merely muddled the waters by speaking from two, rather confused corners of his mouth. How else can one understand that Kant, the shabby sophister of the first (and the three other) antinomy was taken a generation later for the supreme teacher of the Euclidean infinity of the universe?[15] No less easy to understand, provided one is not satisfied with clichés, is Foster's characterization of Kant's philosophy as an almost ideal Christian philosophy of nature at least in "one important aspect."[16] Part of that aspect is seen by Foster as a fundamental achievement of Kant, namely, that Kant spelled out finally and clearly that the source of ideas on which modern science and scientific method rested was Christian revelation. Foster kept a revealing silence on the fact that Kant, as he amply proved by his *Religion within the Limits of Reason*, did not take for an intellectually respectable source that very revelation.

A most important among those ideas, according to Foster, was the unknowabiltiy of the very nature of substance. As long as the opposite was held either by the Greeks or by the Scholastics, modern or empirical science could not arise for a very simple reason. To know the very nature or substance of things, Foster argued, is to possess about each of them a definition from which it is possible to derive all their properties. Clearly, there would then be no need for experimentation and observation.

Since Foster presented this reasoning as one embodied in the history of philosophy, it would have been his duty to proceed in the manner of a historian. He should have shown by appropriate quotations that in speaking about substances Aristotle and the Scholastics (and Thomas in particular) had indeed viewed substances in such a light and, even more importantly, had derived various qualities, so many accidents, of this or that thing from the definition of its substance. Had he made that effort, Foster would have found out something about both Aristotle's and Thomas's keen awareness of the far from direct connection between what they called substance and accidents. Foster provided no documentary evidence on a related though equally important point. It is still to be demonstrated that the doctrine of substantial form, as held by Aristotle and the great Scholastics, made them suspicious of the reality of matter. Had he been pressed, Foster would have, in all likelihood, granted that Christian opposition to the detractors of matter had been strong long before the time of the Reformers. It would have been difficult to take lightly the resistance of pre-Reformation Christians to Gnostics, to Manicheans, to Cathars, to Bogomils and many other lesser known threats to human civilization. But then Foster would have said that pre-Reformation Christians, especially their Scholastic brand, failed to be nearly as perspicacious in their philosophy as they were in their theology. But this is precisely the concession which the Reformers would have refused to grant. To a man they were far more interested in their insights into theology than into philosophy.

No less fortunate turns out Foster's predicament with respect to his interpretation of Kant. As an unabashedly self-centered thinker, Kant would have been flattered by the evaluation of his philosophical aim as an effort to demonstrate the possibility of science, that is, of Newtonian science. Kant certainly gave much impetus to the disease plaguing modern philosophers that their ideas would have a built-in credibility if presented in scientific wrappings. At any rate, Foster's interpretation of Kant implies some serious expertise on Kant's part about Newtonian science, an assumption without any foundation in facts. With a knowledge of geometry restricted to elementary trigonometry, Kant was not equipped to follow most of the proofs of the propositions, corollaries, and lemmas in the *Principia*, where proofs are usually given in terms of differential geometry, a subject more arcane than that differential calculus about which Kant knew nothing.[17]

Apart from Kant's utter amateurism in Newtonian physics, his real aim was not to demonstrate its possibility. Rather, with specious references to that physics, he tried to show, partly through the four antinomies, that universe, soul, and God—the three principal topics of traditional metaphysics—were the illegitimate products of the metaphysical cravings of the intellect. Now, if one recalls the Popperian rephrasing of a very old truth, namely, that all science is cosmology,[18] the possibility of science should seem to depend on the reliability of one's intellectual approach to the reality of the universe. It was Kant's principal aim to discredit that approach so that the approach from the universe to God (the cosmological argument) may also appear unreliable. Kant's aim was not to show that Newtonian physics, which he knew only by hearsay, was possible but that the cosmological argument, and therefore a rationally respectable surrender to God, was not worthy of man as a rational being. Kant failed to realize that his blows aimed at natural theology would reach their target only by posing first a deadly threat to science itself.

As a child and champion of the Enlightenment, Kant aimed at securing the absolute sovereignty of man vis-à-vis any possible or imaginable transcendental constraint. It was not senility but strict logic that inspired Kant's repeated dictum, "Ich bin Gott," in the *Opus postumum*,[19] in which he tried to apply the epistemology of the *Critique* to the various branches of science, that, according to him, had to be of five basic kinds because man had five senses. That the *Opus postumum* is still to appear in English is partly responsible for the persistence of the cultural cliché that Kant was one of the greatest philosophers because his philosophy was scientific.

Foster, who did his doctoral work in the 1920s with R. Kröner in Kiel, and went back for a few years to Germany after the War, had an excellent mastery of German. He therefore cannot be excused for not having explored this rather shady side of Kant's mental world. Of course, studying with Kröner meant a commitment to put Kant in the best possible "Christian" light. Foster's dissertation and other writings on Hegel were part of a long-standing strategy of Kantians to exculpate Kant from the charge of having inspired Fichte's rank voluntarism and Hegel's brazen flights of fancy. There is much more than meets the eye in Foster's remark in his first essay that something in it had been anticipated in a paper he had just delivered at the Third Congress of the International Hegel Society.[20] As to the "Christian" light, it had much in common with the Reformers' way of looking at reason, and especially with Luther's profound distrust, if not contempt, of it. It was not a light as understood by the Reformers' hero, Augustine, who emphasized the priority of reason whenever faith was searching for understanding.[21] Foster's endorsement of Kant as a "Christian" philosopher was an echo of Kröner's echoing the thesis that Kant had made room for faith (taken for sentiment) by putting the intellect in its place, a dubious place indeed. It is in this light that one should see Foster's distrust of natural theology.

Foster suspected nothing of that fact that attacks on natural theology, or the cosmological argument in particular, invariably went hand in hand with disastrous legislations for the methodology to be followed in science. Suffice to recall Bacon, Hobbes, Hume, Kant—yes, Kant—J. S. Mill, and Ernst Mach—to say nothing of logical positivists and the even more illogical paradigmists and Popperians, to boot.[22] Let it here merely be registered that for Christians with Protestant background—and Foster was one—the corpus of Western intellectual history must be cast in a bed, however Procrustean, in order to justify the great break with Tradition.

Protestantism demands discontinuity with the historic past in a sense far deeper and broader than it may appear. This is why the Aristotelian and Scholastic doctrine of substance is systematically misconstrued by Protestant thinkers. Foster's dicta are an illustration.

Contrary to the Protestant tradition, Aristotle and the Scholastics held fast to the notion of substance not because they wanted, consciously or unwittingly, to promote paganism. They rather formulated and upheld the doctrine of substance for a reason which had nothing to do with paganism or with Christianity. The reason related to safeguarding human sanity by securing intellectual coherence in a world of change. For if nothing remains unchanged while changes go on, there remains no ground to predicate the change itself insofar as it connects a starting point with an endpoint, at times very different from one another. The very etymology of the word 'substance' (to stand under, from *sub-stare*) is a proof. It refers to that very thing which stands or stays unchanged underneath while on the observational level exactly the opposite takes place. Thus substance is a postulational entity and unobservable by definition. This is why Aristotle and Thomas did not claim to know the nature of things, let alone to divine the empirical consequences of such knowledge.

Aristotle's derivation of some properties of the ether and of the four sublunary elements from their "substance" or nature was only apparent. In the case of the ether, he postulated its existence in order to safeguard the eternity of the world, as a consequence of his pantheism. At any rate, in speaking of the ether he was not a whit less logical than all classical physicists who swore by the existence of the ether. To make matters even more illogical, they attributed contradictory properties to it and took it for an empirically known entity.[23] At any rate, similarly apparent was Aristotle's derivation of the properties of the four sublunary elements from their substances or natures. His empirical knowledge of those properties merely made it easier for him to create the impression that those properties followed from the manner in which he postulated that only those four elements should exist. Neither Aristotle, nor any of the great Scholastics have tried to derive the properties (accidents) of a thing (say a statue) from its substantial form. They knew that the substantial form was as much a postulational entity as substance was.

Substances were indispensable for the chemists of Newton's time, in particular for Robert Boyle, who worked just across from the walls of Christ Church in Oxford. Reading Boyle's works Foster would have realized that Boyle's researches did not derive any direct benefit from the belief that God was free to create anything. Also, if Foster, who constantly spoke of Newtonian science, had read the *Principia*, he should have canvassed it very carefully to find there the word substance. The reason for this is simple. Newtonian physics, of which Galileo's physics tried to be an anticipation, was not a physics of substances, but a physics of things or masses in motion, regardless of what they were.

In fact, this was true even of Aristotle's physics which, of course, is not in his *Physics*, but in his *Meteorologica* and *On the Heavens*. He too stated in a generic form that the acceleration of bodies was proportional to their masses. Only his reasons for doing this were very different from those of Newton, a point which needs retelling in order to understand where Foster did go wrong in pivoting all his reasoning on the Aristotelian (and Scholastic) notion of substance. Foster said not a word about a most important facet of Aristotelianism insofar as it grew out of Socrates' overriding concern. Faced with the mechanistic ideology of the pre-Socratic *physikoi*, Socrates felt that only if one attributed purposive striving to each and every body, could he justify his own purpose in obeying his conscience. As a result he threw out the baby (the science of physics) with the bathwater (mechanistic ideology).[24]

Such is the source of the inference, fully developed by Aristotle, that the greater was the nature, that is mass, of a body, the more intense was its purpose and the faster its motion either upward or downward. That inference appears with particular sharpness in perhaps the most hapless phrase in the entire Aristotelian corpus. In that phrase Aristotle claims that of two bodies, the one twice heavier than the other, must fall in half as much time from the same height to the ground as the other. Had Foster looked up that glaring passage in Aristotle's *On the Heavens*,[25] his keen analytical mind might have made him perceive a crucial point. The foregoing theory of motion implied that the speed or acceleration of a body depended far more on its "nature" or intensity of purpose, which was proportional to the mass, than on its being given what in modern physics became called the imparting of momentum as the start of motion. Aristotle could not, of course, be expected to know what Newton discovered, namely, that in the case of the free fall of a body, its rate of acceleration does not depend on its mass. Newton did not have to disentangle himself from real or imaginary problems about substances in order to formulate his laws of motion.

That Foster failed to see this and the true character of Aristotle's dicta on substance and acceleration may have had to do not so much with his apparently elementary training in the sciences than in his being a Kantian, however well-meaning. As such he readily set up his categories in terms of which the history of modern thought had to unfold itself. Kant's arbitrariness with the facts of history, intellectual and political,[26] paved the way to Hegel's running roughshod over them, an attitude capsulized in his contemptuous rejoinder: "So much the worse for history."[27] It is difficult to find excuse for Foster's staking all his arguments on some inept dicta of Bacon and Locke on substance, unless the excuse is the proverbial difficulty, even in the best places of learning (including Oxford's Christ Church), to suspect the reliability of some hallowed patterns of explanation.

However, this excuse will appear rather feeble if one recalls a remark of Arthur Koestler that has a much wider applicability than he himself may have thought. Koestler could rightly argue that no academic (or intellectual) could plead ignorance about outstanding Nazi atrocities because it is the primary duty of academics to become informed about facts, let alone salient facts.[28] Concerning the topic analyzed by Foster, some salient, indeed towering facts had been conspicuously available for two full decades before Foster's first essay appeared. Not perhaps in *that* England where the fog in the Channel is readily taken for the non-existence of the Continent.

It was on that Continent that the most dramatic event of modern science had taken place, an event that initiated that very science. The place was the Sorbonne, *the* university *par excellence*, about the time of that event, or around 1330. The *dramatis persona* is John Buridan of whom around 1934 even such better-grade dons as Foster did not know more than the information capsulized in the legend known as Buridan's ass. As such all those dons seemed to be resolved to sit back safely, although the epoch-making information had for twenty years been available in all major libraries in the learned world. I mean the third volume of Pierre Duhem's *Etudes sur Léonard de Vinci* published in 1913 by no less a prestigious publisher than Hermann et Cie in Paris. It was preceded by its first and second volumes, published in 1906 and 1909, respectively, and by Duhem's publication in 1905 and 1906 of his two-volume *Les origines de la statique*,[29] that should have become an academic blockbuster. The academic world, and certainly its Kantian sector, merrily carried on with its learned slumber. Already *Les origines de la statique* provided enough evidence to shatter the myth codified in the preface Kant wrote to the second edition of the *Critique* where he credited Galileo (and Stahl, a scientific non-entity by comparison) with initiating that Copernican turn which he considered to be his historic privilege to spell out with philosophical incisiveness. Never before or after was Copernicus was so rudely turned upside down, but this Kantian headstand in viewing Copernicus has become the normal academic posture.

It is one of the most telltale aspects of Foster's tale about the rise of modern science and its connection with Christian theology that in those three essays he never mentioned Copernicus. One wonders whether Foster had ever read at least the introductory chapter (with not even a simple trigonometrical figure in it) of Copernicus' immortal book. (Possibly, Oxford's program of Greats did not yet include such truly great writings.) There Copernicus answers objections to the earth's motion with references to the doctrine of impetus, without feeling the slightest need to name his source. This time the lack of reference was due not to an academic's ruse to appear more learned in his own right, but to the fact that the information had been common knowledge for a very long time. This is why no injustice is done to Newton when today one speaks of the inverse square law of gravitation or of the theory of central field of force, without referring to him by name.

Duhem indeed pointed out in the third volume of his Leonardo studies (and was to propound in great detail in the second five and posthumously published volumes of his *Système du monde*[30]) that countless scholars before and after Copernicus held that impetus theory. No less importantly, for Foster's Christian concerns, Duhem also showed the unmistakably Christian origin of Buridan's impetus theory, though only at the heroic price of deciphering manuscripts of Buridan that had by then been gathering dust for almost half a millennium. Thus Duhem found that in commenting on Aristotle's claim in *On the Heavens* that the world was eternal and that therefore the motion of the heavens too had no beginning, Buridan declared, as all Scholastic commentators of *On the Heavens* had done before him, that the world had a beginning because it was created in time. Having the bent of mind of a natural philosopher, Buridan also felt prompted to say something about the manner in which cosmic motions were initiated:

> God, when He created the world, moved each of the celestial orbs as he pleased, and in moving them He impressed in them impetuses which moved them without His having to move them any more than except by the method of general influence whereby He concurs as co-agent in all things which take place. . . . And these impetuses which He impressed in the celestial bodies were not decreased nor corrupted afterwards, because there was no inclination of the celestial bodies for other movements. Nor was there resistance which would be corruptive or repressive of that impetus.[31]

Herein lay the true, concretely scientific as well as genuinely theological connection between Christian faith and modern natural science. The connection long antedated the Reformers, as well as Bacon and Locke, and even John Hus and John Wyclif. It had nothing to do with William Ockham to whom the Reformers owed much of their philosophical tradition. That John Buridan belonged to a very different tradition is clear from his categorical endorsement of the cosmological argument,[32] an anathema to Ockham. In Kant's time it would have been still possible to talk away salient facts of intellectual history, facts incompatible with his "critical" reading of it. At that time such a champion of the Enlightenment as d'Alembert could attribute to Aquinas absurd ideas on worse than flimsy grounds and boast that it was not necessary to read Aquinas in order to know what he really had written.[33]

Had Kröner, Foster's "Christian-Kantian" or "Kantian-Christian" teacher in Kiel, learned about the true origin of science (which is the origin of the Newtonian laws of motion, of which the first, the law of inertial motion is the fundamental), he might have had the greatest intellectual shock of his life. Or possibly, he might have taken the easy academic way out of dealing with the specter of troublesome facts. It consists in not reconsidering one's favorite perspective until such a change becomes safe through the shift of academic consensus.

A few observations about Foster and his articles are in order, before making an educated guess about the characteristics of his possible reaction on being confronted with that origin. In discussing the eternalism of Plato (and Aristotle), Foster made much of that chief feature of pantheism which is the necessary generation or birth of the universe from the divine principle which is, of course, but a *demiurgos* even if called by Plato the Father of all. Foster is very clear about the difference between that "Father" and the Father Almighty of Christian revelation who is a Creator in the strict sense of the word.[34] Curiously, Foster left undeveloped a no less important contrast. The latter is between Plato's application of the term *monogenes* (or *unigenitus*) to the universe and the special application of that same term within Christian revelation to a single individual, Jesus of Nazareth. The first chapter of John's Gospel could pose a cosmic shock to any educated pagan of Late Antiquity. By the same token any Christian found there a powerful antidote to the temptation of cavorting, however slightly, with pantheistic ideas.[35] It was that antidote which made the medieval Christian commentators on Aristotle so different from most of their Jewish and Muslim counterparts. It was that antidote within genuine Christianity, and long before

Reformation times, that led to the spontaneous affirmation of creation out of nothing and in time. Buridan's formulation of the impetus theory and all the modern science it made possible, was a choice fruit of that spontaneity.

The Reformation, on which Foster heaped many encomiums,[36] was not needed for that fruit to be produced. Whether by knowing about Buridan, Foster would have recognized the true Christian provenance of that fruit, is most unlikely. Foster's own Christianity was not without some perplexities. One, of course, can never fathom the true reason for suicide, the end Foster chose for himself. The kind of Christian Foster was could perhaps be best speculated upon by Eric Mascall, his fellow theology student in Christ Church. The two worked strenuously on the material improvement of the life of undergraduates, only to find that undergraduates were surprisingly clever in looking after themselves. However, one still has to consider a point, raised unwittingly by the Rev. Dr. V. A. Demant, Canon of Christ Church, who preached Foster's obituary on October 18, 1959. He tried to cope with Foster's suicide by falling back on an apparently inspirational, but in fact subtly dispiriting paradox. Foster, he said, "had all the marks of holiness but just missed the joy of saints."[37] This is the kind of evasiveness that should make all serious Christians shudder. If that evasiveness has any truth to it, it may be the suspicion that no Christian Kantian or Kantian Christian can ever know that joy and keep that character of Christian understanding which, in Paul's words, is *logike latreia*.[38]

With all this in mind, one may not be entirely at a loss about how Foster would have reacted had Duhem, Buridan, and the rest floated within his ken. His reaction would have shown characteristics, both academic and Christian, though hardly in a constructive sense. One of his options would have been to damn Buridan and the rest with faint praise, and with the condescension of more than one Oxford don, in much the same way as he did with Gilson. This is possibly the best a Protestant can do with the fact of the pre-Reformation Christian origin of modern science, unless he chooses to imitate the ostrich. Taking the other option, he would have joined forces with some eminent historians of science who knew of Duhem fully and found him a supreme threat. Such was the case with Alexandre Koyré who cultivated pantheism as much as he championed the Enlightenment.[39] That as a pantheist Koyré could not tolerate the prospect of the birth of science as an event tied to the greatest Birth, should seem obvious. No less categorical was his espousal of the basic dogma of the Enlightenment: Christianity had to be discredited in the minds of men so that science might at long last find a receptive soil there.[40] That most of Koyré's disciples could not come to terms with Duhem, should be seen in this light. As to the very few Christians among those disciples, Protestants in more than one case joined the rationalists in an unholy alliance if it served the cause of denigrating further the allegedly Dark Middle Ages.

This is well illustrated in the recourse which Canon Charles E. Raven made to George Sarton's scholarship as a means of disposing of Duhem's specter.[41] Perhaps the good Canon was unaware of Sarton's virulent allegiance to Freemasonry and of its coloring of Sarton's scholarship as a historian of science, especially of medieval science. It was less excusable to ignore Sarton's systematic slighting of Duhem.[42] In general, fleeting references were at best made to notable historians of science by those Christian theologians who, eager to promote a Holy Alliance between science and Christian faith, discovered in postwar years Foster's articles. Some of them had some philosophical training, some of them dabbled in science, but none of them served evidence of being a serious student of the history of science. All too often they lacked as much as a bachelor degree in science. But they made it a fashion to refer to Foster's essays as if they contained a profound and unassailable analysis together with a proper grasp of history, scientific and philosophical.

Thus was the thesis of Foster turned into an apparently solid doctrine. It constituted a somewhat elaborate variation on the dictum of Whitehead, who with his catchy phrases first called broad attention to the Christian origin of modern science. Whitehead's claim, made in 1925 at Harvard, that modern science is an unconscious derivative of the Scholastics' keenness on logic and of their belief in the imperious Jehovah,[43] had, of course, even less Christian content to it than any stereotype description of Scholastics as medieval. Strangely, Whitehead's claim about the lack of awareness on the part of the Scholastics went uncontested for half a century.[44] Other, no less important, faults can also be found with Whitehead's dicta that hardly did justice to medieval scholasticism and standard scholarship about it, especially from the viewpoint of the history of science.[45]

That the myth Foster helped create has not come in for due criticism has in part to do with the failure of nerve on the part of many Catholic scholars who could and should have cultivated Duhem, the philosopher and the historian of science. The reception of Duhem among Catholics illustrates the truth of the words: He came into his own but his own did not receive him. Duhem proved prophetic when he registered the fact that Catholics were not reading his works on the history and philosophy of science.[46] He exaggerated somewhat. But it is true that Catholics in France missed a tremendous opportunity as they failed to mine Duhem's writings for powerful weapons against scientism, the official ideology of the Third Republic. What he said of Buridan and other medievals may have appeared too good to be true.

Duhem's masterly unmasking of the claims of a scientistic philosophy of science may not have impressed French Catholics for two reasons. One was that it could appear in places almost platitudinous. But this is a prime characteristic of all basic truth. The other reason was that as he praised Ockham's scientific insights, he underplayed the enormous dangers of his occasionalism. This imbalance could appear intolerable to such leading neo-Thomists as Maritain and Gilson. The latter in fact did not stir up enthusiasm around 1936 for the publication of the last five volumes of the *Système du monde*,[47] left in manuscript at Duhem's death in 1916. In addition, to continue with the French Catholic scene, there was the proverbial French craving for novelty, especially when packaged in superb prose generously studded with scientific neologisms. Duhem's solid reasoning and painstaking documentation could have no place on that bandwagon that carried the dizzy-eyed admirers of Teilhard de Chardin's quasi-mystical nebulosity down to a pseudo-philosophical primrose path.

More difficult is to explain the lack of proper reaction to Duhem among English speaking Catholic intellectuals. From 1911 on they had at their disposal a great deal of evidence about the medieval origins of Newtonian physics in the long and eye-opening essay on the history of physics which Duhem contributed to the pre-World War I *Catholic Encyclopedia*.[48] It created no echo as Catholics in the United States developed their vast systems of colleges and universities where the teaching of the history and philosophy of science has been non-existent for the most part. Worse, when such courses were offered, they followed patterns set by secularist gurus in the field. It was not a Catholic publishing enterprise that brought out Duhem's masterful analysis on the aim and structure of physical theory.[49] The general lack of proper appreciation of Duhem's work on the part of American Catholic intellectuals is well evidenced by the lackluster article on Duhem in the *New Catholic Encyclopedia*.[50] These remarks represent but a few outstanding details in a much broader picture which is outright scandalous.[51]

This is not the place to argue the merits of Duhem's discovery of the origin of modern science, or to justify some of his shorthand dating of it. His statement that the condemnation in 1277 by Etienne Tempier, bishop of Paris, of a hundred or so Aristotelian theses marks the beginning of modern science has often been taken out of context. Little attention has been given to another statement of his with which it should seem rather difficult to find fault. It is in the Preface of the third volume of his Leonardo studies, published in 1913, where he wrote, with an eye on Buridan's passage, quoted above: "If one wanted to separate with a clear line the realm of ancient science from the realm of modern science, it should be drawn, we believe, at the moment when Buridan conceived that theory [of impetus], . . . at the moment when it was admitted that the celestial motions and sublunary motions depended on the same [laws of] mechanics."[52] At any rate, no less an expert on medieval science than Anneliese Maier was prompted to say, following her painstaking re-examination of much of the material Duhem brought to light, that "Duhem is essentially right."[53]

But can anything or anyone be essentially right if there are no essences or substances? And is not the reality of essences recognized if one, with Kant, claims that the substances (the noumena) are essentially unknowable? Did not already the more courageous among Kant's students warn the master—and in his lecture room at that—that he was inconsistent in speaking of substances at all? Such an inconsistency keeps plaguing the Kantians if, like Foster, they try to build so portentous a conclusion on the alleged misunderstanding of substances by Aristotle and the Scholastics.

To compound the irony, Foster's fellow dons at Christ Church did not gain the impression that he had attributed much importance to his three essays here discussed.[54] He did not refer to them when in late 1947 he communicated an essay, "Some Remarks on the Relation of Science and Religion," to *The Christian News-Letter,*[55] although he relied on points made in them. In that essay he tried to cope with the enormous disparity which the explosion of the atomic bomb revealed between man's power over nature and his ability to use that power properly. Foster saw in that disparity an unhealthy aspect of the mastery which man obtained over nature through modern science. This mastery Foster took for the hallmark of true or modern science as distinguished from ancient science.

Curiously, Foster took only for a hyperbole the characterization that the ancients worshiped nature while modern science enabled man to dominate it. He was more interested in another contrast, namely, that while pre-scientific man lived in harmony with the rhythm of nature, modern scientific man imposed himself on nature even in

agriculture, and, more importantly, in matters of determining
"whether or not children shall come as a result of sexual intercourse
and even perhaps their sex."[56] Such and similar abilities of science
were in Foster's eyes part of the truth of science and he saw the
superiority of Christian religion over pagan religion in its ability "to
be compatible with the truth of natural science."[57]

The peril which this statement of his implied for Christian
religion remained hidden to Foster. The reason for this casts further
light on his miscomprehension (in spite of his reading Gilson) of
what pre-Reformation Christianity was about concerning the relation
of faith and philosophy, the natural and the supernatural, and, in
particular, of faith and science. All that miscomprehension, and a
number of pivotal terms left in studied vagueness, were compressed
by him in a not-too-long paragraph which was a sequel to his
observation that the negative reaction to science, triggered by the
explosion of the bomb, had in it something of the nature worship of
the ancients:

> We may see an example of this erroneous reaction in the
> resistance which was offered in the name of the Church in the
> seventeenth century to the new view of nature, upon which the
> modern science of nature was based. I speak without first-hand
> knowledge of the controversies of that time, but I think it is clear
> that among the things which churchmen defended was that pagan
> view of nature which had been sytematized by Aristotle and
> domiciled in a Christiain setting by the Mediaeval Scholastics.
> They defended it in the name of Christianity, but the scientific
> view of nature was more truly Christian. Theirs was a Greek
> philosophy of nature, which had been adopted into a Christian
> framework; whereas the modern scientific view of nature
> represented the break-through of a Christian metaphysic into
> natural philosophy.[58]

In speaking of the seventeenth-century Church did Foster have in
mind the Anglicans, or the Puritans, or both? Or did he look beyond
the Channel at the Church on the Continent where there was a
Roman Catholic Church as well as growing varieties of Lutheran and
Calvinist Churches? In speaking of "seventeenth-century churchmen"
he may even have had in mind the spokesmen of Protestant scholasticism who realized, however reluctantly, that it was impossible to do
theology without subscribing to metaphysics. In view of what has
been said of Duhem's discovery of the origin of Newton's first law,
one can merely register a grievous lack of information in Foster's

portrayal of medieval scholastics as ones who defended and domiciled in Christian setting Aristotle's pagan view of nature. But what about that "Christian metaphysic" which the modern scientific view of nature "implanted into natural philosophy"?

In the remaining seven pages of his article Foster had ample opportunity to come clean about that "Christian metaphysic." What he said in those pages could have claim neither to metaphysics, nor to Christianity, and in particular to that Christianity which is tied to Christ in a way far stronger than vague phrases, however scriptural in tone, can assure. Yet it was precisely that Christianity which Foster tried to vindicate against three deviations. One was what he called, 'archaism' (a term he borrowed from Toynbee without apparently seeing the pagan in him). Obviously, the clock of history and technology could not be turned back. It was in vain to dream about a return to a quasi-bucolic state of affairs.

The second deviation was social engineering which Popper had just decried in his *Open Society*. The liberalism Popper stood for did not, of course, offer an answer to man's ultimate hopelessness. Foster had no sympathy for Popper's exhorting his contemporaries "to carry the cross of being human" and stop asking further questions. The answer, Foster argued, was to be sought in Christianity, but as it turned out, Christianity became subservient to natural science through its failure to probe into the ways whereby whereby God's will was revealed to man. One was through nature not yet understood scientifically, the other through nature interpreted by science. Science, however, made all too manifest its inability to assure its proper use. The remedy was therefore to be found in the Body of Christ, the Church, provided its understanding was put at safe remove from its supernaturalized (and insitutionalized) deviation, or the third of deviations Foster had in mind.

In looking for that remedy Foster fell back on Cullmann's freshly published book, *Christus und die Zeit,* where the time between Christ's resurrection and His second coming is viewed as a progressive subjection of all to Christ through the Church. In other words, the resolution of the Cartesian dilemma, or the inability of science to secure its own proper use, was to be found in the gradual integration of all into the body of Christ which is the Church. But could Foster really defend himself against the charge that what he actually meant by integration was a subordination of the Body of Christ to natural science? Foster, who saw in scientifically mediated birth control and sex selection a deeper comprehension of Christianity, would have found it very difficult to defend himself against the charge that what he ultimately held uppermost was not the life to come after Christ's second coming but a life made comfortable by science on earth for the greatest possible number.

Was not this utilitarianism couched in studiedly vague references to the Body of Christ, the Church? Did that Body, as Foster's printed words made it appear, have anything to do with Christ's words, very harsh and very "archaic" words, on sexual conduct? Could that Body of Christ retain through centuries an awareness valid and normative even in an age of science, or was that awareness to be remodeled according to the latest progress in molecular biology, gene-splicing, and cloning? What would Foster have said about substitute mother-hood, one-parent families, megafamilies, and premarital sex that pose today a far more pernicious threat to mankind than the atomic bomb in his time? Would it not have been more appropriate, in speaking of the Body of Christ, to speak of the indissolubility of marriage, which provided the ground for Paul's assertion of an indissoluble tie between Christ and his body the Church?

For ultimately, the gravest deficiency of Foster's dicta on the Christian origin of natural science lies not with his amateurism about Newtonian science and his ignorance about its origin. The deficiency in question lies with his unwitting reduction of Christianity to a purely human understanding of it, a form of naturalism. In falling victim to the lure of that reductionism Foster may have been misled by the splendid estheticism of the religious monuments of Oxford, itself now a monument more to culture than to religion.[59] A telltale proof of this was provided by Foster himself and once more in a self-contradictory way. He did so as he tried to answer the question: What to do with culture which man needs and yet can be subservient to? The question mirrored the dilemma he had already dealt with in connection with nature. In this latter respect, as was seen, he abolished the dilemma by taking science for specific guide while leaving for the Church the muttering of unctuous phrases left in the glitter of their generalities.

This outcome could be suspected by anyone able to see through the hollowness of H. Asmussen's analysis of the German disaster from which Foster took his cue. Tellingly, Asmussen's analysis had its own touch of contradictoriness or at least left much unexplained. One could, of course, argue that the institutionalized unity of State and (Lutheran) Church in the Second Reich resulted in identifying Christian Revelation with a particular form of culture. But Asmussen left unspecified the kind of Church which was to be salvaged from a two-fold threat. One was the disaster of World War I, the other the

Barthian onslaught on all natural connections of Christianity, cultural and philosophical, the latter especially embodied in natural theology. The result was a cultural uprooting of the (Lutheran) Church (in Germany), an outcome not at all to Asmussen's liking. He also left unspecified the measure in which the Church (invariably taken for the Lutheran community) ought to form a culture and in turn to be nurtured by it. Asmussen should have first aired the condition of the (Lutheran) Church in Scandinavian lands instead of trying to diagnose its condition elsewhere. Most importantly, he should have avoided suggesting, however implicitly, that the Church in Germany was simply Lutheran, and much less that the Lutheran Church was simply the Church in Germany, let alone elsewhere. Had he given a reasonably accurate phenomenology of the Church, Asmussen might have prevented Foster from talking about the Body of Christ as if it had no visible body at all.

This was, however, not likely to happen. For Foster did not take kindly to the visibility of culture itself insofar as it was Christian, unless it was such in a subtly British way. A return to Christian culture appeared to Foster to be a mistaken reaction to the sense of having been caught in a cultural vacuum. He strengthened his point by recalling his analysis of the mistaken reaction of the Church (once more left unspecified) to the rise of modern science. There the Church, by clinging to Aristotelian science, unwittingly promoted nature worship as she failed to see the voice of God in modern science: "Is not the reaction," Foster asked, "towards re-establishing the sanctity of historical institutions in danger of falling into another form of idolatry?" Foster's answer was unequivocal though softened with typically British reservation: "There may have been a time (namely, the period of Christian civilization out of which we are just passing) in which God used historical institutions (in somewhat the same way in which I suggested above that He used nature), as in a special way the vehicle for conveying His will to men; so that the naive piety of 'my station and its duties' was a genuine service of God, and not an idolatry. But God is perhaps now bringing that period to an end."[60]

It must have been exceedingly difficult for a Christ Church don to consider that Christianity and Church may have to do one day without Oxford and without bishops sitting in the House of Lords. At any rate, Foster seemed to be fully aware of the drastically negative aspect which his answer to the dilemma posed by science and culture caused to loom large. Owing to the rise of science and the dechristianization of culture God "has detached us from nature and uprooted us from our civilization. He has made it impossible for us to worship either nature or culture." Why?—Foster asked. "Certainly not in order to leave us without worship and without guidance. But perhaps in order to show us that our need of worship and of guidance can find no satisfaction except in Him. Perhaps we are really resisting God's intentions when we try to arrest the process, and to root ourselves again in nature or in culture."[61]

The Barthian ring of this answer is unmistakable. Coming as it did from Foster, living off the emoluments of a 'religious culture', the answer lacked consistency. Worse, it made it impossible for him to give meaning to the question: If science owed much of its rise to Christian Revelation, in what sense could the full grown fruit, modern or Newtonian science, to say nothing of its post-modern form which is 20th-century physics, still be spoken of as a genuine chip off the old block?

To elaborate that sense would lead us far beyond the aim of this essay which is merely to point out some telltale remarks of Foster and give the perspective in which the true story, suggested by his articles but so far untold, may be set forth. It is a story steeped in inconsistencies, both on Foster's part and on the part of those who found in him a guide for spotting something genuinely worthwhile in the relation of Christian Revelation and modern science, Newtonian and truly modern. It is a story in which mistaken assumptions, deficient information, inconsistent argumentation, and a good deal of wishful thinking are allowed to let the blindfold of sectarianism appear as a respectable academic hood.

Such is a story in which historians and historians of science do not, as a rule, find much instructiveness. A major exception would be Pierre Duhem who, in portraying the strange ways of scientific progress, was not afraid even to resort to the analogy of rivers that at times disappear underground.[62] He had no fear for allowing even for such a possibility in intellectual development, be it that of discoveries or of their interpretation, because he had put the history of the origin of modern science on a sound basis. He did so not by getting lost in arbitrary conceptual analysis about substances and in the equally unsafe distinction between the absolute and ordained power of God, but by knowing thoroughly the very foundations of Newtonian science, which is about motion and things in motion, and by courageously following up faint indications about the long forgotten record of those foundations. He was thus able to unmask the *Deus-ex-machina* conception of the origin of science which some before him had tried to cover up with copious references to the liberation of man's mind through the Reformation and others to the liberation which the Enlightenment brought even from reformed Christianity insofar as it held on to Christ and sacraments. To heighten the irony, those who voiced these two very different contentions all too often lived like jolly bedfellows and they did so certainly at a time when Duhem performed his historic feat. He did so almost exactly to the hour when Bergson enshrined that *Deus-ex-machina* with the priceless but worthless phrase about "the descent of science from heaven to earth along the inclined plane of Galileo."[63]

Had Foster studied the works of Duhem, which were at the Bodleian from the moment of their publication,[64] perhaps he would not have written his articles, or, had he mustered a truly Christian intellectual courage, he would have told a very different story with very different telltale remarks.

[1] This article will be referred to as Foster 1934; see pp. 446-48.

[2] These two articles will be referred to as Foster 1935 and Foster 1936.

[3] Foster 1934, p. 448.

[4] Ibid.

[5] Foster 1936, pp. 26-27.

[6] Foster 1934, p. 453, where Foster slights that knowledge as "antiquarian."

[7] The expression is of Leopold von Ranke, who with Theodore Mommsen was the initiator of the study of the original sources in writing history.

[8] The two basic meanings are random and dependent on a choice. Needless to say, even the best dictionaries are reluctant to undertake the task shunned by most philosophers (and scientists) to give a definition of randomness (or chance) which would be an answer to the question: "What *is* chance?" For further discussion of this crucial semantic problem with respect to modern science, see my *God and the Cosmologists* (Edinburgh: Scottish Academic Press, 1989), pp. 142-49 and 167-68, and my essay, "Determinism and Reality," *The Great Ideas Today 1990* (Chicago: Encyclopedia Britannica, 1990), pp. 277-302, reprinted here as ch. 6.

[9] Foster 1934, p. 453.

[10] Ockham was very consistent in arguing, on the basis of his occasionalism, that it was possible to have starlight without stars. Whether it was possible to have astronomy on that basis was another matter.

[11] In his Gunning Lectures, delivered at the Faculty of Theology of the University of Edinburgh in 1969, under the title, *Religion and the Rise of Modern Science* (Edinburgh: Scottish Academic Press, 1972). In giving a mere page to the medievals, Hooykaas ignores not only Duhem's vast findings about medieval science (of which more later), but also the far more accessible work of A. C. Crombie, *Medieval and Early Modern Science* (1953) which by then had gone through several re-editions and reprintings. Possibly Hooykaas would not have done so had he thought that in his presumably scholarly audience somebody was aware of medieval science as an area of inquiry that had by then been studied intensely for two decades. Hooykaas' references (pp. 32-34) to Buridan and Oresme are signs of crass of ignorance.

[12] A well-known remark on Bacon by one of his prominent contemporaries.

[13] To speak, as Hooykaas does, of Descartes' theological voluntarism (pp. 41-42) is a howler.

[14] Newton, of course, could claim in Query 31 of the *Opticks* that it was no contradiction to assume that God could create particles of all sizes "and perhaps of different Densities and Forces, and thereby vary the Laws of Nature, and make Worlds of several sorts in several Parts of the Universe," but he failed explain how those Worlds could constitute one single Universe. For quotation see edition by Dover Publications (New York, 1952), pp. 402-03.

[15] The most telling case in this respect is W. Olbers' famed paper of 1823 on the transparency of cosmic spaces. See for details my *The Paradox of Olbers' Paradox* (New York: Herder & Herder, 1969).

[16] Foster 1936, p. 26.

[17] Many details about Kant's amateurism in science are given in my translation, with Introduction and Notes, of his *Universal Natural History and Theory of the Heavens* (Edinburgh: Scottish Academic Press, 1981).

[18] K. R. Popper, *Conjectures and Refutations: The Growth of Scientific Knowledge* (1962; New York: Harper Torchbooks, 1965), p. 136.

[19] For this and other glimpses of the scientific absurdities filling everywhere that work of Kant, see my Gifford Lectures, *The Road of Science and the Ways to God* (Chicago: University of Chicago Press, 1978), pp. 125-27.

[20] The Congress took place in April 1922. The title of Foster's paper was "The Opposition between Hegel and the Philosophy of Empiricism."

[21] Epistula 120, cap. 1, section 3, in Migne 33:453.

[22] A major theme developed in my Gifford Lectures, quoted above.

[23] In fact, such a sober-minded physicist as J. C. Maxwell claimed the ether to be the largest body of which we have direct knowledge and did so in the columns of the famed 9th edition of the *Encyclopedia Britannica*! For details, see my *The Relevance of Physics* (Chicago: The University of Chicago Press, 1966), pp. 79-85 and 166-67.

[24] See my article, "Socrates, or the Baby and the Bathwater," in *Faith and Reason* 16 (Spring 1990), pp. 63-79; reprinted here as ch. 3

[25] *On the Heavens,* 274a.

[26] Thus after having laid it down in writing that Napoleon must land in Portugal and nowhere else, he refused to concede the truth of the official news about Napoleon's landing in Egypt. For this and similar details, see my Gifford Lectures, p. 115.

[27] Even if this dictum of Hegel is apocryphal, it does full justice to Hegel's handling the facts of history in his philosophy of history.

[28] On behalf of the authenticity of this remark of Koestler, I can offer only my memory of having seen it quoted in one of the major British newspapers, following his death in 1982.

[29] For details, see the full list of Duhem's publications in my *Uneasy Genius: The Life and Work of Pierre Duhem* (2d ed.: Dordrecht: Martinus Nijhoff, 1987). It shows something of the perennial value of Duhem's *Les Origines de la statiques* that almost a century after its original publication has just been published in English translation by Kluwer (Dordrecht).

[30] I have given in my article, "Science and Censorship: Hélène Duhem and the Publication of the *Système du monde,*" *Intercollegiate Review* 21 (Winter 1985-86), pp. 41-49, a glimpse of that startling story which is presented in full in my book, *Reluctant Heroine: The Life and Work of Hélène Duhem* (Edinburgh: Scottish Academic Press, 1992). French translation is forthcoming.

[31] A proof of Duhem's awareness of the significance of this passage is the fact that he had also quoted it in the Preface to the third volume of his *Etudes sur Léonard de Vinci,* in addition of discussing it in great detail in that book in chapter 1. For the English translation, see my *Science and Creation: From Eternal Cycles to an Oscillating Universe* (Edinburgh: Scottish Academic Press, 1974), p. 233.

[32] See ibid., and my Gifford Lectures, p. 43.

[33] For this and similar dismissals by d'Alembert of medieval philosophy, see R. Grimsley, *Jean d'Alembert (1717-83)* (Oxford: Clarendon Press, 1963), p. 226.

[34] Foster 1935, pp. 444-45.

[35] As shown in my *The Savior of Science* (Washington D. C. : Regnery Gateway, 1988), pp. 74-76.

[36] Foster 1934, pp. 448-49.

[37] *The Christian Scholar* 43 (1960), p. 5.

[38] Rom 13:1.

[39] On Koyré's sympathies for pantheism, see my Gifford Lectures, pp. 231-32.

[40] Best seen from in the conclusion of his *From the Closed World to the Infinite Universe* (New York: Harper Torchbooks, 1958).

[41] Raven did so in his Gifford Lectures, *Natural Religion and Christian Theology* (Cambridge: The University Press, 1953), vol. 1, p. 77. To make matters more glaring, Raven, in the same breath, also dismissed the praises of Duhem by L. Thorndike, a far more original historian of science than Sarton.

[42] Even more revealing evidences than the ones in my *Uneasy Genius* are given in *Reluctant Heroine*; see note 30 above.

[43] A. N. Whitehead, *Science and the Modern World* (1926; New York: New American Library, 1948), p. 19.

[44] That is, until the publication of my *Science and Creation*, quoted above.

[45] See my *Savior of Science* and *Scientist and Catholic: Pierre Duhem* (Front Royal, Va: Christendom Press, 1991). The latter work was also published in French, *Pierre Duhem: L'Homme de foi et de science* (Paris: Beauchesne, 1991).

[46] In a letter of March 25, 1913, to his daughter, Hélène. For details, see *Reluctant Heroine*, p. 53.

[47] See ibid., pp. 173-75.

[48] "Physics, History of," *The Catholic Encyclopedia*, vol. 12 (New York: The Gilmary Society, 1913), pp. 47-67. See especially, pp. 51-52.

[49] The translator was P. P. Wiener, the publisher, Princeton University Press, 1954.

[50] See volume 4, p. 1095.

[51] I plan to expose that scandal in a special essay.

[52] *Etudes sur Léonard de Vinci: Ceux qu'il a lus et ceux qui l'ont lu.* Troisième Série (Paris: Hermann, 1913), p. xi.

[53] See *Uneasy Genius*, pp. 426-27.

[54] As testified by such a close observer of Foster as Canon Demant, who stated in the sermon he preached following Foster's death: "A good many years ago Michael Foster wrote some articles in a philosophical journal on the origin of the scientific impulse in Western civilization, and connected it with the world outlook brought about the influence of the Bible and Christian Theology. This apparently paradoxical thesis has been quoted over and over again by others who have shown its importance by building on it. But Michael never seemed to think they were of much importance or value, and did not take up the matter again" (p. 6).

[55] It was carried as Supplement to Nr 299, November 26, 1947, pp. 1-16. The *News-Letter* was published for the Christian Frontier Council and printed by the Church Army Press, Cowley, Oxford.

[56] Ibid., p. 7.

[57] Ibid., p. 8.

[58] Ibid., p. 8.

[59] One need not go as far back as the times of Wesley, not even to the days of the Oxford Movement, to see this. What stands out most sharply in my memory from the days I spent in Oxford as I delivered my Fremantle Lectures at Balliol College in 1977, was a conversation with the outgoing President of Trinity College. What he told me about the vanishing of Christianity in the Colleges of Oxford, still helps me against being unduly impressed by their gothic splendor, built though it was by a Christianity more germane to the Gospel.

[60] Ibid., p. 16.

[61] Ibid.

[62] This picture Duhem developed in masterful prose in the conclusion of the second volume of his *Les origines de la statique*, a prose based on his personal exploration of the river Foux in the arid plateaux of the Cevennes, a scenery which he also drew in magnificent landscapes. For a reproduction of some of them, see my work, *The Physicist as Artist: The Landscapes of Pierre Duhem* (Edinburgh: Scottish Academic Press, 1988).

[63] H. Bergson, *Creative Evolution*, tr. A. Mitchell (1911; New York: Random House, 1944), p. 364.

[64] Information based on a letter from the Bodleian.

6

Determinism and Reality

The old determinism

In its broadest sense *determinism* means that not only purely physical events but conscious human choices too are the inevitable consequences of their antecedent conditions. In modern times champions of this universal determinism heavily banked on mechanistic or Newtonian physics. Its spectacular successes were taken for a proof that mental and volitional acts follow one another in the same ironclad sequence which, according to that physics, regulate the material world.

Those who endowed mechanistic causation with this kind of universal validity did not engage in an enterprise free of perplexities. Doubts that were bravely suppressed by Hobbes, Spinoza, Bayle, de la Mettrie, Helvetius, and d'Holbach surfaced now and then in the writings of Voltaire and Diderot. Subtly worrisome was Voltaire's witticism as he wondered why puny man should have a quality, freedom, which huge celestial bodies did not possess. Diderot felt tormented by the possibility that his love for Mme de Maux might be as blind as a comet's submission to the law of gravitation: "It makes

First published in *Great Ideas Today 1990* (Chicago: Encyclopedia Britannica, 1990), pp. 276-302. Reprinted with permission.

me wild," he wrote to her, "to be entangled in a devil of philosophy that my mind cannot deny and my heart gives the lie to."[1]

No such perplexities are noticeable in that celebrated testimonial to universal determinism which Laplace offered in 1819 in his *Philosophical Essay on Probabilities*. Not for a moment did it dawn on Laplace that the *Essay* lacked that elementary philosophical ingredient which is attention to the inexorable force whereby logic takes its due. The force in question finds the smallest loopholes in reasoning and works on it like water does on a ship that springs a leak, big or small.

Laplace's reasoning could hardly appear watertight to anyone attentive to his ambiguous and inconsistent use of words. He failed to make it clear whether all truths rested on probability considerations or whether what he called "eternal truths" formed an exception. He leaned towards granting universal validity to mechanistic causation which he seemed to equate with sufficient reason. As he turned free acts into the effects of one's motivations he did not care to consider whether he had written his book freely in spite of his own obviously strong motivations for writing it.

The phrase that could appear least objectionable to a contemporary reader in the crucial second chapter of the book related to chance. By endorsing the notion of chance as "merely the expression of ignorance of true causes," he had to write that

> Given for one instant an intelligence which could comprehend all the forces by which nature is animated and the respective situation of the beings who compose it—an intelligence sufficiently vast to submit these data to analysis—it would embrace in the same formula the movements of the greatest bodies of the universe and those of the lightest atom; for it, nothing would be uncertain and the future, as the past, would be present to its eyes.[2]

To this Laplace added that for all its advances in the sciences, actual and future, the human mind would forever remain "infinitely removed" from that superior intelligence. This, however, was not to be taken for a concession that shortcomings in man's scientific knowledge could ever weaken strict determinism in the physical world: "The curve described by a simple molecule of air or vapor is regulated in a manner just as certain as the planetary orbits; the only difference between them is that which comes from our ignorance."

Laplace's reference to the trajectory of vapor molecules reappeared in the reminiscences which T. H. Huxley wrote in 1885, at the request of Francis Darwin, about the first reactions to *The Origin of Species*. A chief among them consisted in the charge that Darwin attributed evolution to chance and this smacked of the absence of causes. To dispose of this "misinterpretation" of Darwin's thinking Huxley resorted to the tactic that attack was the best defense. He asked Darwin's critics what they meant by chance as if they and not Darwin had set so great store by it. "Do they believe that anything in this universe happens without reason or without cause?" To that rhetorical question he was ready with an answer full of rhetoric: "If they do, it is they who are the inheritors of antique superstitions and ignorance." And if they were to convert to science, they would have first to subscribe to the creed of science with only one article of faith in it, namely, "the absolute validity in all times and under all circumstances of the law of causation."[3]

Laplace's reference to the trajectory of vapor molecules may have directly inspired Huxley's further elaboration of the topic. He invited Darwin's critics for a stroll along the seaside. There they were to be coaxed into taking the view that the apparently irregular splashing of the waves against the rocks, the play of colors on the myriads of bubbles and "the roar and scream of the shingle as it is cast up and torn down the beach" were so many chance events. Then Huxley would let Darwin's critics perceive some deity in the gaps of causality where chance is supposed to operate without doing anything. Such perception, Huxley warned, radically differed from the perspective of the "man of science" who

> knows that here, as everywhere, perfect order is manifested; that there is not a curve of the waves, not a note in the howling chorus, not a rainbow-glint on a bubble, which is other than a necessary consequence of the ascertained laws of nature; and that with a sufficient knowledge of the conditions, competent physico-mathematical skill could account for, and indeed predict, every one of those "chance" events.

Although he spoke of purely physical entities and events as subject to strict causation Huxley did not wish to make exceptions to acts of free will. Whatever philosophical loopholes he wanted to secure by coining the word agnosticism, he certainly did not want to weaken thereby faith in universal determinism. When presented, on the occasion of the death of his seven-year-old son, with the prospect of the soul's immortality, he referred to the inverse-square law of gravitation as the only reliable truth to have faith in.

Such a faith is insensitive to its blindness. Led by that faith Huxley did not see that if universal determinism were true, scientific faith had to be blindly predetermined. It remains impervious to arguments, however concise, such as the one formulated by Poincaré, certainly a "man of science." Poincaré's phrase, "c'est librement qu'on est déterministe,"[4] dating from 1902, shows how easy it is to turn the table on a universal determinist, provided he has some respect for logic.

The new indeterminism

At that time such a determinist would not have as much as suspected that science might soon deprive him of the table itself. Determinists could still be confident that no objections would come from science even to strict determinism in the interaction of material objects. Yet the eventual uncritical acceptance of those objections gave credence in the long run to a radically new form of indeterminism. In the latter the ultimate bone of contention is neither the status of free will nor the precision of material interactions. What is truly at issue touches on that fundamental or ontological aspect of determinism whereby a things is unequivocally distinct from mere nothing. In that new indeterminism not only ordinary objects, such as a table, may lose their reality, but the same fate is in store for that supreme totality of objects which is the universe.

Around 1900 or so, few physicists took seriously the claims of Poincaré and Mach about scientific laws as purely conceptual tools to facilitate the economy of thought. Their claims followed, of course, from their rejection of ontology with mechanistic causation as its conspicuous victim. Most physicists would have agreed with Alfred Cornu, of physical optics fame, who declared at the 1900 meeting of the International Congress of Physics in Paris: "The more we penetrate into the knowledge of natural phenomena, the more developed and precise is the audacious Cartesian conception of the mechanism of the universe."[5]

Cornu's words did not seem to take into account that statistical theories as applied to physical problems, molecular gas theory in particular, began to be taken for a proof of indeterminism. In 1905 the British physicist, J. Larmor, had those theories in mind as he warned "mental philosophers" (speculative philosophers as distinct from natural philosophers or physicists) that determinism "is not a conception universally entertained in physical science."[6] Philosophers, bent not so much on speculations as on facts and logic, could have easily replied that statistical gas theory was indeterminist only in appearance. It started with the assumption that molecules were strictly defined entities with exact physical properties and so were their individual interactions.

It was a signal failure in elementary logic to forget that starting point and take average values of probabilities for an absence of strict precision in individual interactions. Even more illogical was to present most improbable events as being a-causal. Yet it was in this vein that Rankine spoke of the chance reconcentration of light into massive stars as a means for the universe to reconstitute itself. The same is true of Boltzmann's suggestion that a table might suddenly rise from the floor whenever all atoms in it happened to move in the same upward direction.

Disregard for logic, once given quarters however narrow, could but claim ever more spacious accomodations. Tellingly, no major physicist protested when in the late 1920s Eddington claimed that the table in front of him was more real when described as a bundle of wave functions than as an object of plain sensory perception. Two generations later no prominent protest was heard when Professor A. H. Guth of MIT claimed that he could create universes literally out of nothing, a claim that made the headlines in *The New York Times* (April 17, 1984).

It made no headlines that soon physicists were busy in turning those "universes" into a single, well-determined universe. Their re-awakening to the fact that only such a universe gives meaning to science illustrates an elementary lesson. A restitution is in order not only when bank robberies come to light but also when "scientific" sleights of hand obviously get out of hand.

Compared with a sleight of hand that pretends to have the very universe for its object, the great train robbery of the 1960s should appear a puny matter. Since only the latter touched on a well-determined reality, such as the sum of five million sterling pounds, the gist of the comparison relates not to the object but to the skill underlying the two actions. Those who performed that robbery had to precondition themselves through practicing petty thefts and minor robberies over a few years at least. It took the relentless immersion of two generations of physicists in the Copenhagen philosophy of quantum mechanics to let the claim be hatched that physicists can conveniently rob the "nothing" and literally create thereby a universe. Were that claim reliable, it would make senseless any talk about determinism, and certainly about its deepest or ontological kind.

Physical theory as mental conditioning
The seeds of that claim could but appear the purest and best science. It would indeed be difficult to think of a context more purely scientific than the pages of the *Zeitschrift für Physik* which carried in its issue of April 1927 a paper by Heisenberg, "On the visualizable content of quantum-mechanical kinetics and mechanism." The cunningly philosophical title of the paper should have served warning to its physicist readers that physics was not its real subject. The very end of the paper made this all too clear. There, in a stylistically overloaded sentence, Heisenberg drove home what in his eyes was the all important point, a point essentially philosophical. The definitive truth of the point rested, according to him, with the uncertainty relation he had just derived and referred to as equation (1):

> Much rather [vielmehr] one can much better [viel besser] characterize the [paper's] true real content [wahre Sachverhalt] [as follows]: Because all experiments are subject to quantum mechanics and therefore to equation (1), the invalidity of the law of causality will thereby definitively be established by quantum mechanics.[7]

A least noted though most revealing part of this declaration was Heisenberg's reference to the *definitive* disproof of causality by quantum mechanics. He may have thought that he had said enough about what had preceded that definitive proof by referring to the bearing of statistical theories on the status of causality. They, he noted, bore only on a weak form of causality, namely, that "from exact data only statistical conclusions can be inferred." What he called the "strong formulation of causality" had a distinctly Laplacian touch to it: "If we know exactly the present, we can predict the future." It is this kind of causality that was definitively disproved by quantum mechanics, or rather by the uncertainty principle, because "we *cannot* know, as a matter of principle, the present in all its details."

The uncertainty principle proved, in Heisenberg's words, "the imprecision of all perception" and therefore it was futile to look for a "hidden 'real' world ruled by causality." What later became known as "hidden variable theories" formed the target of Heisenberg's next declaration: "Such speculations seem to us—and this we stress with emphasis—useless and meaningless." There followed a phrase, laden with philosophy, but not for Heisenberg who noted in a matter of fact style: "For physics has to confine itself to the formal description among perceptions." Perhaps Heisenberg felt that he had gone deeply enough into the philosophy of perception as he had just stated: "All true perception is a choice out of a wealth of possibilities and a limitation of the possible future [perception]."

The philosophical instructiveness of these phrases, replete with *non-sequiturs*, cannot be emphasized enough. They contain much more than a blunt declaration about a new indeterminism, far more treacherous than the one implied in the accidental swerving of atoms postulated by Epicurus. They also vitiate the enterprise of the quantum physicist. First, if physics is but a formal or quantitative description of relations among perceptions, it then justifies no statement about causality and not even a statement about the objective real world. The physicist who subscribes to Heisenberg's definition of the aim and method of physical theory cannot consistently communicate his own construction of it to other physicists if these are but mere bundles of his own perceptions. Similarly inconsistent should appear the same physicist's reliance on laboratory instruments which would not cost at times hundreds of millions of dollars of taxpayers' money if they were but *his* perceptions.

The Copenhagen philosophy and its roots
This formalistic and self-defeating view of physical theory is a mainstay of the Copenhagen interpretation of quantum mechanics as worked out by Bohr. It entails a denial of causality regardless of quantum mechanics. Three years before Heisenberg formulated the uncertainty principle, Bohr implicitly denied causality by postulating a wide departure from the principle of the conservation of energy in the interaction of X-rays with atoms. His theory, proposed together with Kramers and Slater, quickly turned out to clash with observational results.

There is much more to the Copenhagen philosophy of quantum mechanics than its customary image. The latter is similar to a naive account of an iceberg as if almost all of it were confined to its visible part or peak. The culminating or widely perceived point of that interpretation consists in the assertion that causality operates only partially on the atomic level and that atoms have complementary aspects (waves and particles).

The second part of that claim may, when compared with the first, seem a very innocent affair but not when taken in its full philosophical consequences. In working with atoms the physicist registers sensory evidences some of which are best interpreted as the result of actions by waves, others as actions of corpuscles. Patterns of X-ray diffraction are illustrations of the former case, while the latter is indicated by sparks produced by alpha-rays on a scintillation screen. If these two forms have ever been observed simultaneously there would be some justification for the inference that one and the same material entity has mutually irreducible characteristics.

Irreducibilities are never to the liking of physicists as their immediate aim is to turn their sensory findings into quantitative data transformable into one another. Notes of despondency are struck when such a transformation appears to be impossible. No physicist in modern times has, of course, imitated the Pythagorean of old who threw himself into the sea on encountering an irreducibility in the relation of the hypotenuse of a right-angled triangle to its unit sides. Later the fact that one cannot reduce by geometrical means the area of a circle to that of a square became a source of despondency to not a few. The frustratingly unsuccessful attempts to quantize Einstein's gravitational equations are a recent phase in that story of which, in this century, the mutual irreducibility of waves and particles represent a major chapter.

In the measure in which a physicist is insensitive or hostile to philosophical questions about the real as such he will not blame the limitations or shortcomings of the physics at his disposal as he encounters this or that kind of irreducibility. Rather he may blame reality itself for being more subtle than are his conceptual and experimental tools. He then may try to take revenge on reality by sublimating it into high-sounding words and, in fact, may try to abolish it altogether by not talking about it. He will then present his discourse about the irreducible aspects of reality as the last word in philosophy and science.

The philosophical heritage on which Bohr grew up (and of which more shortly) certainly predisposed him for taking such a revengeful posture vis-à-vis reality. It revealed itself in his systematic avoidance of ontological questions, as noted in a major analysis of his thought.[8] He seemed to be unconcerned about the fact that his theory of complementarity was as severed from reality as are two cheeks that can have no claim to a head. Such is the gist of the horns of complementarity on which he had impaled himself.[9] The complementarity of Bohr is a doctrine of indeterminism in that deepest sense in which the real itself loses a determinate meaning because it ceases to be the ground and supportive ontological matrix for what are mere aspects of reality.

The threat to reality should appear more immediate in connection with the denial of strict causality on the atomic level. About that threat, which is essentially philosophical, the first thing to realize is that it has no scientific merit, whatever its alleged connection with Heisenberg's uncertainty principle. The reason for this is that there can be no scientific method of measuring, either on the atomic or on the ordinary level, the process known as causality. The latter is a philosophical and, indeed, a thoroughly metaphysical inference, however spontaneous. Its validity rests on one's view of knowing external reality.

Here the options are essentially two. One can take external reality as the very factor that activates, in the first place, man's ability to know, an ability much more than having purely sensory impressions. This view, which is the classical realist position in epistemology (as very distinct from mere empiricism) is recommended for various reasons. One is that it corresponds to common sense or good sense, a commodity not at all co-terminous with commonly held opinions. Another is that it finds support in the best modern studies of early intellectual development in children. Still another is that by holding to that view one is spared the inconveniences of the other view. Among them is the dreadful necessity of turning external reality into a function of one's thinking.

This necessity unfolded itself in the development of philosophy from Kant through Fichte and Schelling to Hegel. While the Hegelian Left tried to rescue real matter from evanescing into mere ideas, it rescued but the mechanistic properties of matter. Throughout its checkered history, Marxist philosophy remained stuck with mechanistic causality in its effort to become genuinely realist. The Hegelian Right tried to thrive in the rarified atmosphere of disembodied ideas from which the Neokantians hoped to escape by calling for a return to Kant. They merely endorsed as remedy a virus that had already brought epidemics to epistemology.

Despair about man's ability to account intellectually for the real as such prompted, in the closing decades of the 19th century, the rise of philosophies such as Mach's sensationism, Poincaré's commodism, the pragmatism of William James and Harold Hoeffding, Nietzsche's apotheosis of the will, and the intellectually even less respectable Lebensphilosophies. Early in his university studies Heisenberg felt torn whether to specialize in Lebensphilosophie or in physics.[10] Part of the Lebensphilosophie he so enthusiastically subscribed to consisted in denouncing mechanistic causality as a threat to human initiatives and creativity. Sometime before he had written his historic paper Heisenberg explicitly denied causality and knew that not a few prominent German physicists were doing the same.[11] There is much more than meets the eye in his claim that his uncertainty relation has *definitively* proved the invalidity of causality. As so often before and after him, in his case too a grave philosophical error took on the glamor of indisputable verity once it was tied to unquestionably good physics.

As one unable to see that mechanistic causality offered but a surface view of causality, Heisenberg could hardly suspect that once ontological causality was disregarded, a road opened up with solipsism as its logical dead-end. This possible outcome was certainly protested by Bohr. While rejecting ontology he also claimed that complementarity was the only realist philosophy! Recognition of the connection between complementarity and solipsism is still widely resisted by the champions of the Copenhagen interpretation of quantum mechanics, although solipsism comes in view in the measure in which the ultimate implications of that interpretation are being fearlessly drawn. A telling illustration of this is the multiworld theory developed in the early 1970s according to which there are as many universes as there are observers. One wonders whether the universe can be turned more effectively into an undetermined and undeterminable entity.

Ineffective criticisms

That the Copenhagen philosophy of quantum mechanics logically leads to solipsism has been repeatedly noted. The ineffectiveness of its leading critics derives from the fact that they endorse an elementary equivocation underlying it. They do so as they take aim at Heisenberg's claim that it is useless and meaningless to speculate about a hidden real world ruled by causality. For what they look for in theories of hidden variables is a causality which they turn into a function of exact measurability. This is precisely the idea which Heisenberg called in his historic paper "the strong formulation of the causal law" although it should appear such only to one weak in a philosophy that includes unconditional respect for ontology as well as for logic. No wonder that he dismissed that apparently strong but in fact very weak form of causality on the basis of the fallacious inference: since we cannot know (that is measure, a purely operational procedure) exactly the present, we cannot predict the future as it takes place exactly (an ontological procedure, independent of its being measured or not).

The basis was not only bad logic but also a very defective thinking about physical theory. Being essentially non-definitive or revisable, physical theory cannot justify definitive conclusions even within its own realm let alone within other realms such as philosophy. Among leading proponents of quantum theory there has not been, for over half a century now, a single one who would have considered the bearing on it of Gödel's incompleteness theorems first proposed in 1930. This is especially startling in the case of John von Neumann who for many years was a colleague of Gödel at the Institute for Advanced Study in Princeton. In spite of this he did not develop second thoughts on the "definitive" truth of quantum theory which he proposed in 1932 and on the basis of which he celebrated the final overthrow of causality.[12]

There is no evidence either that Gödel's theorems prompted Dirac when at the Einstein-centenary conference in Jerusalem in 1979 he predicted a new form of quantum mechanics which "will have determinism in the way that Einstein wanted." Moreover, in doing so, Dirac did not refrain from chastising the mental inertia prevailing among quantum physicists. Determinism will be introduced in quantum mechanics "only at the expense of abandoning some of the preconceptions which physicists now hold, and which it is not possible to try to get at now; . . . for the time being physicists have to accept Bohr's probability interpretation—especially if they have examinations in front of them."[13]

Although the context of these remarks of Dirac and their biting tone should have guaranteed them wide publicity, they produced hardly a ripple. At any rate, most prominent physicist-critics of the Copenhagen philosophy remained caught in the misleading tracks which Planck had charted in his defense of causality and determinism.[14] Einstein merely followed Planck in propagating the fallacy that only the possibility of perfectly accurate measurement and prediction can give solid basis to determinism and realism, in that order. As will be seen shortly, Einstein failed to see that realism came first, with determinism as a distant second step insofar as it could be useful for the physicist.

Failure to see this sequence meant a shift on the part of the physicist from the grounds of very good physics, whatever its essentially revisable character, to the grounds of plain *non-sequiturs*. A road was thereby thrown wide open into the land of pseudo-metaphysics where irresponsible games could be played with the real. Tellingly, the farce in philosophy went hand in hand with leaving the ledgers of physics unbalanced. For the uncertainty principle when taken for incomplete causality in the interaction between two atoms implied an ontological imbalance or more bluntly, a plain "cheating" with real matter.

Cheating with real matter
The point should have been surmised by Heisenberg in 1927 as nothing is more natural than to think about the collision of subatomic particles (say, an electron and a photon) in connection with the form of the uncertainty principle. As given by him, this is expressed as $\Delta x \cdot \Delta mv$, where Δx is the uncertainty (margin of error) in measuring the position x of the electron and Δmv is the uncertainty (margin of error) in measuring the momentum mv which is a product of mass m and velocity v. By itself the formula states no more than that the product of those uncertainties, as measured by the physicist, cannot be smaller than $\hbar$ (Dirac's $\hbar$ which equals Planck's constant h divided by 2π). By taking that very small operational inexactitude for an inexactitude in causality Heisenberg implied an inexactitude on the ontological level, namely a defect Δ touching not only on v but also on m. This consequence, which he curiously overlooked, was equally overlooked by countless others after him.

The reason for this may lie in the perception which relativity theory brought about velocity being less than a reality than mere relation. Thus in considering the defect in measuring the momentum Δmv, the physicist could be tempted to tack it on v instead on m. There is no such easy escape for the physicist from real matter and therefore from ontology should he consider an alternate form of the uncertainty principle, $\Delta E \cdot \Delta t \geq \hbar$, a form postdating Heisenberg's historic paper. Just as the form given by Heisenberg, this form too involves two *conjugate* variables, energy E and time t. Just like position x and momentum mv, these two parameters are also conjugate variables because one cannot be measured without influencing the other. Theirs is the physically most inseparable "conjugal" connection.

In order to bring out the ontological relevance of this second form of the uncertainty principle, it should be rewritten, with the help of the famous Einsteinian formula $E = mc^2$ as $\Delta mc^2 \cdot \Delta t \geq \hbar$. If further rewritten as $\Delta mc^2 \geq \hbar/\Delta t$, the inequality shows that if the time of the action is measured with perfect accuracy, that is, if $\Delta t = 0$, then the uncertainty of measuring the energy becomes $\Delta mc^2 \geq \hbar/0$ or ∞. This uncertainty can, however, affect only the mass m because c (the speed of light) is an invariable constant.

The presence of an infinity sign in an equation which relates to an actual physical situation makes it meaningless for the physicist. He reaches a dead end whenever his equations conjure up what is usually called the infinity catastrophe. This should make plain the irrelevance of references, first made by Heisenberg himself and then greatly emphasized more recently by Karl Popper, that the uncertainty principle leaves intact the possibility of measuring with perfect accuracy one of the conjugate parameters.[15] Apart from that any perfectly exact evaluation of only one of two conjugate variables is based on data that are themselves the result of an actual measurement. The latter always involves an interaction between photons and the object, be it the marking on any ruler or scale or the position of spectral lines, and is therefore subject to the uncertainty relation. Furthermore, the evaluation, however exact, of one of two conjugate parameters, can have no bearing on causality. The latter is not a mere position in place, nor is it an action that does not take place in space or in time or with no energy-transfer involved. Causality is a *real* action in the broadest and deepest possible sense of that word.

No less real is that constant of physics, usually called Planck's quantum, but most appropriately already called by Planck himself the quantum of action. Of course, for a physicist Planck's quantum of action, the minimum of uncertainty involved in actual measurements, is so small a quantity that he might be tempted to write it off. The temptation may not seem to matter at all if he thinks of the ontologically real as something "determined" insofar as he can measure it with complete precision. But for one respectful of the real insofar as it is "determined" in the sense of simply being, the incredibly small quantity of Planck's quantum of action stands, if taken for a minimum of inexactitude, for an infinite distance that separates being from non-being. It is the distance between to be or not to be, a distance evident to Hamlets, though hardly obvious to most prominent physicists of our times.

An ontologically sensitive thinker, physicist or not, must take reality for something really real and not for a mere construct of his intellect. Such a reality cannot have for its contours a grayish margin of transition between being and non-being. To assume the existence of a margin would land one in the most pathetic spot of Alice's wonderland where the queen claimed herself the right to graft any meaning she wanted to on any word. But even that gruesome lady stopped short of engaging in what has become a favorite game in realms where thinking is governed by the Copenhagen philosophy. There the word nothing may denote some real thing, and some real thing may be taken for "nothing," whenever this dubious transaction can be used as a mental barbiturate for desensitizing one to basic philosophical questions.

From petty thefts to cosmic robbery
When Heisenberg proposed in 1927 the uncertainty principle, gone were the days when positivist physicists could slight atoms as pure fictions of mind. Then the problem for physicists related to various operations of atoms, such their radioactive emission. Most extensively investigated among such emission was the alpha-radiation or the escape of helium nuclei (two protons and two neutrons) from the nucleus of radium atoms. Quantum mechanics came to the rescue in Gamow's famous theory of alpha-tunnelling. It meant to resolve the question of how alpha-particles, whose average energy as measured in cloud chambers fell far short of the height of the energy barrier posed by the force keeping the nucleus together, nevertheless manage to cope with that barrier.

In Gamow's theory the alpha-particles "tunnelled" through the potential barrier, though at a price. During the time they were in that tunnel (a wholly fictitious entity), they too were fictitious, that is, unobservable. The time corresponded to Δt as set by the uncertainty principle. Gamow and countless others, who had by then been conditioned by relativity theory to take time for a purely mathematical relation, could be forgiven for enjoying their triumph. Their explanation, being statistical in character, could keep but fictitious ties with individually concrete physical reality.

Their attitude should seem quite cavalier with respect to a problem that represented the other side of the coin, namely the mass defect Δm corresponding to the uncertainty in time Δt. For if the uncertainty principle meant defect in ontological causality, the mass defect Δm stood for something physically real and wholly unaccounted for by physics. Gamow could have easily estimated the average amount of that unaccounted mass or Δm by taking the average amount of energy of alpha particles. The amount would have been of the order of the millionth of the mass of an alpha particle, in itself an exceedingly small bit of matter, though very real matter. Neither Gamow nor his many colleagues, who hailed his explanation, cared to calculate the missing amount in order to set the balance straight. They may have realized that in doing so they would have revealed the engagement of the Copenhagen interpreters of quantum mechanics in systematic petty thefts with real matter.

They looked the other way and in doing so they fostered a mental attitude, soon to turn into a climate of thought. Already in 1931 some cosmologists talked about the emergence of matter out of nothing and met with no rebuke on the part of fellow physicists. The latter suddenly became oblivious to the enormous and indispensable services which the principle of the conservation of matter and energy had given them during the previous three hundred or so years. This could only embolden the steady-state theorists when in 1947 they claimed that hydrogen atoms were popping up out of nothing and without a Creator at a steady rate everywhere in cosmic spaces. Had they summed up the total mass coming in this way into existence every second, the result would have shown a new matter equivalent to the mass of several stars. Such was the apparently insensible, but actually massive "mechanism" whereby they tried to dispose of the temporality of the universe, so strongly evoked by its expansion.

None of the steady-state theorists thought it necessary to justify the claim that such an emergence was within the ken of reason in general and of science in particular. Nor did their scientific critics call attention to the fact that such a "mechanism" struck at the very root of determinism insofar as there is a well determined basic difference between a thing and nothing. Rather, scientific criticism centered on the detection of an extra amount of radiation at 21-centimeter wavelength, natural to free hydrogen. No physicist dared to suggest that no such observation would conceivably prove that it was due to atoms that had just emerged out of nothing. Such an emergence, a most incisive philosophical inference, is infinitely beyond the competence of physics which by definition can deal only with things already existing.

Lack of philosophical sensitivity did not fail to encourage further furtive actions with reality, that is, with real matter. The claim that our universe might just as well have been "created" out of nothing in a basement laboratory in another universe[16] is but the latest phase in a most dubious and extremely dangerous intellectual process. Although it claims to parade in the garb of the finest science, quantum mechanics, the garb is a most dubious cavorting in philosophical fallacies. The dangerousness of the process will transpire only to those aware of an invariable connection: Presentations of moral principles as mere transient patterns of thought have always sought support in ontological indeterminism.

Some moral perspectives
A recent case about this connection is Karl Popper's advocacy of an "open society" ruled by what he called "Democritean ethics."[17] He also argued at length the merits of an "open universe" as the supreme embodiment of indeterminism.[18] Where Popper is most inconsistent is his determination to appear as a realist philosopher. He has resolutely opposed the Copenhagen interpretation of quantum mechanics. What he failed to see, or perhaps wanted not to see, is that the basic issue with that interpretation is a question of ontology and not whether exact measurements of physical interactions are feasible or not on the basis of the latest in physics. His aversion to ontology[19] may have indeed led him into the erroneous claim that it is possible to measure one conjugate variable independently of the other.

The realism of a philosopher who champions a universe as the supreme entity in which everything can happen and will ultimately happen should seem highly suspect. The immediate reason for this is that Popper based his idea of an ever novel universe on probability reasonings which are but so many means of obtaining a purely pragmatic or practical way around the actually and individually real existent. He seems indeed anxious to keep out of sight that ground of all existence whose best philosophical name was given as HE WHO IS. This ground alone guarantees the truth of realism which Chesterton put in an inimitably short but grave phrase, "There *is* an Is."[20] Compared with such an elemental dictum all philosophical discourse pales into relative insignificance.

Only within such realism can both freedom and complete ontological determinism be upheld with consistency, because both will be seen as created by the One who alone in his ontological infinity can call forth ontologically finite entities into existence. Such a call is an act of creating something out of nothing. Further, because the conceivably most determinate difference is the one between something and nothing, any material reality must have strictly determined quantitative contours insofar as quantity denotes something real. Whether with the actual tools, conceptual and experimental, of physics a completely precise measurement of those contours is possible or not is a secondary or operational question. At any rate, the realism set forth in this paragraph certainly implies that such a measurement may intrinsically be possible.

Within that realism, biblical in its deepest roots, there follows naturally the truth of that biblical phrase that "God arranged everything according to measure, number, and weight" (Wis 11:20). Within that realism, so intent on the ontologically first step, there is no temptation to start an intellectual argument with the second or third steps. Within that realism there is no occasion to explain such firsts as reality, intellect, and freedom of the will in terms of secondary and derivative notions, such as quantities, seductively easy and sweeeping as their handling may appear. Within that realism, and in it alone, it is possible to uphold the vision of a superior intelligence to which all past, present, and future are fully known. It may be doubted that in speaking of such an intellect Laplace had not subconsciously given a feeble deistic twist to an ontologically vibrant biblical passage about determinism that leaves intact human freedom and responsibility:

> The works of God are all of them good . . .
> He has to command and his will is done;
> nothing can limit his achievement.
> The works of all mankind are present to him;
> not a thing escapes his eye.
> His gaze spans all the ages;
> to him there is nothing unexpected (Sirach 39:16-20)

It would be tempting to go on quoting. The next phrase, "No cause then to say: What is the purpose of this?" offers the very commodity, existential confidence with a firm sense of purpose, of which our boasted scientific culture stands in far greater need than of science, enormous as may be its scientific needs. Physicists and philosophers of science will consider the realism set forth in the last two paragraphs for a brazen intrusion of religion, or at least of a philosophy which Gilson aptly called "methodical realism."[21] Had they pondered its merits, they might have spared themselves being entangled in the most notorious paradox of the last half a century.

A misplaced paradox

The paradox saw formulation in a paper which Einstein published in 1935, with B. Podolsky and N. Rosen in *Physical Review,* under the title, "Can quantum-mechanical description of reality be considered complete?"[22] Here too, as in the case of Heisenberg's paper, one is faced with an essay with a markedly philosophical title in a leading journal of physics. Here too a philosophical question was discussed as if it could be decided by the methods of physics. Indeed, the question touched on that chief task of philosophy which is to determine reality, or rather to take with firm determination reality as being determined in the radical sense of differing from non-reality. For such is the ultimate target of what later became known as the Einstein, Podolsky, Rosen (EPR) paradox. Today it is considered experimentally resolved against its original proponents in particular and philosophical realism in general.

The physics in the EPR paper is a thought-experiment in which the simultaneous measurement of position P and momentum Q in one system affects the same measurement in another system not in physical connection with the former. The upshot was that unless one insisted "that two or more physical quantitites can be regarded as simultaneous elements of reality *only when they can be simultaneously measured or predicted*" would one not arrive at a conclusion which "no reasonable definition of reality could be expected to permit." The conclusion stated nothing less than that the Copenhagen interpretation of quantum mechanics "makes the reality of P and Q depend upon the process of measurement carried out on the first system, which does not disturb the second system any way."

The philosophy evident in this argument about physical reality and the method of physics was vintage Einstein. The very first sentence of the paper emphasized the distinction between "the objective reality which is independent of any theory and the physical concepts with which it operates." This could but remind the readers of the EPR paper of Einstein's ringing declaration made four years earlier that "belief in an external world independent of the perceiving subject is the basis of all natural science."[23] One wonders how many of them recalled Einstein's half-hearted acknowledgment, made in his Herbert Spencer memorial lecture in 1933, that the physicist should "leave all questions of the structure of theoretical science to the epistemologist."[24] In his defense Einstein could have, of course, pointed out that epistemologists notoriously disagreed with one another on almost any point, let alone on points of fundamental importance. This, however, did not dispose of the philosophical nature of an epistemological question. Much less did it dispose of the logic whereby one's starting point in defining reality was to unfold its consequences in a remorseless way.

Indeed, Einstein (and his colleagues) made it rather easy for any moderately careful reader of their essay to spot the point from which logic would start exacting its due. Such a reader could, by giving the benefit of doubt, assign an unobjectionable sense to Einstein's opening distinction between a "comprehensive definition of reality" and a definition sufficient for physics, namely, that "every element of physical reality must have a counterpart in the physical theory." The same reader could indeed assume that Einstein reserved for physics only the right to deal with the quantitative aspects of reality as he declared that human experience, "which alone enables us to make inferences about reality, in *physics* takes the form of experiment and *measurement*." (Italics added).

If such was the case, the physicist could indeed declare as Einstein did that a "comprehensive definition of reality" was not "necessary" for his purposes. But Einstein's very next phrase was too sweepingly clear to allow a benevolent interpretation: "We shall be satisfied with the following criterion, which we regard as reasonable. *If, without in any way disturbing a system, we can predict with certainty (i. e. with probability equal to unity) the value of a physical quantity, then there exists an element of physical reality corresponding to this physical quantity.*" To prevent any misunderstanding, Einstein and his colleagues let the passage appear in italics.

The criterion offered by them about reality was most unreasonable and certainly contradicted Einstein's ringing endorsement of an objective physical reality existing independently of the perceiving subject, whether he had measuring instruments in his hands or not. For the criterion meant nothing less than that unless a physical quantity was measured with a probability equal to unity, that is, with complete quantitative exactness, that physical quantity could not be considered to exist unambiguously. In other words, Einstein, without being aware of it, espoused the very basis of Heisenberg's denial of causality, or the fallacious inference that an interaction that cannot be measured exactly, cannot take place exactly. Worse, Einstein went much farther than did Heisenberg who stopped short with a denial of causality. By proposing the foregoing criterion, Einstein made the existence of all physical reality dependent on whether the physicist can measure it exactly or not.

That this is the point where Einstein gave away the game of realism is still to be perceived by interpreters of the EPR paradox, although their number is legion. The point was not, of course, taken up by Bohr, the first to respond to the EPR paper. Here too Bohr was most careful not to be dragged into questions of ontology. He merely insisted that a complete theory had to do but with the aspects of reality and never with reality as such. In defense of this contention he rehashed his ideas on complementarity as a "new feature of natural philosopy" and its ultimate scientific support, Heisenberg's uncertainty principle. Bohr was far from ready to unfold in full the consequences of that new feature. Nor did he seem to be aware of all the dire consequences as he stated that this new feature "means a radical revision of our attitude as regards physical reality, which may be paralleled with the fundamental modification of all ideas regarding the absolute character of physical phenomena, brought about by the general theory of relativity."[25] Once more the word *radical* failed to evoke its true etymological trust which is to touch on the very roots of a question or a thing with the distinct possibility of uprooting it completely.

A passionate universe

If Bohr was right, the only absolute truth that remained was that everything was relative, even reality itself, and in a subjectivist sense much more sinistrous than Bohr might have suspected. It took twelve years for Einstein to voice, in 1948 in a letter to Max Born, his forebodings that "spooky actions at a distance" were to invade physics once Bohr's ideas about complete physical theory had been taken for the last word on the subject. Even when that letter was published in 1971[26] Einstein's conjuring up of such spooky actions could appear but a morbid concern about the abstract consequences of a purely theoretical matter. Physicists were still to devise experiments to test the EPR paradox as further elaborated by D. Bohm in 1952 and given a very specific form by J. S. Bell in 1964. It was only sometime after Aspect and his co-workers successfully tested in 1981 the quantitative prediction specified by Bell that physicists began to face up to its deepest challenge. Even then they failed to realize that the challenge was posed by their own thinking about some facts of physics rather than by physical facts themselves.

Aspect's famous experiment consists in a count of photons (emitted from a common source in two opposite directions and screened through identical polarizers) whenever they simultaneously hit their corresponding targets. These are photosensitive detectors that can be rotated at different angles. The number of coincidences is not the same when predicted respectively on the basis of quantum theory and of a theory that, in principle, allows exact measurements of individual atomic interactions. The number registered is in clear support of the quantum theoretical prediction.

Such are the bare facts. Beyond that every step becomes more and more theory-laden and revisable in that very proportion. As to the experimental apparatus, the observations of its operation remain, regardless of its sensitivity and precision, subject to the uncertainty principle. In other words, no measurement of coincidences, however accurate, can be fully exact. The physicist, who subscribes to the Copenhagen fallacy that a physical interaction that a physicist cannot measure exactly cannot take place exactly, is then forced to deny that plain matter can be the carrier of those coincidences. Since as a physicist he cannot live without a universe which is coherent, he will have to look for its cause in a non-physical factor.

Most likely he would take the view that it is neither reasonable nor fashionable to rehash the occasionalism of old. As worked out independently and at very different times by al-Ashari, Ockham, and Malebranche, occasionalism leaves to God the task to make every moment and event coherent. Since the Copenhagen philosophy does not permit the physicist to credit matter with coherence, he will have no choice but to fall back on some kind of "soul." For this is what the physicist does when he credits the coherence of those photons to some "passion" operating in them whereby they can communicate with one another at any distance.[27] But then why not attribute a "soul" to all matter, nay to the universe itself? After all it is now becoming fashionable to look at the earth as some semiconscious "Gaia."

This is not to suggest that physicists, who seem to attribute such passion to photons, speak of the soul of the universe. Nor do they methodically list the three main objects of metaphysics— universe, soul, God—and, having no use for God and bartered away the objective material universe, they attribute some passion if not soul to things to make them coherent. In their customary philosophical amateurism they just grope their way among the only possible choices, being aware more or less of the restrictions imposed on them by the Copenhagen philosophy and the fashions of the day. Of course, most physicists just do their good quantum mechanics and ignore philosophy, including its Copenhagen version.

Physicists who care for the Copenhagen philosophy to the point of conjuring up passions at a distance, would do well to take stock of their procedure's immediate and remote antecedents. The remote kind relates to the most monumental stillbirth which science suffered in the great ancient cultures, in classical Greece of all places.[28] There the attribution, within the Socratic tradition, of a striving to all bodies nipped in the bud any promising move toward an anticipation of Newton's first law, or the law of rectilinear inertial motion. As to the immediate antecedents, a quick look at them may illustrate the point that a diffuse climate of thought must for some time be on hand before its raw nature can suddenly reveal itself. Passions at a distance, that for a physicist should seem far more disreputable than actions at a distance, relate to the realm of will, a realm far removed from and potentially most hostile to the subject matter of physics. Yet, no sooner had the uncertainty principle crowned the young edifice of quantum mechanics than will and psyche were invoked as factors of coherence in physical interactions.

The scene that first witnessed this act was the famed Solvay Conference on physics held in Bruxelles in late 1927 with Heisenberg and Dirac as its youngest participants. Dirac was still to make his famous postulation of the existence of antimatter and to publish his classic axiomatization of quantum mechanics. In retrospect he should seem to have displayed penetrating insight when at that Conference he challenged Heisenberg to account for the coherence of ionization tracks produced by alpha particles in cloud chambers. The distinguished participants of that conference must have taken for a joke Dirac's remark that, in view of the inability of quantum mechanics to account for that coherence, the individual droplets of condensation somehow know how to cohere into a single track and wish to do so.[29] The joke was an ominous straw in the wind.

A year later, in 1930, George P. Thomson, a future Nobel laureate, published a smallish book, *The Atom*, which in thirty years went through six editions and saw wide circulation as a title in the Home University Library series. There he spoke of the electron's wave-function whose intensity at a particular point is a measure of the probability of the electron's being there and added: "This introduction of probability as a factor in the expression of a fundamental law is very characteristic of the recent trend of physics which is moving away from the rigid determinism of the older materialism into something vaguely approaching a conception of free will."[30]

Such was loose talk about free will on the part of a prominent cultivator of the most exact form, physics, of empirical investigations. It should have been the target of immediate and unsparing criticism on the part of physicists. Far from seeing anything wrong in it, they for the most part quickly followed suit, with Einstein being here too a most noteworthy exception.[31] Pilosophers were almost as guilty of connivance, if not by action at least by omission. This was true even of J. E. Turner, a philosopher at the University of Liverpool who quickly and unanswerably made short shrift of Thomson's assertion of indeterminism. Although Turner's concise remarks appeared in *Nature*, its countless physicist readers all over the world failed to take notice. They went on celebrating "indeterminism" in spite of the logical fallacy which Turner put tersely, though not in a language easily recognizable by physicists: "Every argument that, since some change cannot be 'determined' in the sense of 'ascertained', it is therefore not 'determined' in the absolutely different sense of 'caused', is a fallacy of equivocation."[32]

Turner, who should have used the word "measured" instead of "ascertained," made his real omission by failing to excoriate Thomson's injection into physics "of something vaguely approaching the conception of free will." He might in fact have felt some sympathy with Thomson on that score. Will in the form of *nisus* was the driving force in nature in Samuel Alexander's philosophy to which Turner wanted to give a more realist character. Turner, who even hoped to cast into a realist frame the idealism of McTaggart, was not enough of a realist to see that the real problem with the "new" physics touched on that deepest layer of realism which is ontology. No wonder that he confused realism with mechanistic causation which he tried, in a different context, to defend with an eye on sufficient reason.[33]

Before long the saving of free will on the basis of quantum mechanics had formed the ground on which prominent physicists assured laymen about their deliverance from the shackles of determinism. A series of lectures given in 1934 by A. H. Compton, who had received the Nobel Prize in physics in 1927, is worth recalling for two reasons. As Terry Lectures given at Yale they received wide publicity and they also contained a classic case of a great mistake made by a great physicist in philosophical reasoning. The error consisted in Compton's asserting and abandoning in the same breath the only defense of free will. He did so in his reference to the determinism of classical or Newtonian physics:

> It seems unfortunate that some modern philosopher has not forcibly called attention to the fact that one's ability to move his hand at will is much more directly and certainly known than are even the well-tested laws of Newton, and that if these laws deny one's ability to move his hand at will the preferable conclusion is that Newton's laws require modification. Yet I suppose such an argument would have been scorned by the physicist, who has found it necessary to show in his own way the inadequacy of Newton's laws.[34]

Compton's remark was a genuine gold piece which he immediately bartered away for a piece of fool's gold. There has not been and never shall be a better and more inescapable proof of free will than one's immediate experience of it, which is applicable even to the determinist's arguing against it. The physicist therefore traps himself in a vicious circle when he tries to prove "in his own way," that is, in terms of his physics, the "inadequacy of Newton's laws." By that inadequacy Compton could, in that context, mean only the irrelevance of those laws to the question of free will versus determinism.

He immediately forgot about that irrelevance by turning the discussion, in a page or two, to Heisenberg's uncertainty principle. Less than twenty years later, no less a physicist than H. Margenau spoke with disapproval of endless endorsements of "violation of causal reasoning" on the basis of quantum mechanics.[35] Yet Margenau contributed to the further flourishing of that intellectual orgy when in the mid-1960s he claimed that the physicist's *psi* (he had in mind Schrödinger's wave function) "has a certain abstractness and vagueness of interpretation in common with the parapsychologist's *psi*."[36]

Less shocking though intellectually just as treacherous was Heisenberg's mature interpretation of quantum mechanics. In the 1950s he saw in its probabilistic character something akin to the tendency of the Aristotelian potency towards it fulfillment in act.[37] By then Bohr had devised his own coat of arms with the Yin and Yang as its chief feature. Self-confessed amateurs clearly felt they had obtained the highest licence for casting modern physics into the categories of Tao and the steps of dancing Wu Li masters. The climate was ripe for the introduction of passions at a distance into physics to save the coherence and unity of the physical universe, a coherence lost on the basis of an elementary fallacy in reasoning.

The logic of demoralization

The potentially most destructive aspect of that climate can be best seen in a remark of Wolfgang Pauli who received the Nobel Prize in physics in 1954 for his formulation of the exclusion principle. When two years earlier Max Born wrote to him about his repeated failures over many years to convert Einstein to the Copenhagen interpretation, Pauli, in his reply, put his finger at the heart of the matter and ridiculed it at the same time. He did so by specifying the crux of the difference between Born and Einstein not as something relating to physics but to philosophy. Einstein's concern for reality belonged, Pauli wrote, with the medievals' preoccupation over the number of angels that could be put on a pinhead.[38]

Such a slighting of concern for reality, over which no revulsion is felt among physicists, bespeaks of a thick climate of thought in which one cannot see beyond one's very nose. Pauli failed to see that those who cared for angels did not despair of the reality of pinheads even if they could not measure exactly its dimensions. More importantly, they did not turn into those eggheads who cherish doubts about their own heads as reliable instruments of knowing a reality that exists independently of their thinking of it.

Nor did Pauli see something most crucial to his own predicament. Although victimized by a totalitarian regime that swore by the will of the race, Pauli did not seem to look deep into the roots of that will's rise. He might have found enlightenment in a survey which Heinrich Heine published in 1837 on the history of religion and philosophy in Germany. Heine asked the French to keep their arms while watching German Idealism produce, by running its full logic, Kantians "with sword and axe" who "would mercilessly rummage around in the soil of our European culture in order to eradicate the last roots of the past," a Christian past to be sure. Heine, in fact, foresaw that in the process the Cross, "this last restraining talisman," would be broken to pieces.[39] That Cross was and still is the best reminder of reality in more than one sense.

It may seem most unjust to use Heine's dire prophecy as a warning about long-term consequences of the prevailing interpretations of experimental verifications of Bell's theorem. Unfortunately, they are taken for conclusive proofs that everything in the world is enveloped in "mysteries," or at least in passions that always border on the mysterious. Yet, those "mysteries" are but the by-products of a fallacy in logic on which rests the entire edifice of the Copenhagen interpretation of quantum mechanics. One is faced here with a form of mystery-mongering all the more dangerous as it parades in the paraphernalia of a truly marvelous science. As such it can effectively help usher in the ultimate demoralization which is the condoning of any and all irrationality, conceptual and behavioral.

That counsels of "irrationality" readily seek their justification in the uncertainty principle could be seen in a *New York Times* editorial, towards the end of 1989, when Samuel Beckett's death was still fresh in memory and his chief disciples were widely commemorated. One of them, the Czech playwright, Vaclav Havel, gained further fame by becoming the interim President of Czechoslovakia. His unforeseeable rise to political prominence was taken in that editorial as an illustration of the lesson contained in Beckett's *Waiting for Godot* in which Godot never knows what he waits for: "The uncertainty principle in physics found its counterpart in his [Beckett's] plays and novels, allegories in randomness. . . . Godot seems a surer guide to an unknowable world than all the effusions of the experts."[40]

Political experts proved wrong more than once. The wrong to be wrought by them, or by anyone else, will, however, grow exponentially if "allegories in randomness" are to be taken for guide in real life. There, time and again, one must act now and with a clear goal in mind because the next moment may be too late to achieve any goal. Such was the argument which a President of the United States used twenty-five years ago before a distinguished gathering of acedemics in defense of some agonizing decisions he had to make. He, of course, wished that his had been the luxury available for academics who can indefinitely go on debating two sides of a coin without ever using it. In the real world, he warned, a coin must be used *now* because the next moment may be too late.

Within the Copenhagen view only two sides, two aspects, of a coin or of anything do exist but not the coin or the thing itself. This essay is in a sense a survey of the genesis of that very arbitrary view of reality with references to its consequences indicative of long-range demoralization. No sympathy whatever has been offered in this essay for that view and no apologies either for rejecting it without any reservation. No more is asked from an unsympathetic reader of this essay than to stop and ponder, however briefly, the consequences of a fatal first-step in reasoning, infinitesimal as it may appear from the scientific or quantitative viewpoint. An error, which is infinitesimal science, can become infinite in logic though in a different sense of course.

If the same reader wonders whether so many brilliant physicists could be so wrong in so elementary a matter of logic, he should recall the conclusion of a once famous article on the ether. It was contributed by no less a physicist than Maxwell, around 1873, to the famed 9th edition of the *Encyclopedia Britannica*. "There can be no doubt," Maxwell declared, "that the interplanetary and interstellar spaces are not empty, but are occupied by a material substance or body, which is certainly the largest, and probably the most uniform body of which we have any knowledge."[41] He merely voiced the unanimous conviction of the body physicist.

Within a generation or so physicists began to be tight-lipped about the ether and soon afterwards celebrated its final demise. In doing so they grew doubtful of the reasoning—if there is undulation, there ought to be something that undulates—an inference which was the sole support of their former belief in the existence of the ether. Yet that support, however shaky, should seem rationality incarnate when compared with the fallacy: an interaction that cannot be measured exactly cannot take place exactly.

This fallacy forms the stage on which not a few prominent physicists have now for over two generations been turning their noble art into a glamorous farce. They claim that their physics can perform fantastic feats, both conceptual and factual. According to them the quantum mechanical vacuum is *almost* nothing as if such nothing would make any sense. They are busy indoctrinating their students into believing that the nothing is also something. They conjure up universes out of nothing as so many rabbits from under a cocked hat. For keeping fundamental particles coherent, they prescribe as glue passions at a distance. They hold high randomness as the fundamental feature of reality without giving a truly random or chaotic definition of it. In the name of indeterminacy they ask the layman to take the wonderful science of physics for a mere game, provided it has its rules, always to be determined by them alone.

They speak of quantum mechanical models of consciousness as if that very gist of consciousness, the sense of *now* could be caught in the net of physics, be it quantum mechanics. They pretend to know and not to know at the same time as to what they really know, as if this were a sign of profundity. They claim that their mere thinking about "state-functions" makes them "collapse" into tangible reality as if this were not a collapse of one's stance vis-à-vis reality. They assert ownership over all reality and in return they offer a mere fallacy which leaves nothing determined. The bargain they drive at should seem infinitely more disreputable than the one in which an entire orchard must be bartered away for a single apple. To crown the comedy, they remain firmly determined to treat with a condescending glee their lay listeners as they are being put on the road that leads from mere bewilderment to total demoralization. If one is not to be swept off one's feet by the "liberating" tidal wave of the new indeterminism, one must, in addition of having a clear head, be determined, in a genuinely moral sense, to keep one's feet firmly planted in good old reality.

[1] A. M. Wilson, *Diderot* (New York: Oxford University Press, 1972), p. 577.

[2] For this and the subsequent quotations from Laplace, see his *A Philosophical Essay on Probabilities*, tr. F. W. Truscott and F. L. Emory (New York: Dover, 1951), pp. 4-6.

[3] For this and the next quotation, see F. Darwin, *The Life and Letters of Charles Darwin* (New York: Basic Books, 1959), pp. 553-54.

[4] H. Poincaré, "Sur la valeur objective des théories physiques," *Revue de métaphysique et de morale* 10 (1902), p. 288.

[5] *Travaux du Congrès International de Physique 1900*, ed. C. E. Guillame and L. Poincaré, vol. IV (Paris: Gauthier-Villars, 1901), p. 7.

[6] Larmor did so in his introduction to H. Poincaré, *Science and Hypothesis* (London: The Walter Scott Publishing Co., 1905), p. xiv.

[7] W. Heisenberg, "Uber den anschaulichen Inhalt der quantentheoretischen Kinematik und Mechanik," *Zeitschrift für Physik* 43 (1927), p. 197.

[8] C. A. Hooker, "The Nature of Quantum Mechanical Reality: Einstein versus Bohr," in R. C. Colodny (ed.), *Paradigms and Paradoxes: The Philosophical Challenge of the Quantum Domain* (Pittsburgh: University of Pittsburgh Press, 1972), p. 208.

[9] A theme further developed in ch. 13 "The Horns of Complementarity" in my Gifford Lectures, *The Road of Science and the Ways to God* (Chicago: University of Chicago Press, 1978).

[10] W. Heisenberg, *Physics and Beyond: Encounters and Conversations*, tr. A. J. Pomerans (New York: Harper and Row, 1971), p. 27. More and important light is shed on this point by P. Forman, "Weimar Culture, Causality and Quantum Theory 1918-1927," in *Historical Studies in Physical Science* 3 (1971), pp. 105-6.

[11] Ibid., pp. 80-7.

[12] J. Von Neumann, *Mathematical Foundations of Quantum Mechanics,* tr. R. T. Breyer (Princeton: Princeton University Press, 1955), p. 327.

[13] Reported by R. Resnick, "Misconceptions about Einstein: His Work and his Views," *Journal of Chemical Education* 52 (1980), p. 860.

[14] For a detailed discussion, see my essay, "The Impasse of Planck's Epistemology," (1985); reprinted in my *The Absolute beneath the Relative and Other Essays* (Lanham Md: The University Press of America, 1988), pp. 18-42.

[15] K. R. Popper, *Quantum Theory and the Schism in Physics* (London: Unwin Hyman, 1982), pp. 54-60. As to the hope that physicists might be more tuned to ontological causality if "exact" measurements of conjugate variables (let alone of just one in a pair of them) were to be proven possible, it is difficult to reconcile with the chronic dislike or miscomprehension of ontology evident, now for almost a century, in their dicta on the subject.

[16] See M. W. Browne, "Physicist Aims to Create a Universe, Literally," *The New York Times,* April 14, 1987, p. C4.

[17] K. R. Popper, *The Open Society and Its Enemies* (Princeton: Princeton University Press, 1950), pp. 222 and 641. Revealingly, Popper connects that ethics with the one proposed by Epicurus!

[18] K. R. Popper, *The Open Universe: An Argument for Indeterminism* (Totowa NJ: Rowman and Littlefield, 1982), p. 130.

[19] See ibid., p. 7.

[20] G. K. Chesterton, *St. Thomas Aquinas* (New York: Sheed & Ward, 1933), p. 206.

[21] A collection of five essays, written between 1932 and 1936, first published in 1937, now available in English translation, *Methodical Realism*, tr. P. Trower, with an introduction by S. L. Jaki (Front Royal Va: Christendom Press, 1990).

[22] *Physical Review* 47 (1935), pp. 777-80.

[23] A. Einstein, *The World as I See It* (New York: Covici-Friede, 1934), p. 60.

[24] Ibid., p. 30.

[25] N. Bohr, "Can Quantum-Mechanical Description of Physical Reality be Considered Complete?" *Physical Review* 48 (1935), p. 702.

[26] March 3, 1947; see *The Born-Einstein Letters,* with commentaries by Max Born, tr. Irene Born (New York: Walker and Company, 1971), p. 158.

[27] An expression of A. Shimony of Boston University; see M. W. Browne, "Quantum Theory: Disturbing Questions Remain Unsolved," *The New York Times*, Feb. 11, 1986, p. C3.

[28] For a detailed discussion, see chap. 6 in my *Science and Creation: From Eternal Cycles to an Oscillating Universe* (1974; new rev. ed., Edinburgh: Scottish Academic Press, 1986; Lanham, Md.: The University Press of America, 1990).

[29] *Electrons et photons: Rapports et discussions du Cinquième Conseil de Physique tenu à Bruxelles du 24 au 29 Octobre sous les auspices de l'Institut International de Physique Solvay* (Paris: Gauthier-Villars, 1928), p. 264.

[30] London: Thornton Butterworth, 1930, p. 190.

[31] Einstein's was here too a rather lonely voice as he decried, about the same time, that fashionable ascribing a sort of free will to inorganic matter not merely a "nonsense but an objectionable nonsense." See "Epilogue: A Socratic Dialogue. Planck-Einstein-Murphy," in Max Planck, *Where Is Science Going?* tr. J. G. Murphy (New York: Norton, 1932), p. 203.

[32] *Nature*, Dec. 27, 1930, p. 995.

[33] J. E. Turner, *Essentials in the Development of Religion: A Philosophic and Psychological Study* (London: Goerge Allen & Unwin, 1934), pp. 224-26.

[34] A. H. Compton, *The Freedom of Man* (New Haven: Yale University Press, 1935), p. 26.

[35] H. Margenau, *The Nature of Physical Reality* (New York: McGraw Hill, 1950), p. 418.

[36] H. Margenau, "ESP in the Framework of Modern Science," in *Science and the ESP,* ed. J. R. Smythies (London: Routledge and K. Paul, 1967), p. 209.

[37] W. Heisenberg, "Development of the Interpretation of Quantum Theory," in *Niels Bohr and the Development of Physics*, ed. W. Pauli (New York: McGraw-Hill, 1955), pp. 12-29.

[38] Pauli to Born, March 31, 1954; *The Born-Einstein Letters*, p. 223. There Pauli credits another Nobel-laureate, O. Stern, with that disparaging comment on concern for reality.

[39] *Heinrich Heine. Selected Works*, tr. and ed. H. M. Mustard (New York: Vintage Books, 1973), pp. 417-8.

[40] "What 'Godot' Hath Wrought," *The New York Times*, Dec. 28, 1989, p. A20.

[41] *The Scientific Papers of James Clerk Maxwell*, ed. W. D. Niven (Cambridge: University Press, 1890), vol. 2, p. 775.

7

History as Science
and Science in History

Historians have been the target of many jibes. According to one the only thing they learn from history is that they never learn from history. This is true, of course, of non-historians as well. Another jibe —history never repeats itself, only historians repeat one another—seems to deprive historians of the right to claim that what they say is at least a reasoned discourse. Such a discourse was originally meant by writing history, that is, giving a careful recital of past events.

But even if historians did far better than repeat one another, their discourse would not necessarily qualify today as something really well-reasoned. For such a discourse has now been largely restricted to what science stands for. This is certainly the case in the Anglo-Saxon ambiance. Even the German word, Wissenschaft, which should cover all systematically reasoned inquiry, finds its broad meaning

First published in *Intercollegiate Review* 28 (Fall 1993), pp. 20-33. Reprinted with permission.

steadily narrowed to the exact and empirical sciences. Chiefly responsible for this semantic process is the stunning effectiveness which exact science displays in ever widening forms.

The admiration which scientists enjoy as a result has for some time been looked upon by non-scientists with envy. To retain respectability, more and more philosophers began to write as if philosophy could be handled in the manner of science. In the process—it is enough to think of logical positivists—wisdom and its love disappeared from much of philosophical discourse. Again, in order to be part of the scientific world, cultivators of psychology abandoned their claim to the human psyche taken for soul, properly so-called, as they filled their learned journals with statistics, measurements of behavior, and even with mathematical formulas. In trying to become scientific, many sociologists became mere statisticians. Worse, they readily assisted those who set themselves up as the chief global engineers of society.

To what extremes this aping of the properly scientific method carried the study of history can be measured from the emergence of the word "cliometrics." It is the study of history using advanced methods of data processing and analysis. Cliometrics ties Clio, the Muse of history, to the art of measuring or computing. This might not overly upset her, but one wonders whether she would have been amused by a paper read during a seminar which Professor L. Benson of the University of Pennsylvania held in the Department of History at Princeton University on May 11, 1967. In the paper, "The Quantification of History," Professor Benson claimed that only by feeding into a computer the full voting record of all members of Congress between 1830 and 1859 shall we learn the true causes of the Civil War. This claim could, of course, sway only those ready to trade common sense for the veneer of science.

Others expected some truly recondite information to come from cliometrics. Tellingly, a huge scientific conference, the annual meeting, in 1965, of the American Association for the Advancement of Science, was chosen as the setting for a claim which, if reliable, would have turned political science into one of the exact sciences. According to that claim the ups and downs of Soviet-American relations obeyed Pontrjagin's Principle, or a mathematical function useful in calculating parts of rocket trajectories as subject to external influences. In the sixties, when Soviet rocketry was the envy of scientific and political world, that claim must have particularly appealed to not a few. They were the ones who viewed the Soviet Union as a permanent feature on the global scene and sympathized with the Marxist tenet that history followed ironclad rules of economics. The fact that representatives of radically opposed schools of economics have been awarded Nobel Prizes should be enough of a warning about what to think of the scientific status of that most eagerly pursued field of "scientific" inquiry.

At any rate, in thinking about history in scientifically deterministic categories, Marxists, of whom more later, merely followed the social engineers of the Enlightenment. They all tried to confine history to Procrustean beds of illusory categories. Such beds were fabricated by Turgot, Condorcet, and Saint-Simon, the new "scientific" theoreticians of the development of human thought. They all tried to show that the religious, metaphysical, and empirical or positive, that is, scientific phases of human thought followed one another in an inevitable sequence. Comte's law of three states, a borrowing from Saint-Simon, was received in France for the rest of the 19th century as a genuinely scientific key to the genesis of ideas and of the evolution of society.

This scientistic thinking about history was crystallized in Comte's famous dictum, "science, d'où prévoyance, prévoyance d'où action."[1] Newtonian science was thereby declared to be the key to the understanding of human history and the development of society. Once more a declaration was not a demonstration. Comte merely proved that he was in the line of *philosophes*, all too eager to abuse Newtonian science for purposes it never meant to serve. There was not a line in Newton's writings that would have supported Baron d'Holbach, a *philosophe* of lesser rank, in his declaration in 1771 that "all the errors of men were the errors of physics."[2] Better-grade *philosophes* were not reluctant to make the same disreputable claim. D'Holbach's startling phrase reoccurs almost verbatim in Condorcet's diagnosis of the factor that holds back human progress: "All errors in politics, in morals are based on philosophical errors which in turn are tied to errors in physics."[3] A feat of physics, Laplace's demonstration of the stability of the solar system supported Condorcet's forecast of an unlimited progress for the human race. One wonders whether Bertrand Russell realized the extent to which he was indebted to those *philosophes* when at one point he looked confidently forward, to recall a recollection of his, to a "mathematics of human behavior as precise as the mathematics of machines."[4]

Such precision implied the predictability of human behavior and of history. The hapless short-range performance of the futurologists of the 1950s and 1960s should be enough of a warning about the merits of writing an exact history of the future. But even the past posed unsurmountable challenges to those who tried to present it in a "scientific" way. The fatefully unforeseeable turns of human history demanded a more pervasive listing of causes than the ones typified by the possible difference of the length of Cleopatra's nose. Hume's *History of England* could appear "scientific" only for those who let themselves be taken in by his two sleights of hand. One was a superficial though stylish account of the advent of scientific thinking through the genius of Newton. Few realized, then as now, that the *Principia* was a closed book for Hume. The other was a convenient disregard, or at least a heavy slighting, of religious motivations that played a part in the shaping of English history and even in the rise of Newtonian science.

Hume drew his inspiration for writing a "scientific" history of England after consorting with *philosophes* whose undisputed leader, Voltaire, had already tried to put French history on a "scientific" basis. This meant no more than obsequious references to Newton.[5] In Voltaire's case too, scientific largely meant secularistic. *Le Siècle de Louis XIV*, Voltaire's best historical treatise, should seem most unscientific against the standards of historical accuracy as set by Mabillon and his Maurist confrères. Nor did it follow from Voltaire's portrayal of the century of Louis XIV that the reign of Louis XV should last so long as to make very difficult the reform of the monarchy during Louis XVI, a well-meaning but indecisive king.

Nor could Voltaire, or anyone else for that matter, claim that Louis XVI had no choice but to shun decisive choices. For if Louis XVI, a physically robust and mentally normal being, could be taken for a mere product of strictly deterministic causes, Voltaire's evaluation of the monarchy also had to be seen as a foregone conclusion and not the fruit of free deliberations. Indeed, the question of freedom remained for Voltaire a disquieting topic. This is why he also felt disturbed by the perspective of purposeful action, inconceivable without the freedom of the will. Not surprisingly, Voltaire did his best in his *Essai sur les mœurs* to discredit Bossuet's *Histoire universelle*, the last classic statement of the view of history that had been first set forth in Augustine's *On the City of God*. What must have irked Voltaire most in Bossuet's book was its grand conclusion, a categorical dismissal of chance as an explanation of history or of anything else: "God reigns over every nation. Let us no longer speak of coincidence or fortune; or let us use these words only to cover our ignorance."[6]

A providential view of history, so Voltaire argued, could not qualify as "scientific." But was Voltaire's science of history any more scientific by his roundabout recourse to chance as an explanation? Of course, in Voltaire's time it was still "unphilosophical" to fall back on chance, though not unphilosophical or unscientific to make ample stylistic use of the term as long as one could cover up one's real intentions. Helvetius, a fellow *philosophe*, provided a revealing instance of that stratagem as he spoke of the rise of geniuses as a fortuitous process. In Helvetius' *De l'homme* a mere footnote, in which he warned the reader against taking chance for more than a mere word, let alone for a cause properly so called, balances copious references to the role of chance in that rise.[7] But once divine guidance and human freedom were conveniently ignored, studied references to chance remained the only acceptable technique for suggesting that history was not inevitable. This far from intellectually honest technique could alone save the determinist historian from admitting that he implied the inevitability of his own mental processes.

Such a predicament had to be greatly perplexing to prominent 19th-century historians, bent on assuring to historiography a status which was scientific in at least the sense of being scrupulously factual. Their motto was Ranke's injunction that the historian should render the past "wie es eigentlich gewesen,"[8] that is, exactly as it happened. Not all these "scientific" historians shared Ranke's view that if facts were taken care of, a higher wisdom or Providence would readily show through history. But all shared a faith in progress, writ large. This faith quickly provided stimulus for a memorable formulation, by Thomas Henry Buckle, of scientific historiography. His complaint, "we find that while natural science has long been cultivated, historical science hardly yet exists," was introductory to his grand conclusion that "all events which surround us . . . are but different parts of a single scheme which is permeated by one glorious principle of universal and undeviating regularity."[9]

Any British historian who hoped in the 1850s to justify his scientific status with an eye on science and progress could certainly take inspiration from the Great Exhibition of 1851. Buckle's hopeful

words, "the signs of the times are all around, and they who list may
read. The handwriting is on the wall,"[10] may very well have been
inspired by his reading of the editorial in the May 10, 1851 issue of
The Illustrated London Times about the simultaneous opening, a week
earlier, of that Exhibition and its housing, the Crystal Palace. The
illustrious visitors from all over the world, the Palace, the plethora of
manufactured goods and new machinery suggested to the author of
that editorial the reversal, once and for, of the *mene tekel upharsin*,
the most ominous handwriting ever to appear on any wall.[11]

And why not? It was, for instance, precisely around the middle
of the 19th century that overland travel took on, with the sudden
spread of railroads, a vastly new aspect. Had Lord Palmerston been
called to form a new government, not in 1842 but ten years later, his
trip from Rome to London would not have taken thirty days which
were sufficient even in Imperial Roman times to cover the same
distance. Almost a century later, Winston Churchill still found this
fact worth recalling as he tried, in 1931, his hand on futurology.
Once more the result was a very mixed bag. He forecast not only the
coming of fusion energy, but also, perhaps half facetiously, the
eventual manufacturing of chicken legs and breasts without hatching
entire chickens.[12]

Around 1900 travel from Rome to London took less than two
days and could be done in the luxurious comfort of Pullman sleepers.
People, so Stefan Zweig reminisced, took belief in progress with "the
force of religion." Countless "miracles" were on hand, all brought
about "by the archangel of progress." Moreover, "the possibility of
a relapse into a new barbarity, such as, for instance, war between the
nations of Europe, seemed as remote as demons or witches."[13]

Suddenly the demons of barbarity were back in full force and
with a fury unimaginable before. Machine guns could cause in a
single morning as many casualties as the atomic bomb was to take in
a split second. Synthetic nitric acid, invented by Fritz Haber, a future
Nobel-Laureate chemist, made it possible for Germany to prolong the
war from four months to four years. The same scientist engineered
the chlorine gas attack at Ypres on April 22, 1915, that might have
lead to the quick termination of the war had the attackers realized the
magnitude of the devastation they brought about.

It looked as if all conspired to bury victors and vanquished alike
under the ruins that, physically at least, were the making of that very
science which had until then seemed to assure unlimited progress.

Worse, science proved helpless against the onslaught of new epidemics. Science could but give the useless label, "Spanish flu," to the plague that took more than two million to the grave in the wake of a War that forced the digging of more than twenty million graves. Had pessimism not been rampant, the two heavy volumes of Spengler's *Untergang des Abendlandes* would not have sold in a mere five years in well over a million copies in half a dozen translations.

As always, some diehards refused to surrender. No reference to World War I was in sight when in 1920 Bury published his *Idea of Progress* and dedicated it to the memory of such optimists as Condorcet, Comte, and Herbert Spencer. And why not? After all, their ideas were merely given a more scientific looking cast as Bury declared that historiography is "science, not more and not less." The declaration was part of his inaugural lecture in Cambridge University in 1903.[14]

A "scientific" historian who could ignore World War I in such a non-scientific fashion, must have had an unusual measure of detachment from reality, the realm of facts. With such a detachment, Bury might not have cared, had he lived to the end of World War II, to refer to the surrender which no less a pragmatist than H. G. Wells signalled by publishing in 1946 his *The Mind at the End of Its Tether*. Certainly, Charles A. Beard did not refer to World War I, and much less to the Wall Street crash of 1929, or to the rise of totalitarian regimes, as he wrote an introduction in 1931 to the American edition of Bury's work to help celebrate the "Century of Progress Exposition" in Chicago.

Yet, darker than the specter of global destruction was Bury's own admission that the idea of Progress, writ large, seemed to imply its own refutation. Did not that idea, Bury asked, owe its origin to a reasoning that aimed at disposing with the Christian dogma of finality? But, Bury asked again with commendable candor, "if we accept the reasonings on which the dogma of Progress is based, must we not carry them to their full conclusion? In escaping from the illusion of finality, is it legitimate to exempt that dogma itself?"[15]

In the absence of an epistemology capable of coping with this apparently total futility, some facts of cultural history appeared even more ominous. All cultures seemed to be subject, in Bury's own words, to the rule of "arrest, decadence, stagnation".[16] For the historian this could mean but a surrender to utter relativism, carefully dressed up as it could be.

Escape from that relativism could not be provided by more references to science is if they by themselves could assure "scientific" status to historiography. That status was no more than a variation of recourse to belief in progress. When that belief was defended by those who denied scientific status to history, the tables could readily be turned on them. Thus the Cambridge historian, Edward C. Carr, was right in claiming, in his Trevelyan memorial lecture (1961) that Karl Popper could not have it both ways. Either Popper was right in claiming that the Marxist view of history was wrong because there were no laws to history, or he was wrong in claiming that scientific progress could only be had in an open society. If progress did not imply some law or pattern across history it was void of meaning.

Undoubtedly, Marxist systems were the main target of Popper's declaration: "Wherever the freedom of thought, and of the communication of thought, is effectively protected by legal institutions and institutions ensuring the publicity of discussion, there will be scientific progress."[17] Carr replied: "This was written in 1942 or 1943, and was evidently inspired by the belief that the Western democracies, in virtue of their institutional arrangements, would remain in the van of scientific progress—a belief since dispelled, or severely qualified, by developments in the Soviet Union. Far from being a law, it was not even a valid generalization."[18]

Developments in the Soviet Union, which Carr with his Marxist sympathies would not have thought possible, to say nothing of its demise, makes it unnecessary to comment on Carr's dictum. But a brief look at his Trevelyan lecture may help one see some of the consequences in store for a historian in pursuit of history as an exact science. For those consequences are threatening regardless of whether the historian is in sympathy with social engineering or not, that is, whether he favors the ideology of socialism or liberalism.

Carr's most surprising if not shocking principle in that lecture is that the historian should pass moral judgment only on institutions but never on individuals, be they so horrendous as Napoleon, Stalin, and Hitler.[19] Carr defended that principle on the authority of Weber, although his real argument rested on his claim that questions of morality should cast into purely "cultural" parameters that could easily be "evaluated" as statistical (and therefore "scientific") data. Thus, according to Carr, institutions should be judged good or bad insofar as they prove themselves "progressive" or "reactionary." Recourse to those two categories stood in good stead a historian bent on appearing "scientific." Such a historian could easily present a fair number of similar categories and skirt the value judgments underlying them.

One could praise, for instance, political programs as progressive for their insistence on voting rights, freedom of speech, division of powers, direct representation and so on, without facing up to values that are more than purely pragmatic. Moreover, all those programs had aspects that could be treated as if they were so many patterns, ready to be cast into quantitative terms and distributions. In eliminating the specter of purpose and of genuinely moral perspectives which comes with truly purposive action, the "scientific" historian could flatter himself for having joined the club of "exact" scientists. These, from Galileo on, had consciously barred the consideration of the possible purpose which things in motion might have, and limited themselves to establishing the quantitative patterns of such motions.

As a specialist on Soviet history and not at all unsympathetic to its ideals, Carr found in Marxist ideology further support for his claim about the scientific status of historiography. From its inception on, Marxism claimed to be a "scientific" theory of society, economics, and history. On such a basis Engels and Lenin could seem justified in claiming that the future of science rested with a Marxist recasting of society. While the propagandistic claims made in the 1930s about the superiority of science in Marxist realms carried conviction only with relatively few scientists in the West, the situation became very different in the 1950s and 1960s. Partly because Western democracies were on the defensive vis-à-vis Soviet expansionism, and partly because the West seemed to fall behind in space exploits, quite a few Western intellectuals looked upon Marxism as the wave of an obviously very scientific future. Unlike many "apostles" of culture, they did not fail to recognize that this was precisely the message of C. P. Snow's once famous *Two Cultures*.

Around 1960 or so a prophetic truth could seem to be attached to the claim which Joseph Needham had set forth in 1946 in his collection of essays, *History is on Our Side*, that is, on the side of the Marxists.[20] Yet by then computers were in the making that anticipated what twenty years later entered the market as PC's. In fact, already in 1983, when the Soviet Union still seemed to be on a par with the United States with respect to military and industrial power, those in the know were aware of the fact that this parity was largely a matter of well orchestrated propaganda. But propaganda could not be exposed with any effectiveness when at the same time liberal newspapers and university presses readily played second fiddle to tunes set by Marxist ideologues from well-endowed chairs in capitalist American universities.

Of course, information from sensitive sources could not be revealed without further ado. Yet, one wonders whether the 1992 presidential election was the appropriate time for disclosing that already in 1983, or eight years before "Desert Storm," responsible people in the Soviet military knew that they had lost the cold war and that they lost it not on the battlefield but in the laboratories. For never before in history did science decide history with such a lightning effectiveness as was the case with the four-day war against Iraq. It would not have been possible without stealth bombers, without Patriot missiles, without laser-guided bombs. And none of these could have operated without computers and a global satellite communication network that brought together the fastest and largest computers in the world.

Of course, the Chief of the Soviet General Staff, Marshal Nikolai Ogarkov could know in 1983 only in general terms about most of these items of scientific military hardware. But it took no crystal-ball gazing to know at that time about the awesome potentialities of computers which only a year or so earlier became available for anyone's desktop in the United States in the form of IBM PC's. But at that time not even every office in the Soviet Ministry of Defense had a computer. So remarked Marshal Ogarkov to a delegate, Mr. Leslie H. Gelb of the State Department, who specialized in foreign affairs reporting.

To Mr. Gelb's utter astonishment, the Marshal, in the course of a reception in Moscow, took as irrelevant his question why the Soviet Union kept a great standing army if its intentions were purely defensive. According to Mr. Gelb, "Numbers of troops and weapons mean little, he [the Marshal] said. We cannot equal the quality of U.S. arms for a generation or two. Modern military power is based upon technology, and technology is based upon computers. In the U.S., he [the Marshal] continued, small children—even before they begin school—play with computers. Computers are everywhere in

America. . . . And for reasons, you know well, we cannot make computers widely available in our society."[21]

That this extraordinary piece of information was made public by Mr. Gelb at the height of the 1992 presidential campaign should speak for itself. The disclosure was not meant to expose those many Democratic members of Congress who decried Reagan's Star Wars and all his programs to let the U.S. take a commanding military and technological lead over the Soviet Union. Mr. Gelb, in an unwitting illustration of those who do not want to learn from history, used that disclosure to undercut the Republicans' claim about winning a major confrontation with minimal bloodshed. He tried to undercut Republicans who, as led by Reagan and Bush, could rightly claim that *they* and not the Democrats won freedom for hundreds of millions in that Soviet Empire that included dozens of captive satellite nations. Their liberty was of little concern for certain liberals who kept saying with their idol, Roosevelt, that "we can live with Uncle Joe." Mr. Gelb even failed to remember that it was liberal Democrats who decried Reagan for his having characterized the Soviet Union as "an evil empire."

For contrary to Mr. Gelb's strange reasoning, the Soviet Union did not collapse because it was decaying from the inside. The Soviet Union and its satellite system would still largely be in place had not Gorbachov miscalculated. Three years after Marshal Ogarkov was removed from office, Gorbachov did indirect justice to the Marshal's logic by declaring *perestroika* and *glasnost*. Gorbachov thought that by playing for time it was still possible for the Communist system to catch up technologically and militarily with the United States. In view of Gorbachov's firm adherence to Communism, it is most likely that he saw in Saddam Hussein a useful tool to produce another Vietnam for the U.S. Clearly, it was reasonable to expect that the first three or four days of hostilities would produce a few thousand U.S. casualties. This in turn would have most likely been used by liberal newspapers as ammunition to stir popular sentiment against President Bush and force him thereby to seek a "negotiated" solution. This would have kept Gorbachov in power to the delight of those Democrats in Congress who opposed military intervention.

Clearly, the shoe was on the other foot when Mr. Gelb charged the Republicans with "shameless distortion of the record" and characterized as "unpardonable . . . their continuing blindness to the principal lesson of the cold war—the Soviet empire collapsed abroad because it had failed at home." And one wonders whether the present administration's professed interest in the welfare of Americans at home could be voiced at all if they still had to face another Super-power. It is sheer skullduggery to claim, as Mr. Gelb did, that Reagan and Bush merely "slayed a Red Dragon already dying" and that therefore there was no excuse for them "to virtually ignore America for 12 years."

Against that hapless reasoning about current history, a Reagan one-liner stands out as a beacon of insight into the role of science in history. The Soviet Union was still in place, the satellite countries still had no inkling about their imminent liberation, when Ronald Reagan spoke in Guild Hall in London, following his induction as honorary member of the Order of the Garter. There, on June 11, 1989, he confidently predicted that "the microchip of David will vanquish the Goliath of totalitarianism." The truth content of this brief phrase compares very favorably with lengthy chats about four freedoms from which so many were excluded for so long over so large stretches of the globe with the ready connivence of liberal chatterboxes interested in everything except liberty for all.

Their latter-day epigons have just announced the death of Star Wars research on the ground that there is no longer any intercontin-ental threat to the United States. They still have to get off the ground of pedestrian thinking about science. For just as there can be no science of history which is, as exact science has to be, strictly predictive, there is no way of predicting the course which scientific discoveries will take in the near future, let alone in the distant future. This is why what is actually feasible, such as the Superconducting Supercollider, must be seized upon, no matter the cost. For whereas there is no intercontinental ballistic missile threat (at the moment) to the United States, science knows no bounds set by continents. A major scientific and technological breakthrough can occur at any time in lands very distant from the United States. The Supercollider may indeed reveal entirely new forces at work in nature, forces far stronger than the force that keeps the atomic nucleus together.[22]

Such are most realistic vistas against which the smug registerings of the "end of history" reveal their futility. Fukuyama's much touted book has that dubious saving grace which is its author's drastic insensitivity to what goes on in science and technology.[23] This is typical of an author whose hero, Hegel, best revealed his intellectual insolence in his encyclopedia of the natural sciences.[24] Hegel failed to see their openendedness as much as he failed to note forces at work in history other than the self-unfolding of the German race.

One may bemoan the overweening importance which scientific and technological breakthroughs play in modern history. One may deplore mankind's inability to break out from the hellish circle of manufacturing for the sake of more manufacturing. One may agonize over certain charateristics of man's pursuit of scientific and technological goals that evoke Captain Ahab's mad chase of the big white whale: "All my means are sane, my motive and my object mad."[25] The fact remains that history is made increasingly by science although one cannot write a "scientific" history, and not even a history of science along scientific lines. But history will remain a source of insight for those who want to learn from it instead of declaring it to be at its end, let alone predicting its likely future course.

But even to the history of the last one hundred years, so full of the impact of science on it, one can rightly apply the dictum almost two millennia old: "History is philosophy [drawn] from paradigms [examples]."[26] To draw its lessons one has to have better categories than the one offered by "paradigmizing" historians of science.[27] The gathering of the genuine paradigms or lessons of history demands "imaginative sympathy," as noted by H. Butterfield. Animated by that sympathy, the historian "makes the past intelligible to the present. He translates its conditioning circumstances into terms which we today can understand. It is in this sense that history must always be written from the point of view of the present. It is in this sense that every age will have to write its history over again."[28]

But writing history again and again is not a re-writing of it, nor is it is a sophisticated regurgitation of what has already been stated. John Henry Newman here too touched the nerve of the matter as he warned: "History is not a creed or catechism, it gives lessons rather than rules; still no one can mistake its general teaching. . . . Bold outlines and broad masses of colour rise out of the records of the past. They may be dim, they may be incomplete; but they are definite."[29] But a history with such instructiveness will resemble its Augustinian type on which Voltaire poured scorn for not being scientific. It is even less in favor today when cultural relativism runs amok through the history departments and deconstructs teachers as well as students.

The havoc—a quarter of a century long—wrought by the French Revolution had to come to secure a hearing for a relatively brief revival of the Augustinian view of history. The revival had its Romantic ingredients, among them a nostalgia for some unduly idealized past ages, as was the case with Chateaubriand's *Génie du christianisme* (1802) and Schlegel's *Über die neuere Geschichte* (1811). But both authors could point at the colossal failure of the *philosophes* to remove genuinely religious perspectives from modern man's mind.

Since the dire lessons of World War II are rapidly fading, a far greater historical havoc may be necessary to retune mankind to those perspectives. Such a havoc may be generated by the hope that science can nip in the bud the epidemic of AIDS and related diseases which now claim a full fifth (over fifty million) of the population of the United States alone. Another such havoc of historic proportion may be fomented by ecologist gurus more concerned with the number of people than with the number of internal combustion engines and unconcerned about moral resources properly so called. Would that mankind not find out at its own grave peril that no matter what the impact science may have on history, a perspective other than scientific is needed to secure a reasoned discourse about past events which is history and have thereby a safe outlook on the future.

---

[1] A. Comte, *Cours de philosophie positive* (Paris: Bachelier, 1830-42), vol. I, p. 51.

[2] D'Holbach, *Système de la nature* (new ed.; London, 1775), p. 19.

[3] *Œuvres de Condorcet* (Paris: Firmin Didot Frères, 1847), vol. VI, p. 223.

[4] B. Russell, *Portraits from Memory* (London: George Allen & Unwin, 1956), p. 20.

[5] This transpires even in *Voltaire, Historian* by J. H. Brumfitt (Oxford: Oxford University Press, 1958). See especially the section, "Causation and Development," pp. 104-111.

[6] J. B. Bossuet, *Discourse on Universal History,* ed. and tr., O. Ranum (Chicago: University of Chicago Press, 1976), p. 374.

[7] "I understand by chance the unknown chain of causes capable of producing such and such effect." *De l'homme,* sec. I. ch. viii, in *Œuvres complètes* (Paris: Lepetit, 1818), vol. 22, p. 33.

[8] L. von Ranke, *Geschichte der romanischen und germanischen Völker von 1494 bis 1514: Zur Kritik der neuerer Geschichtschreiber* in *Sämmtliche Werke* (3rd ed.; Leipzig: Duncker und Humblot 1885), vol. 33-34, p. vii.

[9] H. T. Buckle, *Introduction to the History of Civilization in England*, new rev. ed. by J. M. Robertson (London: George Routledge and Sons, 1904), pp. 901-02.

[10] Ibid., p. 901.

[11] See my *The Purpose of It All* (Washington DC.: Regnery-Gateway, 1990), pp. 13-14.

[12] He did so in his essay, "Fifty Years Hence," (1931); reprinted in *Amid these Storms: Thoughts and Adventures* (New York: Charles Scribner's Sons, 1931), pp. 269-80.

[13] S. Zweig, *Die Welt von Gestern* (Frankfurt: Fisher, 1970). p. 15.

[14] J. B. Bury, *An Inaugural Lecture: The Science of History* (Cambridge: University Press, 1903), p. 41.

[15] J. B. Bury, *The Idea of Progress: An Inquiry into Its Origin and Growth*, with an introduction by C. A. Beard (New York: Dover, 1960), pp. 351-2.

[16] Ibid., p. 342.

[17] K. R. Popper, *The Open Society* (London: Routledge and Kegan Paul, 1952), vol. 2, p. 322.

[18] E. H. Carr, *What is History?* (New York: Vintage Books, 1961), p. 93.

[19] Ibid., p. 101.

[20] J. Needham, *History Is on Our Side* (London: George Allen and Unwin, 1946). The subtitle, "A Contribution to Political Religion and Scientific Faith," sums it up all.

[21] This and subsequent quotations are from L. H. Gelb's report, "Who Won the Cold War?" on the op-ed page of *The New York Times*, Aug. 20, 1992, p. A26.

[22] The point is made with particular force in S. Weinberg's *Dreams of a Final Theory* (New York: Pantheon Books, 1992), p. 210.

[23] This characteristic of Fukuyama's diction in his *The End of History and the Last Man* (New York: Free Press, 1992) was already in full evidence in his essay, "The End of History?" *The National Interest* (Summer 1989), pp. 3-18.

[24] Translated into English, by M. J. Petry, as *Hegel's Philosophy of Nature* (London: George Allen and Unwin, 1970).

[25] H. Melville, *Moby Dick* (New York: Modern Library, 1926), p. 185.

[26] Dionysius of Halicarnassos, *De arte rhetorica*, xi, 2. See ed. H. K. Usener (Leipzig: Teubner, 1895), p. 124. The phrase was memorably rendered by Lord Bolingbroke as "history is philosophy teaching by examples" in the second of his "Letters on the Study and Use of History." *Works* (London: David Mallet, 1754-98), vol. 2. p. 266.

[27] With Thomas S. Kuhn in the van.

[28] H. Butterfield, *The Whig Interpretation of History* (London: L. G. Bell, 1951), p. 92.

[29] J. H. Newman, *An Essay on the Development of Christian Doctrine* (Garden City, N.Y.: Doubleday, 1960), p. 34.

8

Science: Western or What?

It is a pleasure to be in Moscow and to have the opportunity to speak to a distinguished gathering of scholars and to do so under the auspices of the Academy of Science of the U.S.S.R. Even though the talk of a visitor from the U.S. is not on scientific technicalities, its factuality owes much to science. The jet plane and the radio beams that helped land it here are products of science and so is the amplifying system that makes one's voice audible to a large conference.

In modern times
There was a time, not too long ago, when purely scientific topics offered the only terrain where scholars from West and East could meet with the prospect of achieving a meeting of minds. On more than one occasion scientists held high their example to politicians that agreement between East and West is possible. Of course, not everything in life is science. Indeed, science deals only with a

First published in *Intercollegiate Review* 26 (Fall 1990), pp. 3-12. Reprinted with permission. The meeting was held in mid-June, 1990.

rather narrow aspect of reality, the quantitative features of things. Scientists should have remembered that their products, insofar as they found military application, greatly heightened the tension between East and West.

Scientists should have also remembered that things moved very far from the time of the Napoleonic wars, when Humphry Davy, the leading British chemist of the day, could freely travel all across France and claim that scientists are never at war. This was not entirely true even in the days of Napoleon. His novel strategy, a concentrated artillery fire on the center of the enemy troops, could not have worked without first-rate gunners, many of whom came from the Ecole Polytechnique, the foremost science-school at that time anywhere in the world.

Only some military historians realized, long after Napoleon, that through science Napoleon might have invaded England a few months before Trafalgar. He should have ordered his engineers to make steamboats, such as the ones that were operating on the Firth of Fourth in Scotland. On any windless day, when the British navy would be immobilized, French troops could have been landed on the English coast.

Had the Germans realized the effectiveness of their first use of poison gas—a scientific invention—the outcome of World War I might have been different. We all know about the role which radar, a scientific novelty around 1940, played in the outcome of World War II. If World War III did not take place, it was largely through realization on both sides that destructive tools created by science can easily turn military victory into an utterly self-defeating affair.

It may indeed be said that one reason why these two great Wars had taken place relate to the great advantage which science offered to the West over the last three or four centuries. Prior to those two Wars, history saw the Western European nations conquer America, Africa, the Mid-East, and Africa. Science played a part all the time. The effective conquest of the Americas demanded good science, the only thing that made the sailing across the Atlantic relatively safe. In addition to magnets and sextants, one needed reliable pendulum clocks to keep accurate time, the only way to determine one's longitude on high seas or on land for that matter. The West learned about the Chinese during the seventeenth century, because the Court in Beijing was much impressed by the scientific know-how of the Jesuits. That the West established a global colonial empire by the late-nineteenth century was largely due to its enormous technological superiority. It was then that Rudyard Kipling wrote his "Ballad of East and West," which begins with the legendary lines:

> Oh, East is East, and West is West,
>   and never the twain shall meet,
> Till Earth and Sky stand presently,
>   at God's great Judgment Seat.

Indeed, around 1895, exposure to science meant in those colonial lands an exposure to a way of thinking very different from the mentality characteristic of great ancient cultures, such as India and China, let alone of the mentality of primitive peoples. In China those opposing the Western colonizing powers almost to a man decried the mentality demanded by science as a mentality of lifeless mechanism. Gandhi for over a century fulminated against science while preaching the blessings of a primitive village life, of an agriculture free of mechanization.

Yet, that same Western science has for some time offered a relatively smooth meeting ground between East and West. Science—it is enough to think of the Pugwash conferences and many similar gatherings—proved effective in lessening ideological conflicts. Sakharov would have hardly been so effective in his struggle to loosen up rigid political control, had he not been a prominent scientist. Again, it is scientific prominence which gave weight to the insistence of the Chinese astrophysicist, Fang Lizhi, that the Party should democratize its procedures.

A principal point in the arguments of Professor Fang relates to science. To raise the standard of living, depends, so he argues, on the effective and broad use of science. Yet that use presupposes the free flow of information which is obviously a chief facet of democracy. Moreover, Professor Fang takes science for an embodiment of democracy because the terms and laws of science are universally valid. Or to quote him: "In physics we cannot say that there is Chinese physics and Western physics."

This is true to a very great extent. The laws of gravitation and of electromagnetic induction did not become British because Newton and Faraday were British citizens. There is nothing Russian to Mendeleev's table of elements, nothing French to Carnot's cycle, nothing German to Clausius' law of entropy, nothing Dutch to the Lorentz transforms, nothing Italian to Galileo's telescope and Fermi's neutrinos.

The supranationality of science should be even more evident when it comes to that backbone of exact science which is mathematics. The decimal system, which until recently formed the basis of practically all scientific calculations, saw birth in ancient India, a non-Western culture. There, long before Euclid and Diophantes, the art of counting became generalized to the level of second-degree equations.

In ancient cultures
Formulas that are equivalent to solutions of second-degree equations appear in ancient Babylon and probably also in China. Yet there is no evidence in either place of a system that could be called algebra as such. Even more startling should seem the absence of arithemetic generalization in ancient Egypt or among the ancient Maya. Society in both places was heavily organized, very bureaucratic, one may say, markedly socialistic. The storage and distribution of goods demands in such places a vastly organized book-keeping. Still the ancient Egyptians did not develop an effective counting system. With one exception, 2/3, all their fractions were unit fractions, such as 1/4, 1/5, 1/6, and so forth. Yet it was ancient Egypt that achieved, as early as around 2000 B.C., that enormous feat of generalization and abstraction which is phonetic writing. Their hieroglyphic writing is the basis of all modern alphabets.

The case of the Maya is no less instructive. As they kept improving their lunar calendar and another calendar based on the phases of Venus, the Maya were forced to work with very large numbers. Yet their number notation remained so clumsy that they had to do mentally even relatively simple additions and substractions, to say nothing of multiplications and divisions. No number notation seems to have developed among the ancient Inca, although their tightly organized society could have derived great benefits from it. Throughout the Inca realm, which had a speedy and efficient postal system, information about numbers was carried on quipus or strings with beads. Clearly, social needs are simply not enough to prompt necessarily insights about matters that should seem most universally obvious to the human mind.

A similar conclusion imposes itself when one looks at geometry, which next to algebra forms another indispensable tool for doing science. Here too the ancient Egyptians pose a tantalizing problem. If practical measurement is the origin and mainspring of geometry, then ancient Egypt should have become its birthplace. There each parcel of arable land in the Nile valley had to be remeasured each year once the annual inundations of the Nile had receded. The construction of pyramids involved measurements and calculations that today would seem to be impossible to carry out without geometry. Yet, while the ancient Egyptians had a formula for computing the volume of a truncated pyramid, they did not seem to have its rigorous derivation. Without doubt, they could not teach geometry, properly so called, to Greek visitors, such as Thales and Herodotus.

Geometry is a Greek invention, in fact one of the great glories of ancient Greece. Of course, one cannot help admiring Euclid's Fourteen Books on geometry of which the first two contain all that is being taught to the average educated modern man insofar as he learns the elements of trigonometry as well. A typical engineeer or a physicist is familiar with the contents of Books III to VI. The contents of Books VII to XII are being taught only in graduate courses. Books XIII and XIV contain propositions whose proofs were not given by Euclid. Some of those propositions have yet to be proven, although first-rate geometers have applied themselves to the task. Our admiration for the achievements of the Greeks of old in geometry should not blind us to their comparatively primitive number notation. The same Greeks, who made notable advances in number theory, used letters of their alphabet for numbers and in a way that made calculations even more cumbersome than was the case with Roman numerals.

The chief paradox posed by ancient Greece relates to their failure to invent science. Here a few preliminary remarks are in order, because it has become a cultural cliché that science was born in Greece. Undoubtedly, geometry is science and so is Ptolemaic astronomy. The latter provides, through a complex system of geometrical figures—the superimposition of circles in particular—a means whereby the position of planets can be predicted with as much accuracy as in the heliocentric system of Copernicus. Undoubtedly, it was a great scientific feat when Eratosthenes calculated the size of the earth, or when Hipparchus derived, also with the help of empirical data and geometry, the precession of the equinoxes.

But the Greeks failed to make any advance in the sense in which science, physical science, has been taken for the past 300 or so years. Science in that sense is the science of dynamics that copes with the motion of bodies. In talking about the motion of celestial bodies, the ancient Greeks astronomers did not advance from geometry to dynamics for they imagined celestial spheres, each carrying a planet, as if they resembled a system of cog-wheels.

The structure of a machine reflects geometry as an account of a static situation. Dynamics comes into the picture when one analyzes the motive force that drives the machine. How far the Greeks remained from formulating the laws of dynamics can easily be gathered from Ptolemy himself. Not, of course, from his *Almagest* which contains a purely geometrical formalism of the celestial motions of planets. From Ptolemy's *Tetrabiblos*, still the bible of astrologers, one learns that he took the planets for living beings that influence and determine every event, including all human actions, on earth. In another book of his, the *Hypotuposes,* Ptolemy described the planets as a group of dancers and a group of well drilled soldiers to explain that the planets are never seen to collide with one another.

Ptolemy was not an exception in classical antiquity, looking at the universe as a quasi-living entity, a sort of all-embracing organism. In fact, only the Atomists, very much a minority in ancient Greece, had a cosmology free of animistic traits. By holding that ultimately everything was fire, the Stoics did not deny a principal point of the Platonic and Aristotelian tradition in which the the universe was the ultimate and foremost living being. Aristotle's continual recourse in his cosmology to biological images has much more to it than his being by profession a biologist.

But even among the Greeks only a relatively few abstained from using crude biological analogies in reference to the physical world. Recourse to such analogies was the rule in other ancient cultures. In India the universe was spoken of as the huge body of Brahman, whose perspiration as it came through the pores formed bubbles, each of them a universe appearing without rhyme and reason. In the Confucian literature one finds accounts of the universe in terms of the parts, big and small, of the human body. In the Babylonian genesis the universe is built from the chopped up parts of the body of the great mother, Tiamat. In ancient Egypt the sky is often represented as the body of the female deity, Nut, who is down on all fours over the reclining body of Geb, the male deity, who represents the earth.

It was impossible to think of the universe in such, at times, crudely organismic terms and to have about the universe thoughts that would lead to the birth of a correct science of dynamics. Thinking of the universe as an organism meant at least two things: First, that the motions of the universe and the motions within it were the motions of an animal. Second, if the universe was the ultimate living being, it had to be taken for an entity whose motions were without a beginning and an end. The bearing of all this on the possibility of finding the correct laws of dynamics will be clear later. Also, as long as the universe was looked upon as an organism, one was tempted to understand the universe through introspection. After all, few things are so obvious to man as the fact that he is an organism with laws that seem to be obvious on a little reflection. Last but not least, the universe taken for a huge animal suggests the idea of its going through endless cycles of birth, growth, aging, death and rebirth. It is no accident that all ancient cultures were dominated by one version or another of the doctrine of the Great Year.

But if everything repeated itself in an infinite number of times, what was the point of making a major effort to improve one's lot? This question could but generate a pessimistic or lethargic outlook. It could be dissimulated only by brave rhetoric, such as Aristotle's dictum that all the comforts conceivable were on hand in his time. And he was one of the few lucky ones. Most free people, to say nothing of the slaves, had meat only once or twice a month.

So much for some likely reasons, why the science of dynamics was not born in any of the great ancient cultures. They became so many places for the repeated stillbirths of science. Such stillbirths came about in two ways. Either no effective steps followed a promising start, or the start was already a step in the wrong direction. The former case has no better illustration than ancient China, the place where the magnet, block printing, and gunpowder were invented. Francis Bacon was, of course, quite wrong in thinking that two if not three of those inventions were made in the West. On the basis of that very erroneous Baconian empiricism, science should have been born in ancient China. Had this been the case, China would have developed the laws of dynamics, and with it the science of ballistics. A scientific China, which would then have easily colonized North America sometime in the twelfth and thirteenth centuries, could have also discovered and conquered Australia, as well as Japan, Korea, and India. Yet there was no Chinese Marco Polo, no Chinese Vasco da Gama, no Chinese Columbus, although at that time the Chinese navy was on a par with the best ships available in the West.

The other case, or taking the first step in the wrong direction, that is, toward a scientific dead-end, is illustrated in Aristotle's theory of motion. Why is it that he recalled with no criticism the patently absurd theory called *antiperistasis* about the flight of projectiles? According to that theory a stone thrown forward is kept in motion by the air which closes in behind the stone and thereby pushes it ahead. Even in Aristotle's time it had to be obvious that one could not lift himself by his bootstraps. Also if one were thinking of the universe as one single organism, and this is what Aristotle did, it was inevitable to think that the continuity of motion had to be through some continuous contact between the mover and the moved. The parts of an organism can never be truly separate from one another. As a result, in Aristote-

lian physics, as Edmund T. Whittaker stated, every page was
wrong. In that physics one went with every step farther down a
blind alley.

The physics in which not only the first step was right, but
also prompted further steps in the right direction was classical or
Newtonian physics. Its first step consists in Newton's three laws
of motion. The first of them, the law of inertial motion, is an
impossibility in Aristotle's physics. Within Newton's physics it
is the basis of all other laws.

Breakthrough in the West
Not only was Newton a Western European but so were all the
scientists from whom he learned very important things. In reverse
chronological order they were Huygens, Descartes, Galileo,
Kepler, and Copernicus. Today the whole story of the pre-
Cartesian and, in fact, pre-Copernican development of the idea
inertial motion is well known. The names connected with that
story are all Western names. At the beginning of the story is John
Buridan, a fourteenth-century professor at the Sorbonne, a
Western place of learning if there ever was one. If one takes
science for the study of things in motion, and if one recognizes
the primary importance of the law of inertial motion, one can
specify the date of the Western birth of science.

The time is 1330 or about, when John Buridan took the
chair of philosophy at the Sorbonne. As was the custom of other
professors, he taught by offering a commentary on various works
of Aristotle. One of the most important of those works is a
cosmology, usually referred to as *De caelo* or *On the Heavens.*
There Aristotle states most emphatically that the universe is
eternal and that therefore there had been no beginning to the
foremost of its motions which is the daily revolution of the
celestial sphere.

Buridan was not, of course, the first Christian to read
Aristotle and to reject his teaching about the eternity of the
universe and of its motion. For Christians it had been for many
centuries an explicit tenet of their faith that the past history of the
universe is strictly finite. For this is the meaning of the phrase
that God created the universe out of nothing and in time. But

Buridan did what no Christian philosopher or theologian did before him. He speculated on the manner in which motion was given to the celestial bodies, once they were created.

His thinking was genuinely scientific because it was about the manner in which bodies moved. In substance he stated that in the beginning when God made the heaven and the earth, He imparted to the celestial bodies a certain amount of impetus, by which Buridan meant the equivalent of what later came to be called momentum. Then he added that these bodies keep their momentum undiminished because they move in a frictionless space. Such a motion is inertial motion.

Buridan taught at the Sorbonne for over twenty years and the same is true of Nicole Oresme, his most important student and successor in the chair. Oresme faithfully repeated Buridan's ideas in an even more famous series of lectures. Copies of Buridan's and Oresme's commentaries on *On the Heavens* can be found in such ancient libraries as Oxford, Salamanca, Cambridge, Bologna, Pavia, Cologne, Toulouse, Sevilla, Vienna, and last but not least in Cracow. It was in Cracow that Copernicus learned about inertial motion and put it to a crucial use. He did so by explaining in its terms why birds and clouds and the very atmosphere do not fall behind on a fast-rotating and even faster-orbiting earth.

The formulation by Buridan of the idea of inertial motion is the very spark which functioned with respect to science as does the spark plug in an automobile. The spark plug is but a small part of the entire machine, but an all-important part. It makes the motor start and thereby puts the entire car in motion. That very spark or Buridan's idea of inertial motion failed to turn up in any of the great ancient cultures. The reason for this should seem obvious, if one recalls the theological context in which that spark appeared in Buridan's mind. All those ancient cultures were pagan. The essence of paganism, old and new, is that the universe is eternal, that its motions are without beginning and without end.

Belief in creation out of nothing and in time is the very opposite to paganism. Once that belief had become a widely shared cultural consensus during the Christian Middle Ages, it became almost natural that there should arise the idea of inertial motion. Certainly, the idea appeared very natural to Buridan, to his contemporaries, and to the subsequent eight generations between Buridan and Descartes. In the entire vast manuscript tradition during that period there are but few instances of a rejection of Buridan's ideas, whereas its endorsements are numerous. Insofar as that broad credal or theological consensus is the work of Christianity, science is not Western, but Christian.

This conclusion, which may seem startling, however logical it may be, needs further explanation. A reason for this relates to the circumstances of my very presence here in Moscow. I am part of a group of scholars who were invited here to give their views about various aspects of life and thinking in the West, and especially in the United States. Consequently, this essay may imply that what I have said now is a widely shared opinion in the West. Nothing could be further from the truth. This, of course, does not mean that my conclusion, namely, that in a very specific and all-important sense science is not Western but Christian, may not be true. Truth is not measured by so-called scholarly consensus. The latter is all too often like fashions. They come and go. Truth will come out and survive. Truth is like facts. Facts will prevail and one must be careful not to be found in opposition to them.

Modern peevishness
The facts of the pre-Cartesian history of inertial motion are well-established. They were first listed in the monumental historical studies of Pierre Duhem who died in 1916. His *Origines de la statique*, his *Études sur Léonard de Vinci*, the first five volumes of his *Système du monde* were widely reviewed by 1920 or so. In spite of this, Duhem's chief message, the medieval Christian origin of science, was little spoken of. The message must have been resisted even in the best academic circles where respect for scholarly research, no matter what its message may be, is claimed to be the foremost precept. For the first twenty years the typical resistance to Duhem's message consisted in silence, hardly a scholarly attitude.

A classic example of a seemingly more scholary attitude, or quasi-silence, can be found in the famous lecture series, *Science and the Modern World*, which Whitehead delivered at Harvard in 1925. There in the first chapter entitled "The Origins of Modern Science," Whitehead listed two beliefs that had to be widely shared so that science might be born. One is belief in order—in an orderly world. The other is the conviction, to quote Whitehead, "that every detailed occurrence can be correlated with its antecedents in a perfectly definite manner, exemplifying general principles." Then Whitehead asked: "How has this conviction been so vividly implanted on the European mind?"

Whitehead's answer is that "when we compare this tone of thought of Europe with the attitude of other civilizations when left to themselves, there seems but one source for its origin. It must come from the medieval insistence on the rationality of God, conceived as with the personal energy of Jehovah and with the rationality of a Greek philosopher." Whitehead's answer is a classic in suggesting the correct reply, but hiding its true nature in the same breath. To see this it should be enough to take a close look at the basis of the answer, or a comparison between medieval European culture and various earlier cultures and in particular a comparison of the notion of God prevailing in them.

According to Whitehead, "in Asia the conceptions of God were of a being who was either too arbitrary or too impersonal for such ideas to have much effect on instinctive habits of mind. Any definite occurrence might be due to the fiat of an irrational despot, or might issue from some impersonal, inscrutable origin of things. There was not the same confidence as in the intelligible rationality of a personal being." But the real difference between the various Asian conceptions of God and the medieval Christian conception of God lay not in one being impersonal and arbitrary, and the other personal and logical. Even from the purely conceptual point of view the comparison drawn up by Whitehead should seem gravely defective, if not plainly illogical. The more impersonal a factor is, the less arbitrary it has to be. Clearly, the real difference must lie elsewhere. The concept of God in ancient great cultures did not essentially differ from the notion of the universe. All ancient cultures were pantheistic. By contrast, the Christian concept of God has for its essence the belief that He is truly a Creator, that is, a being absolutely transcendental to the world. He exists whether He creates a universe or not.

A most interesting feature of that first chapter in *Science and the Modern World* is that whereas Whitehead speaks there of God as Jehovah, he never speaks of God as a Creator. In fact he does not mention God as a Creator throughout the whole book, not even in its next to last chapter which is on "Science and Religion." In not making any reference to God as a Creator, Whitehead remained consistent with pantheism which was his own religious belief. Toward the end of his life he made it clear that around 1916 or so he abandoned the Christian faith he learned from his father, an Anglican clergyman.

While pantheism might have given personal comfort to Whitehead, it made him distinctly uncomfortable in the face of some major facts of history. Such a fact was the belief of medieval Christians, or of genuine Christians in any age for that matter, in a personal transcendental Creator. Moreover, for those Christians the transcendental Creator was substantially identical with the Incarnate Logos, or Reason Incarnate. They also believed that He could only create a fully logical or rational universe. It may sound most surprising that the first unambiguous declarations about the unrestricted rationality of the universe are found not in Greek philosophical writings but in the writings of Saint Athanasius, the great defender of the divinity of the Logos against the Arians.

None of these points is as much as hinted at in Whitehead's *Science and the Modern World* or in any of his writings, a fact indicative either of lack of scholarship or perhaps of bad faith. Both lurk in between the lines of his often quoted declaration: "The faith in the possibility of science, generated antecedently to the development of modern scientific theory, is an unconscious derivative from medieval theology." Facts, fully established by scholarly research, show that the derivative in question was the result of a fully conscious reflection. As to Whitehead's bad faith, it gives itself away by the phrase that precedes that declaration: "I am not arguing that the European trust in the scrutability of nature was logically justified even by its own theology."

It seems that Whitehead was most eager to make sure that his readers should not give substantial credit to medieval Christian theology in connection with the rise of science, let alone to that faith's pivotal point which is the very divinity of Christ himself. Would it have been difficult for a man with Whitehead's mind and learning to see something most crucial in the belief that held Christ to be the only begotten Son of God? Was not that belief the principal safeguard for Christians that saved them from sliding into pantheism? Did not classical Greek and Roman antiquity provide enough evidence that in pantheism the universe is looked upon as the only begotten (*monogenes*) procreation from the divine principle?

So much for quasi-silence (by way of illustration) as a means of coping with the momentous significance of Duhem's historical researches. They constituted a revolution in Western man's understanding of the very origins of his greatest pride, science. That revolution, which remains largely to be assimilated, has been from about 1940 on resisted by the claim that there is a revolutionary break between the science of Buridan, or of the science of impetus, and the science of Galileo. The claim was first made by A. Koyré, whose religious history parallels that of Whitehead, with the difference that Koyré reached pantheism not from Christian but from a Jewish background.

Revolution or Revolutions?
Undoubtedly, it would pay to look into the impact that Koyré's pantheism had on his historical researches into the origin and chief characteristics of Galileo's science. Here, let me note only the price one has to pay if one accepts Koyré's contention that Duhem was wrong in claiming a continuity from Buridan through Oresme and Leonardo to Galileo and beyond. The price is that if Koyré is right, science must be taken with him for a succession of disconnected periods, a mere sequence of revolutions. Such a sequence is not a continuity and therefore cannot represent a progress.

In other words, if Koyré's critique of Duhem is accepted—and many modern philosophers and historians have accepted it—one cannot give a logical account of a *fact*, the fact of scientific progress which it would be absurd to deny. A telling point of that logical conundrum is that neither Koyré nor his disciples—such as Thomas Kuhn of MIT, Paul Feyerabend of Berkeley, Bernard Cohen of Harvard, to mention some principal ones—give a clear definition of what they mean by revolution, while they profusely use that word. If they mean a complete break with the past, that is, with former ideas, they invite incomprehensibility of the pre-revolutionary phase as seen from the vantage point set up by the revolutionary change. To ward off the specter of incomprehensibility, they usually resort to some scientific expression, such as incommensurability, mutation, and paradigms.

The last of these is best left to Latin grammarians. They never expected their students to undergo a mental mutation or a revolutionary reorientation as they proceeded from a paradigm noun of the first declension to a paradigm noun of the second declension. As to genetic mutation, it consists in an extremely minute rearrangement of the chromosomatic material and not in its complete replacement. This is why one species can be instrumental in the rise of another species.

As to incommensurability, it occurs in a right-angled triangle with unit sides. The measure of the hypotenuse is an irrational number. Yet, no rationality was displayed by that Pythagorean of old who, on discovering the strange nature of that measure, drowned himself on the high sea. As to those moderns who cavort in the idea of incommensurability and do so in the name of their philosophies of science, they should rather take note of the Bulgarian proverb: Those who want to drown should not torture themselves in shallow waters. At any rate, they seem to ignore a principal lesson about revolutions, the point best conveyed in the French saying: *plus ça change, plus ça reste la même chose*.

This is certainly true of the American Revolution. It was a revolution only inasmuch as it wanted to gather the best from past political wisdom. It emphatically asserted continuity with the past. And this was precisely the professed aim of Marx and

Lenin. Undoubtedly, the results have become very different. The differences in question could and did create enormous conflicts, but also have promoted a serious reconsideration. The latter has come about mainly because of science, Western science, that is, the very last point in this essay.

There was a time when one could argue that science is a principal tool of enslavement and misery. Of course, Marx did not think that this should necessarily be the case. He in fact thought that once wholesale misery sparked revolutionary uprisings, and as a result the tools of production got in proper hands, poverty would be eliminated. He would be very much surprised, were he to see today that those tools of production achieved a substantial rise of living standards only insofar as they were handled by capitalists. The credit for this should not go to capitalists as such. Capitalists did not create the belief that man is free and that therefore man is creative. Capitalists played very little part in that creativity explosion that has characterized science for the past hundred years and increasingly so with every passing decade. The principal part is played by man's urge to know and to invent. Unlike classical capitalism that thrived on loans and interests, modern capitalism thrives on inventions that come in at an accelerated rate.

That exchanges between East and West are today extending far beyond meetings of scientists has much to do with science. Industrial applications of science are very much at work even when in all appearence such exchanges have nothing do with science. The meetings of the World Bank and of top financiers have much more to do with technology than it appears at first sight. Any issue of the *Wall Street Journal* or of the *Times Financial News* is a proof of this.

Herein lies both an opportunity and a danger. The opportunity is that the more two potentially hostile sides talk to one another, the better the chance that they discover a great many things they share or aspire to, such as a good road toward a more securely established peace and prosperity. The danger lies in the fact that to preserve peace and broadly shared prosperity much more is needed than a greater availability of material goods and conveniences. An undue preoccupation with such goods, with the technical and scientific tools needed for their production, may promote a shallow pragmatism which has plain self-interest as its chief standard.

Unbridled, unprincipled self-interest, be it the self-interest of individuals, of nations, of social classes, of races, has always been the source of conflicts. To keep that self-interest under control, better and deeper motivations are necessary than the ones science can deliver. This received a momentous reminder in 1950 from Bertrand Russell, hardly a champion of ethical rules or a friend of Christianity. At a time when the Cold War was at its height and the arms race got on a seemingly runaway course, he suggested nothing less than that what the world really needed was Christian love. "If you feel this [Christian love], you have a motive for existence, a guide in action, a reason for courage, an imperative necessity for intellectual honesty."

All these commodities—motivation, guidelines, courage, and intellectual honesty—are indispensable in scientific work. To do physics today, one need not be Western, one need not even be a Christian. Science or physics has its highly developed and well-proven techniques—theoretical and experimental. Such techniques remain universal even if their origins show some specific connection with Christianity. But they require a philosophical and ethical underpinning if the purely quantitative results of physics or science are to be integrated into the broader human context.

With philosophy and ethics on hand, one has within easy reach religion, which recognizes all just demands of reason, while rightly resisting its unjust demands. Those unjust demands are nowadays couched in specious references to science. Such is the claim, for instance, that science has proved experimentally the eternity of matter and therefore such an entity was in no need whatsoever of a Creator.

I was a member, together with Professor Ambartsumian, of the panel on cosmology at the seventeenth World Congress of Philosophy in Dusseldorf in late August 1978. There I and a thousand-strong audience heard him claim—and in the name of science, at that—that matter was eternal. Of course, that was still the Brezhnev era. I am certain he would not today make that claim which is absurd philosophically and nonsensical scientifically. Today even the church bells are free to ring out their voice without fear all over Holy Russia. It is a land with as many brave and honest men as can be found in any other land.

One of those lands is the land of Afghans, where the British tried to do a hundred years ago what you tried recently and failed. A hundred years ago a famed British poet, Rudyard Kipling rode around the Khyber pass, an area which seemed to prove that there can be no meeeting between East and West. There Kipling also learned a heart-warming story about two brave and honest men: Kamal, an Afghan chieftain, and a young British cavalry man, the son of a colonel of the Boarder Guards. The story is about the recovery of the colonel's favorite horse. Through their encounter in which both Kamal and the soldier have the opportunity to kill one another they learn about their bravery and sincerity. The result, far more important than the restitution of mere material goods, is, to quote Kipling:

> But there is neither East nor West,
>   Border, nor Breed, nor Birth,
> When two strong men stand face to face,
>   though they come from the ends of the earth.

9

Gilson and Science

A host of scholars honored Gilson on his seventy-fifth birthday in 1959 with the publication of an unusually big Festschrift. As usual with Festschrifts, the *Mélanges offertes à Etienne Gilson* contained his full bibliography up to 1957. The total of 648 titles, including three scores of books, makes for a formidable list.[1] In all those titles the word "science" occurs only twice—a fact that may cast doubt on the merits of this essay. Gilson was sixty-eight when, in 1952, he published his first essay with the word "science" in its title.[2] During the next five years he produced only one more, and very brief, essay where the title carried the word "science".[3] Even with an eye on words related to science, such as "scientific" or "physics", one cannot discover in that huge bibliography more than a couple of essays relevant to our topic.[4]

However, one would be wrong in drawing the inference that Gilson was not interested in science. Countless readers of the twenty-some printings of his *God and Philosophy* have been treated, in its last chapter, to a penetrating exposure of what is usually called scientism. His particular targets were Julian Huxley and Sir James Jeans, both of whom were unable to see the difference between their science and the dubious philosophy they grafted onto it.

First published in *Saints, Sovereigns and Scholars: Essays in Honor of Frederick D. Wilhelmsen*, ed. R. A. Herrera *et al* (New York: Peter Lang, 1993), pp. 31-47. Reprinted with permission.

This is not to suggest that Gilson's reading of first-rate popular-izations of science was wide. Towards his seventies he expressed, somewhat indirectly, his regrets on that score. In the same context he put, in fact, a decisive emphasis on science for the purposes of Thomist philosophy—an emphasis that should have sent a shockwave through Thomist realms. In his eighties Gilson did his best to take the medicine he had prescribed to his fellow Thomists. The result was the crowning of a distinguished philosophical career with a first-rate interpretation of the science of biology, including Darwinian evolution. And in his very last lecture given at the Medieval Institute in Toronto, Gilson came to grips with the notion of matter in modern physics.[5]

Gilson was certainly a latecomer to science even as regards a diligent reading of books about science and by scientists. In his intellectual autobiography[6] he made no reference to any course in science during the years he spent in Notre-Dame-des-Champs, a minor seminary under the direction of priests of the archdiocese of Paris. What he gained from them above all was a lifelong commit-ment to the highest Christian ideals. Next to that came a passionate love of the humanities, of classical and modern literature. Gilson's first ambition was to become a teacher of humanities in a better-grade high school. Whatever he had learned from those priests in mathe-matics and science, it apparently made no impression on him.

Since he could hope for a decently paying teaching job only in State schools, he decided, with the full encouragement of his parents and those priests, to find out what secular education looked like. He spent the last three years of his teens in Henry IV, then as now one of the leading *lycées* in Paris. In recalling those years, he mentioned some teachers, none of whom taught science. What he remembered best was that for all the philosophy courses he took at Henry IV, he failed to gain even a minimal understanding of what philosophy was about. As he was mulling over this problem during his year of military service, Gilson decided to probe into it in a most methodical way. He entered the Sorbonne as a student of philosophy.[7]

During his years as a student in the Sorbonne's department of philosophy, Gilson could have time and again developed a special interest in the sciences, but he did not. This is all the more strange since he soon felt a great admiration for Bergson, who was just writing his *Evolution créatrice*. Whatever the shortcomings of that book, it conveyed powerfully the message that a careful study of living organisms was irreconcilable with mechanistic philosophy, the rage of the day. It took more than sixty years before Gilson discovered the usefulness of the study of biology for a philosophical purpose far more reliable than the one which Bergson tried to demonstrate.

The department of philosophy at the Sorbonne, where Gilson spent three years (1904-1907), resounded with references to science. Comte's positivism, in which science crowns everything else, was the official dogma of the academe. Among the older professors the towering figure was E. Boutroux, whose fame rested on his doctoral dissertation, published in 1873, on the contingency of the laws of nature. Yet it was a hollow fame. In speaking of Boutroux and Lachelier, also a senior professor, Gilson reminisced: "They were rarely seen; they were heard still less; and they were hardly read at all."[8] It took half a century for Gilson to discover the importance of Boutroux's book.

Then there was Durkheim, who with his "scientific" sociology hoped to provide answers to any and all questions. While one could easily see through the hollowness of such a hope, Gilson felt perplexed on hearing Frederic Rauh state in class that "there are times when one feels almost ashamed to call oneself a philosopher." Did this mean that philosophy was an enterprise beyond remedy? Or was it from science alone that salvation could come to philosophy? Rauh seemed so think so. On hearing from young Gilson that he was passionately interested in art and religion, Rauh replied: "Very well, but this can wait. For the time being study the sciences." To Gilson's question, "Which sciences?" came Rauh's reply: "Any sciences. Provided they be sciences, they will teach you what it is to *know*."[9]

Luckily, Gilson did not follow this potentially destructive advice. Then as now it was almost impossible to study science and not to imbibe at the same time what scientists were thinking about what knowledge they gained in doing science. Most scientists who articulated their thoughts on that score ended up by saying that they knew only their thoughts, but hardly what the layman calls reality and what scientists themselves claim to know in their non-scientific hours. Young Gilson could hardly have failed to learn about the philosophy of science and knowledge which the great mathematician Henri Poincaré, a luminary of the Sorbonne, was setting forth in more than one bestseller. Written in a style most commodious for non-scientists, those books spread far and wide Poincaré's commodism, or the idea that a scientific law is but a convenient arrangement of data and perhaps even less. Since *bons mots* (if not self-defeating utterances) uttered by luminaries in academia are well remembered there, young Gilson could have heard of a famous remark of

Poincaré, uttered before the Académie Française: "Tout ce qui n'est pas pensée est le pure néant."[10]

Such declarations revealed their pathetic character as soon as the mathematician cared to communicate his thoughts to others whom he could hardly take for "pure nothing." At any rate, such utterances posed no threat to young Gilson, who even prior to his entry into the Sorbonne felt "plagued with the incurable metaphysical disease of what they call *chosisme,* that is, crass realism."[11] In all evidence he was ready to parry possible invitations to do philosophy by doing science. One of these came as he proposed a topic in speculative philosophy as his doctoral thesis to be directed by Lucien Lévy-Bruhl, whose clarity of thought and exquisite phraseology had made a deep impression on him. Lévy-Bruhl told him that he "should undertake something positive, that speculative philosophy just wouldn't do." As one, who made a name for himself with a book on morality and the *science* of morals, first published in 1903, Lévy-Bruhl obviously meant by "positive" something scientific. Gilson was ready to deflect the thrust of the remark: "All right. I will do history of philosophy. That's positive enough, isn't it?"[12] So Gilson became a historian of philosophy, one who always treated even the most universally valid epistemological questions from a historical perspective. A very positive approach on the part of the one who loved to talk of the history of philosophy as the laboratory where philosophical propositions are tested, and mercilessly at that. But in that laboratory, as run by Gilson, very few references to science could be heard for at least half a century.

Gilson's apparent insensitivity to science should seem particularly startling in view of the fact that the very system of a philosopher-scientist, Descartes, became the subject of his doctoral thesis and his first field of study. Neither in his first major works on Descartes nor in his continual return over several decades to various aspects of Descartes' thought did Gilson take up Cartesian science as such. Here again one cannot help wondering, since it was precisely in those formative years of Gilson, the philosopher, that there appeared in thirteen volumes Descartes' correspondence, a mine of information about Descartes' science.[13]

The reason for Gilson's lack of interest in Descartes' science could not be a lack of adequate scientific training. Descartes's physics contains not a single mathematical formula. But while trying to find out what Descartes had done with a long list of philosophical terms used by the Scholastics, Gilson discovered Thomas Aquinas' philosophy, which retained much of his attention for the rest of his life. Compared with Albertus Magnus, Thomas Aquinas showed minimal interest in the sciences as they stood around the middle of the 13th century, or even as he found them in the writings of Aristotle, regardless of his full mastery of them. Something similar is true of Gilson when compared with various medievalists' work in the 1920s and 1930s.[14]

Gilson himself offered a striking though unintended proof of this in his famous Gifford Lectures, *The Spirit of Medieval Philosophy*. Among the twenty chapters there is one on "The Middle Ages and Nature." The medievals' idea of nature was based, Gilson argued, on the notion that nature always acts in the same way. Therefore, Gilson continued, "it is quite easy to conceive the medieval universe as a possible object of scientific explanation in the sense in which scientific explanation is understood today." This should have called for at least two or three notes or references in a book abounding in well over a thousand of them, so many witnesses to Gilson's bent on meticulous documentation. Instead, Gilson suggested that medieval science was a dubious topic: "I trust I have no illusion as to the extent and quality of medieval science, but it seems to me necessary to draw a clear distinction between scientific knowledge of the world on the one hand and the general conception of the world that science interprets on the other."[15]

Gilson would have been the last to dispute the fact that the universe as seen by the medievals eminently lent itself to scientific discussion, mainly because that universe was even more deterministic than the Aristotelian universe. As proof, Gilson listed Aquinas' conviction that the motion of stars rules all terrestrial phenomena, as well as the medievals' fondness for astrology. He also mentioned Grosseteste's physics of forms, based on the geometrical properties of light rays. His fourth and last example was Roger Bacon's encomiums on experimental science.

In summing up in a mere dozen or so lines what would qualify as the positive achievements of medieval science, Gilson clearly revealed his lack of interest in those "positive" data. It was the philosopher disguised as a historian of philosophy who asserted himself as Gilson quickly went off on a very valuable tangent by returning to the physical determinism held by Aquinas. This was a determinism mitigated by chance: a notion as important for Aristotle as for Aquinas. Mechanistic determinism could not be complete as long as efficient causes could at times work without being ruled by final causality. Chance, Gilson insisted, "is by no means there [in peripatetic philosophy] conceived as a pure indetermination, that is to say as something that happens without cause, and, in this respect, it makes no breach in the universal determinism; nevertheless, it is incompletely determined, it is accidental with respect to the efficient cause because not produced thereby in view of an end, or because the thing produced is other than the end for which the cause acts. In nature, then, the fortuitous is that which lacks an end."[16] The importance of this detour will be clear later.

Of course, if what Gilson said about medieval science was in substance all that could be said about it in the 1930s, then Gilson was right in defending himself against the possible charge that he was entertaining illusions about the science of the medievals. But there was in fact much more to medieval science, and it should have come within Gilson's own definition of the Middle Ages as extending well beyond the thirteenth century. This was true not only of *The Spirit of Medieval Philosophy* but even more so of another masterpiece of Gilson's, his *History of Christian Philosophy in the Middle Ages,* which he published in 1954. There the Middle Ages comes to a close around 1400. And therein lies the rub.

In his discussion of the nominalists, Gilson has only a page for the science of John Buridan and only two for that of Nicole Oresme.[17] Concerning Buridan, the proponent of the theory of impetus, Gilson should have gotten fired up. According to his own admission, he had for well over two decades come to realize that medieval philosophy was a *Christian* philosophy, that is, a philosophy done in full awareness of the dictates of the Christian Creed. In fact, Gilson credited this insight of his, which he considered one of his two most important insights, to his having had to come to grips, in connection with his Gifford Lectures, with the true nature of medieval philosophy.[18]

But then why did Gilson fail to mine the very theological context of Buridan's formulation of the impetus theory of motion? Was it not full of philosophical significance of great interest to the historian of philosophy and to the defender of Christian culture? Publishing his own book in 1954, Gilson could not, of course, utilize the sixth volume of Pierre Duhem's *Système du monde,* first published in that same year, almost forty years after Duhem's death, where Duhem cited at great length Buridan's statements. But Duhem had revealed enough concerning Buridan already in 1913, when he published the third volume of his Leonardo Studies, which alone could have served as a mine of information for Gilson. There, in the introduction, Duhem characterized Buridan's achievement as the line of demarcation between the old, that is, Aristotelian physics, and the new physics, subsequently to be known as Newtonian physics. While this statement of Duhem's did not escape Gilson's attention, he undercut its philosophical significance by saying that it "belongs to the history of science."[19] Yet in that very volume Duhem quoted that epoch-making passage where Buridan confronts in the same breath both the ontological (and theological) origin of all motion and also the very scientific question of *how* that motion originated.[20]

One wonders whether Buridan would have remained for Gilson a mere nominalist had Gilson taken up some science while at the Sorbonne. A born historian, Gilson then would have perceived a golden opportunity. He might have spotted something of the line that leads from Buridan (and his disciple Oresme, who faithfully echoed his master's great insights) to Copernicus, and beyond him to Descartes and Galileo. And in view of Gilson's profound conviction that all intellectual work should promote the Kingdom of God as a service under Christ the King,[21] he could not have failed to note an all-important point and the very reverse of a point made by Bergson in a priceless though largely false phrase: "Science has descended to earth on the inclined plane of Galileo."[22] By then something similar had become a shibboleth of a secularist modern culture, largely hatched in Gilson's France. The message of that shibboleth was that science is the true savior and that for it to be born, belief in the traditional savior, or Jesus Christ, had first to be discredited in the mind of Western Man.

No one could have more effectively battled that shibboleth than Gilson, who, because of his prodigious learning and sparkling diction, quickly became the toast of the American secularist academia. Not that Gilson had ever made a secret of his being a dogmatist, and a Roman Catholic dogmatist at that. It is almost dizzying to think of some what-might-have-been's. One can, for instance, imagine Gilson as he delivered his William James lectures at Harvard University in 1936, the same Harvard that had heard Whitehead deliver his famous Lovell Lectures in 1925. In the latter, published as *Science and the Modern World,* Whitehead made the claim that modern science is a subconscious derivative from belief in Jehovah and from the scholastics' bent on logical rigor.

The claim should have jarred ears brought up on encomiums of Francis Bacon's inductive method and on the equally inane references to Galileo's dropping balls from the Tower of Pisa. Many of those ears had also been attuned to the equally inane tenet that the rise of reformed Christianity and that of science were two sides of the same coin. But this coin had some value in the eyes of those whose

Christianity largely amounted to a mere anti-Romanism with little positive supernatural content. For those ears, few dicta were so melodious as contemptuous references to the darkness of the Middle Ages and scholastic logic-chopping.

Whitehead's claim was a classic exercise in telling far less than half of the truth. For the truth of the matter was that the Scholastics, Buridan and Oresme in particular, were very conscious of what they were doing. Moreover, their belief in God was not a belief in Jehovah but in the Father who revealed Himself in His only begotten Son, Jesus Christ. This is why, unlike their Jewish and Muslim counterparts among medieval students of Aristotle, the Christian Scholastics steered clear of Aristotle's pantheism and eternalism. The medieval Scholastics, precisely because they believed in Christian dogmas, held fast to the tenet that the universe was created out of nothing and in time. Herein lies the chief clue to Buridan's breakthough toward the idea of inertial motion, or Newton's first law.[23]

Nobody could have said this better than Gilson did at Harvard in 1936, when Whitehead still held court there. It was not said for another half a century, though not without an indirect influence of Gilson.[24] Having failed to expose himself to science, Gilson's broad perspectives narrowed somewhat. He never warmed up to Duhem. There is a touch of slighting in his reference to Duhem's achievement as an "original and intelligent pioneering work." The work of a genius like Duhem need not be called intelligent. Also Gilson contradicted his own praise of that work by adding that Duhem's work "perhaps runs the risk of causing us to imagine the University of Paris in the fourteenth century as peopled by physicists completely absorbed in statics, kinetics, and astronomy."[25]

It would be tempting now to say that no intelligent reader of Duhem had ever fallen victim to such imagining. But this would, of course, cast a doubt, however slight and unintended, on Gilson's superb intellectual powers. In a genuinely Gilsonian sense, one therefore has to fall back on the elementary, namely, on the limitations of every human mind, however great. Its powers of appreciation are always limited. To appreciate science in a convincing sense, one has to be a scientist, which Gilson was not. Thus he treated Buridan as a nominalist, which Buridan was not, as long as Ockham sets the pattern of nominalism. Buridan firmly upheld the possibility of proving God's existence from visible things, which is the kind of exercise in traditional metaphysics that would have been anathema to Ockham.

Appreciation of science, coupled with exposure to its practice, might have prevented Gilson from doing a signal injustice to Duhem. For science, with its stunning ability to deal with the quantitative aspects of things, can easily make one unappreciative of the fact that while science ascertains facts about things, it does not provide the things. This is why many prominent scientists, and in particular physicists, who write about the philosophy of science fall victim to idealism or pragmatism, neither of which offers room for asking questions about reality as such. In view of this, Duhem's achievement in his *Théorie physique* should seem all the more outstanding. For in that work, which caused many a headache to philosophers at the Sorbonne[26] while Gilson was studying there as well as when he returned there to teach, Duhem firmly upheld the primacy of registering the real as it exists outside and independently of the knower. In Duhem's visceral affirmation of the real, one may indeed see anticipated Gilson's own methodical realism. Gilson, however, presented Duhem as a good, though sadly mistaken, Catholic and as a "physicist of good repute" who "deemed it necessary to revive the nominalistic interpretation of science, and to pit Ockham once more against St. Thomas Aquinas."[27]

Duhem did not pit Ockham against Aquinas, although he emphasized, with some asperity, that Aquinas borrowed from various philosophical systems. The heavy Platonist veins in Thomas's writings were, indeed, well known long before their systematic presentation by Fr. Robert J. Henle.[28] As to Ockham, Duhem's chief aim was to present his scientific attainments, which were numerous. Ockham merely showed what is demonstrated by most Nobel-Laureates in physics, namely, that it is possible to do excellent science while espousing shabby philosophies.[29] But it takes a scientist, with keen eyes on what is a fine scientific contribution, to see this. Those scientifically keen eyes Gilson did not possess.

This can be seen in those two articles of Gilson from 1952 and 1953. His starting point in the former, "Science, Philosophy, and Religious Wisdom," was the phenomenal expansion of scientific knowledge. While a Greek and even a Descartes could still have a mastery over all science, two centuries later a scientist had, of necessity, to be a specialist. Even more so was this true of our times: "Modern science has become much too big to lodge entirely in the brains of any one man."[30]

Gilson then exposed the illusion that science is a stable enterprise and that it is certainly such in comparison with philosophy. Anyone forty-seven years old in 1952 had already lived in three scientific universes: that of classical physics, that of Einsteinian space-time universe, and that of Heisenberg's indeterministic world. With a felicitous phrase that came so readily to him, Gilson compared this succession of scientific world views at an accelerated rate to the succession of the Patriarchs of the Old Testament, who were subject to "the law of diminishing longevity."[31] However, for this law to hold true, Heisenberg's world should have by 1952 yielded to another scientific world. It still holds court.

This is, however, a minor point. Introducing that remark, Gilson portrayed the gist of Heisenberg's world. It was, of course, true that given the particle-wave duality, it was impossible "to situate with complete precision, in space and time, the elementary physical transformations which take place in the world." But Gilson continued as if it had been his conviction too that "for a phenomenon to escape the determinations of space and time is also to escape the determination of causality."[32]

Here Gilson should have paused. The expression "determinations of space and time" could suggest two very different things. One could mean by that expression that physicists, as long as they had to rely on wave-particle dualism or on Heisenberg's uncertainty principle, could not achieve perfect determinations, that is, accuracy, in their measurements. While this could be frustrating, it was simply a matter of operational restriction. But the expression could also mean, and in the context this is what it appeared to mean, an ontological indeterminacy. If this is what Gilson meant, it contradict-ed what he had stated in his Gifford Lectures, à propos the notion of chance in Aristotle and in Aquinas. Chance, he declared there, could not mean that something happened without an efficient cause.

Unfortunately, it is this most considered view of his that seemed to have some doubts cast on it by what he was to say not so much about the world of the new physics, but about the world as revealed by the new physics. In the former case one could simply talk about certain presuppositions of physics and not talk of their essential revisability. In the latter case, one endorsed an ontological indeter-minacy. This is what Gilson seemed to do as he contrasted the strict previsability available in Einstein's space-time universe and the new physics of Bohr, Heisenberg, and de Broglie: "Up to 1927, scientific previsability was supposed to rest upon strict physical determinism; today, scientific previsability results from the global probability arising from innumerable elementary indeterminations." And as if this antiontological slant, most likely unintended, had not been enough, Gilson added: "Incidentally, this means that the strictly determined mechanical world of dialectical materialism, which Marxists still mistake for the world of science, died twenty-five years ago. They don't seem to know it yet."[33]

Gilson did not seem to know that in saying this he was giving an unintended support to the antiontological ideology of the Copenhagen interpretation of quantum mechanics. Still, one wonders how a mind so bent on the real and so keen on ontology as Gilson's could have failed to notice the dangerous drift of what he had extolled as the new indeterminism. He did not seem to subject it to the law of "an always decreasing stability" which he saw exmplified by the happenings in modern science.[34] He tried to lead his reader to the recognition that science is no less subject to reformulations than are philosophical systems, and that the latter are the more subject to reformulation the more science they incorporate. Once more Gilson came up with a sparkling phrase: "All philosophies perish by their science; all philosophies survive by the metaphysical truth which they contain. The constancy of the fact is such that it might almost be called a historical law."[35]

With that, Gilson was back on his own terrain, a far safer one for him than the one on which he had just been treading. He could make much of the modern physicist's puzzlement as to how knowledge is possible. It took no particular insight to show that such a puzzlement is metaphysical and will never be cleared up by scientific methods. Nor was it difficult to point out that if the intelligibility of nature has to be explained on a metaphysical basis, then nature itself has to be taken for a pointer beyond itself. While he was not the first to note this, Gilson could once more put matters in a gripping form: "What is now happening is that, on the basis of their scientific knowledge, some scientists are beginning to ask metaphysical and theological questions. And they are welcome to it, but if they do they will have to look for metaphysical and theological answers."[36]

The physicist's wonderment about the epistemological possibility of science was the starting point of Gilson's contribution to a Festschrift in honor of Louis de Broglie's sixtieth birthday.[37] Gilson affixed his comments to a statement in De Broglie's *Physics and Microphysics*: "The great wonder in the progress of science is that it has revealed to us a certain agreement between our thought and things, a certain possibility of grasping, with the assistance of the resources of our intelligence, and the rules of our reason, the profound relations existing between phenomena."[38]

The reasons which De Broglie assigned for his wonderment were not new. In essence they related to the fact that while physical processes and realities could be visualized in terms of mechanistic physics, this was much less the case for Einstein's physics, and even less so for the physics of the quanta. Gilson then noted what could be taken either for the view of De Broglie and other physicists or for his agreement with that view: "The radical indeterminacy which one must henceforth admit on the level of elementary phenomena [particles] adds to the bewilderment of a mind which more readily parts with visual representation than with an abandonment of determinism."[39]

This situation meant for Gilson a possible parting with the great lesson given by the Greeks to posterity that "determinism and intelligibility are but one thing." In the same breath he took the view that "we are probably at the dawn of a profound reshaping of our traditional concepts of space, and at a price compared with which the transformation which our notions of time had to undergo will appear mere child's play."[40]

Gilson saw two more lessons arise from this new situation imposed by the experimental findings of the new physics. For one, they made sound hollow Kant's chief contention that the mind's categories determined the structure of the physical world. In place of the mind's dictatorship over nature, the new physics invites us, Gilson wrote, "to think of the mind as an intelligent pupil who pays the greatest attention to all which its master chooses to tell him, but no less surprisingly, always finds an answer to his questions." The measure of the surprise, and here Gilson once more quoted De Broglie, "appears far greater than said now and then."[41]

Here Gilson, the philosopher, felt that he could go De Broglie, the physicist, one better. The history of philosophy, old and recent, contains surprising examples of the anticipation by philosophers of ideas found very useful by physicists. Ancient speculations about atoms were one example. Another was the suggestion made by Boutroux in 1873 that "a certain radical contingency of fundamental phenomena was not incompatible with the idea of law as long as laws were given the value of statistical truth." In view of this, Gilson felt entitled to speak of Boutroux's *La contingence des lois de la nature* as a work whose "prophetic significance increases in the measure in which time separates it from us."[42] Such was Gilson's belated discovery of a work he was to recall as hardly having been read during his student days, although he had known its author as one of his senior professors of philosophy.

Gilson wisely made the point that Boutroux no more anticipated undulatory mechanics as such than the ancient atomists had been forerunners to modern atomic physics. Boutroux, Gilson warned, merely meant to show to Comtean positivists that "the universe of science implied contingency at the very origin of its necessity."[43] This was better said than reasoned. The phrase as such amounted to a beautiful morning haze. It is relatively easy to figure out what Gilson could not have meant to convey with that pleasing vision. In speaking of nature's "very origin," Gilson could have meant its creation by God, who of course was free to create or not to create, and who was equally free to give reality to any of an infinite number of possible worlds. In that sense the physical world implied a radical contingency at its very origin.

But insofar as Gilson was speaking of a contingency which science could ascertain at the very origin of nature—or of its laws, for that matter—he could not have meant the origin as specified above. That kind of origin can be seen only with the eyes of metaphysics, but never by those of science. Gilson might have spotted this problem had he reflected on the steady state theory, which had for five years been avidly discussed and given wide publicity when, in 1953, he contributed that essay of his to the De Broglie Festschrift. In that theory, hydrogen atoms were postulated to arise at a steady rate, out of nothing and without a Creator. In other words, the theory provided an example of a thorough miscon-struction of what radical contingency was about.

Boutroux himself never made clear in his book what he really meant by radical contingency. He certainly implied much more than the kind of chance which Aristotle and the medievals had admitted, namely, the absence of a final cause when two separate chains of efficient causes interact with one another. To call those chains independent just because they were separate was already less than precise talk. But the real question was, were they truly independent from one another? Even in 1952 the idea of the expansion of the universe conjured up an erstwhile state of affairs for the physical universe from which all physical phenomena as observed today were a strict consequence. Following the discovery, in 1965, of the 3°K background radiation, much physical research was done on this view of a fully coherent physical universe where the initial conditions strictly determine all subsequent stages. Clearly, here too a philoso-pher could have stolen the march on the physicists had he carefully defined his terms, especially that most crucial term of "contingency".

For just as Boutroux could be seen as a prophet just because he was studiedly vague on a crucial point, T. H. Huxley, a contemporary of Boutroux, would not have missed the point had he been careful with his words. In a famous passage, where Huxley celebrated the strict interconnection of all processes of nature, including the seemingly chaotic interaction among vapor molecules in the midst of sea waves splashing on a rocky shore, he confused strict mechanical interaction with perfect measurability. Of course, every classical physicist knew that his actual measurements always implied some imperfection, owing mainly to friction. Boutroux made much of that imperfection, not realizing that it was merely a matter of practical deficiency in measurements.[44]

Such a deficiency is a far cry from the absence of ontological causality. The deficiency does not cease to be merely a practical one simply because physicists had to learn that as long as they work with wave-particle duality, or as long as they have to use non-commutative algebra coupled with Planck's constant, they cannot achieve perfect accuracy in measuring physical interactions. In speaking of this predicament of theirs, most modern physicists had been studiedly vague, if not wilfully antiontological.[45] Gilson failed to see this.

But this is precisely the kind of vision which a metaphysician should provide as he rightly tells the physicist, as Gilson did at the conclusion of his essay, that "if a physicist does not want to listen to the answers of metaphysics, he should not pose questions to it."[46] Needless to say, most physicists are utterly uninterested in what metaphysics may tell them, even if the word "metaphysics" is replaced by such more palatable terms to them as "epistemology" or "philosophy". But that rara avis, the physicist interested in metaphysical problems, deserves at least a careful specification of crucial terms as he listens to the metaphysician. And even more so is this the case when one deals with Christians bewildered by the onrush of the ever more spectacular discoveries of science about the physical universe. For, invariably, scientists present those discoveries in pseudo-metaphysical wrappings.

Only a metaphysician with solid training in one of the exact sciences should undertake the task of removing those useless and at times positively dangerous wrappings. Otherwise the content will not be properly set apart, and something of the wrapping will be mistaken for the content. Gilson had in mind some such task when, close to 80 years old, and having spent half a century studying Thomas, he pondered the future of Thomism. For in the early 1960's, Thomism was no longer the rage of the day, as it had been in the 1930's and 1940's. Tastes in philosophy can change as fast as they do everywhere else. But something more serious may have been at play in the sudden change of Thomism's fortunes—something which could be spotted by a careful observer.

For nothing is more unfortunate for any entity, including philosophical perception, than to be systematically mistaken for a variety of entities which are very different in nature in spite of all appearances to the contrary. Such a mistake was presented as genuine progress in *The Thomist Spectrum*, published in 1966, in which the chapter on Gilson came to a close with the phrase: "But the fact that there actually exists a numerous and outward-looking body of Thomists to be transformed has been very largely the achievement of Jacques Maritain and Etienne Gilson."[47] Most of these Thomists became transformed before long, and in the process the general perception about Thomism changed drastically.

Here, transcendental Thomism as such is not at issue. The silent treatment given by prominent transcendental Thomists to the universe should be a warning about their not too covert subservience to Kant.[48] With Kant they also claim to be "scientific" though mostly in terms of rhetoric or by cultivating the so-called "soft" sciences (psychology, sociology, and evolutionary theories where rhetoric has a free run), or by mistaking philosophies of science for science itself. Typically, in the entire *Thomist Spectrum* there is not one paragraph on science, and consequently the word "science" is not to be found in its ample subject index. Gilson, however, had the "hard" sciences in mind (physics and biology) when he brought his intellectual autobiography to a close with a chapter on the future of Thomism.

There Gilson argued nothing less than that "the future of a Christian philosophy will therefore depend on the existence or absence of theologians equipped with a scientific training, no doubt limited but genuine and, within its own limits, sufficient for them to follow with understanding such lofty dialogues not only in mathematics and physics but also in biology and wherever the knowledge of nature reaches the level of demonstration."[49] Clearly, he did not want those theologians to be bothered with "soft" sciences. The reason, indicated by his "therefore", is related to his realization that Aristotelian or Thomist metaphysics can no longer take its starting point from Aristotle's world or science, which was still the world and science of Thomas but is a far cry from the world of the 20th century. By "such lofty dialogues" Gilson meant panel discussions to which he and a few other prominent Thomists had been invited to discuss matters of common interest with prominent physicists, such as notions of space, time, matter, causality, and so forth.

The urgency of the task was paramount in Gilson's eyes. He rightly feared that if there are no such theologians around, there will be a runaway increase in the number of those who laugh on hearing Aristotle's definition of motion as "the act of that which is in potency, inasmuch as it is in potency." They laugh, Gilson remarked, because, their thinking having been conditioned by the physics of Newton and Einstein, they do not realize that Aristotle spoke as a philosopher and not as a scientist as he gave that profound definition of becoming, or the generalized meaning of motion. However, if there are no competent theologians ready to incorporate the findings of modern science into Christian philosophy, "there will inevitably be Christian men of science to incorporate the teaching of theology with that of positive science. The result is likely to be, as can be seen today, a mixture of science fiction and of mock theology." Prophetic words, indeed, to which Gilson added, a few pages later: "The really dangerous persons are less real scientists than Christians with a smattering of science."[50] They are the ones most incapable of noticing what plagues scientists themselves: "Wild extrapolation is the pet sin of the wrong kind of imagination in scientific research."[51].

In saying all this, Gilson remained true to himself on two points very essential to his thinking. One was the idea of Christian philosophy. This came through in his insistence that the task in question was to be done by theologians. "The critique of the philosophical reasons by the reason of the theologian is one of its necessary functions."[52] The other was his methodical realism, his resolve to go back to the real, to the physical, at every turn of the metaphysical exercise. This meant metaphysics always had to run a risk—that of making an appraisal of the specifics which the science of a given time added to one's immediate grasp of the real. That appraisal would be subject to constant reappraisals in terms of the development of the sciences. Thus Gilson could rightly give one of his most penetrating warnings: "All metaphysics become outdated because of their physics: that of Saint Thomas (and of Aristotle himself) because the Aristotelian physics became obsolete, that of Descartes because of the Cartesian mechanics, that of Kant because of the Newtonian physics, and that of the last born, Bergson, who lived just long enough to realize that he could not catch up with the physics of relativity."[53]

Almost ten years after he had penned these lines, Gilson, then in his mid-eighties, gave a vast example of what can and should be done. In his *From Aristotle to Darwin and Back Again*,[54] he came to grips with the question of whether it was still reasonable to look at the actions of living beings as evincing some purpose. This is not the place to give even a brief summary of that book full of sparkling phrases, a wealth of data, and rigorous analysis of some basic terms constantly used by biologists, both ancient and modern. In fact the constancy of their falling back on registering the presence of some goal which organisms seem to strive for, made Gilson conclude that one of the constants of biology is that references to purpose in biology are unavoidable.[55]

But in the same book Gilson also had to voice a conviction of his which could serve as a prime guideline in his program of keeping alive Thomism by constantly immersing it in the latest development of science. "Science is revolutionary," Gilson quoted Claude Bernard, and then in the same breath he added: "I am profoundly convinced that philosophy is not."[56] Such a conviction must imply the recognition of two important consequences. One has to recognize that no study of science, not even of its very latest developments, can have for its fruit revolutionary implications for the perennial philosophy. The latter can gather from such study only new illustrations, however startling, of very old truths. And since each age, or rather generation, has its own preferred variations of phraseology, those new illustrations should seem of utmost pedagogical value. This is to be still learned by many Thomists who often speak as if they were brought up in the waning of the Middle Ages.

While this can be expected to change for the better, realism forces one to recognize a rather dispiriting feature of human behavior: Human nature is itching for novelties. Gilson himself once dejectedly registered the unwillingness even of Thomists to hold on to this or that well-established truth, even historical truth.[57] Consequently, somewhat illusory should seem Gilson's dream of what he called "a religious order of scientists."[58] He had in mind a close collaboration among a handful of theologians well trained in the sciences.

Collaboration of this kind may be a pleasing subject for conversation, but it would be a most difficult thing to bring about.[59] Even the collaboration between Aquinas and Albertus Magnus was not what Gilson had in mind. Yet they were geniuses, and saints for good measure. Still, as Gilson the teacher demonstrated, it is possible to produce like-minded pupils who, even if their influence suffers a temporary eclipse, will serve as guideposts for a post-eclipse generation searching for beacons better than the ones who presented the twilight of eclipse as the dawn of a new day. For if it is true, as Gilson aptly put it, that "no time is real except the present, and hence modernism is an ever open possibility,"[60] the converse also must be true: the sun of true philosophy never sets once it has risen.

Gilson's eyes remained wide open to the richness of the light spread by that sun, even in his old age. One can only speculate about the powerful antidote he would have left to a posterity drunk with speculations about artificial intelligence, had he had more strength left as he wrote his *Linguistics and Philosophy*.[61] Even in its philosophical purism, that book remains a mine of arguments against those who think that language, and with it the human intellect, is a mere binary counter with feedback mechanisms. It suggests a "what might have been," a part of Gilson's third great discovery that was only partially achieved. I mean his discovery of the importance of science for philosophical health. Yet even as it stands in its incomplete grandeur, that discovery of Gilson's can take its rightful place next to his two other discoveries: the reality of Thomism as *Christian* philosophy, and the priority which, in Thomas' philosophy, existence has over essence.

The objects of these two discoveries have an intimate connection with science. True philosophy is Christian, even historically. And so is science, which saw its only viable birth in terms of Christian faith. And insofar as science cannot touch on the essence of anything and cannot even say anything about existence, science must keep at least an indirect tie with that philosophy and faith if it is to account for itself in a better than cursory way.

---

[1] C. J. Edie, "The Writings of Etienne Gilson Chronologially Arranged," in *Mélanges offertes à Etienne Gilson de l'Académie française* (Toronto: Pontifical Institute of Mediaeval Studies; Paris: J. Vrin, 1959), pp. 15-58. Equally rare are entries relevant to science in the full listing of Gilson's publications, *Etienne Gilson. A Bibliography. Une bibilographie,* by Margaret McGrawth, that appeared as "The Etienne Gilson Series 3" (Toronto: Pontifical Institute of Medieval Studies, 1982).

[2] "Science, Philosophy, and Religious Wisdom," *Proceedings of the American Catholic Philosophical Association*, Twenty-sixth Annual Meeting, 15 April 1952, Washington, D.C., pp. 5-13 (in Edie, entry 591). Reprinted in *A Gilson Reader: Selected Writings of Etienne Gilson*, ed. A. C. Pegis (Garden City: N.Y.: Doubleday, 1957), pp. 212-221. Much the same material also appeared in the same year as "Religious Wisdom and Scientific Knowledge," in *Christianity in an Age of Science,* Canadian Broadcasting Corporation, n. d., pp. 15-22 (in Edie, entry 583). This essay was republished in

Christianity and Culture, ed. J. Stanley Murphy (Baltimore: Helicon Press, 1960), pp. 112-119.

[3] "The Role of Science in Catholic Education," in *Disputed Questions in Education* (New York and Toronto, 1955), pp. 7-16 (in Edie, entry 629).

[4] One is an essay on the cosmogony of Bernardus Sylvestris (in Edie, entry 150) from 1928; another is a contribution to a Festschrift in honor of Louis de Broglie, a Nobel Laureate in physics (in Edie, entry 603).

[5] See L. Shook, *Etienne Gilson* (Toronto: Pontifical Institute of Mediaeval Studies, 1984), p. 389.

[6] *The Philosopher and Theology*, tr. Cécile Gilson (New York: Random House, 1962).

[7] Ibid., p. 18.

[8] Ibid., p. 30.

[9] Ibid., p. 37.

[10] See my *Uneasy Genius: The Life and Work of Pierre Duhem* (Dordrecht: Nijhoff, 1984), p. 335.

[11] *The Philosopher and Theology*, p. 18.

[12] Shook, *Etienne Gilson*, p. 18.

[13] One of the two editors, Paul Tannery, was in fact the leading historian of science in France.

[14] Particularly influential were the publications of L. Thorndike, C. H. Haskins, and M. Clagett.

[15] E. Gilson, *The Spirit of Medieval Philosophy*, tr. A. H. C. Downes (New York: Charles Scribner's Sons, 1936), p. 366.

[16] *The Spirit of Medieval Philosophy*, pp. 367-68.

[17] E. Gilson, *History of Christian Philosophy in the Middle Ages* (New York: Random House, 1954), pp. 515-18.

[18] E. Gilson, *The Philosopher and Theology*, pp. 177-78.

[19] Gilson, *History of Christian Philosophy*, pp. 357-58.

[20] For text and discussion, see my book, *The Savior of Science* (Washington, D.C.: Regnery Gateway, 1988), pp. 51-54.

[21] See Gilson's essay, "The Intelligence in the Service of Christ the King," in *Gilson Reader*, pp. 31-48.

[22] This statement of Bergson's was carried to the four corners of the world in countless translations of his *Evolution créatrice*, in which Gilson saw much, perhaps too much, redeeming value. See *The Philosopher and Theology*, pp. 108-109.

[23] As I argued in my book, *The Savior of Science* (Washington, D. C.: Regnery Gateway; Edinburgh: Scottish Academic Press, 1988), and especially in its ch. 2, "The Birth that Saved Science."

[24] My first major encounter with Gilson's thought took place during the sixteen hours of a flight from New York to Tokyo in November 1973. By then I had already written my *Science and Creation: From Eternal Cycles*

to an Oscillating Universe (Edinburgh: Scottish Academic Press, 1974), but it was my reading of Gilson's *The Unity of Philosophical Experience* during that flight that gave me the insight into the correlation between a realist metaphysics (which issues in a demonstration of the existence of God) and a truly creative method in science. This theme I developed in my Gifford Lectures, given in 1975 and 1976 at the University of Edinburgh under the title *The Road of Science and the Ways to God* (Edinburgh: Scottish Academic Press; Chicago: University of Chicago Press, 1978).

[25] *History of Christian Philosophy in the Middle Ages*, p. 520.

[26] See *Uneasy Genius*, pp. 352 and 359-60.

[27] E. Gilson, *The Unity of Philosophical Experience* (New York: Charles Scribner's Sons, 1937), p. 293. Three pages earlier, Gilson quoted with approval Lenin's evaluation of Duhem as a successor to "Humean agnosticism." Clearly, very good French Catholics are apt to turn themselves into a very quarrelsome lot.

[28] R. J. Henle, *Saint Thomas and Platonism: A Study of Plato and Platonic Texts in the Writings of Saint Thomas* (The Hague: Martinus Nijhoff, 1956).

[29] In fact it is possible to do excellent theology while being stuck with less than adequate philosophizing. Saint Augustine is a case in point. Duhem may have overlooked the fact that, as Gilson points out, Thomas' theology gave a unifying force to his apparently syncretistic philosophical material. See *The Philosopher and Theology*, p. 103.

[30] "Science, Philosophy, and Religious Wisdom," in *Gilson Reader*, p. 213.

[31] Ibid., p. 215.

[32] Ibid., p. 214.

[33] Ibid., pp. 214-15.

[34] Ibid., p. 215.

[35] Ibid., p. 216.

[36] Ibid., p. 218.

[37] E. Gilson, "En marge d'un text," in *Louis de Broglie: Physicien et penseur* (Paris: Albin Michel, 1953), pp. 153-58.

[38] L. De Broglie, *Physics and Microphysics*, tr. M. Davidson (New York: Harper and Brothers, 1955), pp. 208-09.

[39] Gilson, "En marge d'un texte," p. 154.

[40] Ibid., p. 154.

[41] Ibid., p. 155.

[42] Ibid., p. 156.

[43] Ibid., p. 157.

[44] See my article, "The Cosmic Myth of Chance," originally published in German in *Zur Kritik der wissenschaftlichen Rationalität. Festschrift Kurt Hübner* (Munich: Karl Alber, 1986); in English, in my book *The Only Chaos and Other Essays* (Lanham, MD.: University Press of America, 1990), pp. 17-30.

[45] See my essay, "Determinism and Reality," in *The Great Ideas Today* (Chicago: Encyclopedia Britannica, 1990), pp. 273-302.

[46] Gilson, "En marge d'un texte," p. 158.

[47] Helen James John, *The Thomist Spectrum* (New York: Fordham University Press, 1966), p. 49.

[48] A point developed in my Père Marquette Lecture, 1992, under the title *Universe and Creed* (Milwaukee: Marquette University Press, 1992).

[49] *The Philosopher and Theology*, p. 221.

[50] Ibid., pp. 221-22 and 227.

[51] Ibid., p. 225.

[52] Ibid., p. 227.

[53] Ibid., p. 232.

[54] Translated by John Lyon, with an introduction by S. L. Jaki (Notre Dame, In.: University of Notre Dame Press, 1984).

[55] Ibid. This is thematically developed in Ch. 6, "The Constants of Biophilosophy."

[56] Ibid., p. xx.

[57] For evidence, here I can refer only to my memory of having seen this remark of Gilson somewhere in his latest writings.

[58] Ibid., p. 221.

[59] My call for a Duhem Society of Catholic Historians of Science, coupled with a plea that these historians support one another's research, a plea made at the University of Notre Dame in the Spring of 1983, produced no results. A major prerequisite for such a Society is a readiness on the part of those concerned to place no premium on being accepted by their secularist counterparts. They should learn from what happened to Gilson himself (or to Maritain, for that matter). Both were at best politely listened to at Harvard, Princeton, the University of Indiana, and so forth, but their philosophy was never seriously taken up by the luminaries there. Did Whitehead ever express any regret for not having offered a single paragraph on Gilson, even after the two had very pleasant conversations at Harvard in the mid-1930's and even before?

[60] Ibid., p. 222.

[61] Translated by John Lyon, University of Notre Dame Press, 1989.

10

The Nonsense and Sense
of Science

Science is organized common sense. Of that foremost commodity which is common sense there was little in Thomas Henry Huxley who coined that most useful definition of science. Huxley was most nonsensical when he boasted, at the death of his only son at the tender age of seven, that the certainty of the inverse sqaure law of gravitation gave him more assurance about the meaning of existence than all Christian talk about an eventual resurrection to eternal life. For it made no sense—logical sense, that is—to weigh a law of physical science against any proposition with an imponderable object, be it the very reality of anything on earth or in heaven. The laws of physics, or of science in general, are about the empirical or quantitative properties of things and never about the existence of anything material or non-material, not even about the inverse square law as a mere conceptualization. The notion of quantity is an idea that cannot be weighed in a scale or measured with a caliper.

Wilful oversight of the inability of the scientific method to cope with the phrases, "to be or not to be" or "thou shalt not do," has be-

First published in *A Warning Is Given*, essays by Pope John Paul II *et al.*, ed. H. Owen (Woodstock, Va.: Apostolatus Uniti, 1992), pp. 43-46. Reprinted with permission.

come the epidemic of modern culture. One is, in fact, faced with something more than an epidemic, if this were not bad enough. When an ordinary epidemic runs its fearsome course, the corpses scattered right and left serve as so many alarm bells that only the deaf and blind can ignore. It is different with the intellectual and moral disease triggered by the foregoing nonsensical understanding of science. Symptoms of mature scientific culture are seen in the widespread beliefs that everything is relative and that things happen for no cause in ultimate analysis.

Both these most mistaken beliefs are all the more dangerous because they are wrapped in science in the name of which almost anything can be sold nowadays and with the greatest ease. Yet the theory of relativity is the most absolutist theory ever proposed in the history of physics. Far from having to do anything with causality, quantum theory has for its basic claim the realization, very sensible in itself, that no one can cut thinner than the thinnest instrument at his disposal. This gem of common sense was turned half a century ago into the nonsensical inference that an interaction that cannot be measured 'exactly', cannot take place 'exactly' in the very different sense of that word whenever it is invested with an ontologically causal sense. Hence the 'scientifically' legitimized celebration of randomness and the supreme accolades paid to all sorts of behavioral and misbehavioral patterns when their practitioners form a statistically 'significant' number, which may mean something very different from true significance.

The cultural epidemic germinated in terms of Darwinian ideology is better known, because whatever one's inability to intellectualize one's misigivings about patent nonsense, no one can function without full trust in one's acting for a purpose. But it is precisely that sense of purpose which defeats not so much evolutionary theories but Darwinian ideology. Its champions throw common sense to the wind as they devote their lives to the purpose of proving that there is no purpose, which is the standing or falling tenet of the Darwinian interpretation of the origin of man, life, and universe.

Indeed, whenever an evolutionary scientist with Darwinist ideology is seized with the urge of being consistent, a hallmark of common sense, he has no choice but to close ranks with the High Priests of Darwinism. In our days, it has become their dubious privilege to take the moral sting out of AIDS by taking it for the kind of biological epidemic that decimates each and every species time and again and which therefore should be borne with equanimity. Against such 'reasoners' only that reasoning is effective which is one's existential resolve to stick to common sense through thick and thin even when that menacing growth is bathed in academic sunshine.

The same is true when one is faced with high-faluting claims of genetic engineering. Common sense is needed in a special measure if sufficient echo is to be produced by the insistent question: "Who will engineer those who claim to themselves the role of engineering the rest?"[1]

Common sense is especially needed to resist the lure of a runaway technology which makes modern capitalism so successful by providing a staggeringly vast flow of ever new products and depleting beyond repair natural resources. Whatever the idiocy of some Greens who try to reinstate a bucolic past, the snuffing out of progressive man by his scientific progress has become a distinct possibility.

In the face of these threats more is needed, however, than an elemental reassertion of common sense. For as long as one lives in a universe of elements, that is, of specifically quantitative material units, whatever else they may be in ultimate analysis, a quantitative know-how is absolutely necessary to cope with problems which, however philosophical and ethical in their deepest aspect, pose challenges that are quantitative, and therefore scientific and techno-logical. Those who ignore this are so many babes in the woods, genuinely innocent as they may be. Unfortunately innocence of this type is all too often a tool of sinful self-serving, aimed at avoiding the need of facing up to pressing tasks.

Among those tasks is the acquisition of proper scientific training by as many as possible. To be sure, as was noted at the outset, skill with quantitities can become a boomerang if it does not to go hand in hand with a clear awareness of what cannot be delivered in quantitative terms. While all quantities can be turned into patterns, no amount of them would ever issue in principles. To know this, and to hold fast to this, is the very condition of never turning science as common sense into a fearsome nonsense.

To gain strength for taking that posture one can derive enormous assurance from at least one point about the relation of science and that common sense which has for its indispensable source the Christian faith, this apparently most nonsensical form of religion. Exact science owes its birth to Christian belief in creation out of nothing and in time.

This is not the place to give details. A brief reference is, however, in order to the one who first saw this culturally most important point. He was Pierre Duhem (1861-1916), an outstanding French physicist of the turn of the century.[2] It was he who, through heroic historical research and fearless pursuit of truth, spotted the medieval Christian origins of modern science. He also viewed his illustrious career as an apostolate to common sense. Study of his life and work should indeed seem a most effective means of acquiring the skill (intellectual and moral) needed to keep struggling for the sanity of science when, in our times, it seems to be enveloped in nonsense, intellectual as well as ethical.

---

[1] This question of Paul Tillich, aired at the Massachussetts Institute of Technology at its centenary celebration, is, of course, a variant on Juvenal's "quis custodiat ipsos custodes" (Satire VI), aimed at the duplicity of male sexual behavior.

[2] See my *Uneasy Genius: The Life and Work of Pierre Duhem* (1984; 2nd paperback ed., Dordrecht: Kluwer Academic Publishers, 1987), or my *Scientist and Catholic: Pierre Duhem* (Christendom Press: Front Royal VA.: 1991), half of which is a selection from various writings of Duhem.

11

The Mind:
Its Physics or Physiognomy?

The book begins with no small encouragement: The reader may safely be satisfied with the verbal explanations that follow the mathematical formulas—not a few in a very long book. This type of encouragement can in itself be trusted. In 1865 Faraday commended Maxwell as one of those very rare physicists who can translate fully "their hieroglyphics" into ordinary language. Faraday, who knew little mathematics, thanked Maxwell for giving him "a perfectly clear idea of conclusions, which though they may give me no full understanding of the steps of your process, gave the results neither above nor below the truth, and so clear in character that I can think and work from them."

The process in question meant the genesis of the electromagnetic theory of light, one of the greatest feats in physics. Without that theory there would be no computers, nor anything of the vast technological backup (telephones, radio-satellites, fiber optics, lasers) that enable the owner (today their number is legion) of a personal computer to feel like an emperor. Some of them feel so elated as

A review essay of *The Emperor's New Mind: Concerning Computers, Minds, and the Laws of Physics* (New York: Oxford University Press, 1989), xiii + 466pp, by Roger Penrose. First published in *Reflections* 10/2 (1991). Reprinted with permission.

to cultivate a mock humility tied to the prospect that they soon will become "humble" slaves of an artificial intelligence (AI) already in embryo in their desktop computers.

The first of the two major contentions of this book is to discredit this prospect, exhilarating to a few, ominous to many. According to the author's second major contention, physics is *the* tool whereby one can unravel the mystery, not only of the brain but also of the human mind no matter how un-mathematical some of its operations may appear.

Professor Penrose makes no effort to reconcile this contention of his with his admission of a problem to which he devotes his book's last chapter, entitled "Where lies the physics of mind?" It is not overly enlightening to say that "the physics of mind" will be a radically probabilistic physics, a future mutation of present-day quantum mechanics, about which nothing specific is given. Such a physics, as will be seen later, implies an absolute improbability.

The claim that physics is *the* means for the ultimate unraveling of the mind and the admission of not knowing in any specific form that physics represent a pair of not too subtly contradictory propositions. The shock of this contradictoriness is not allayed by the author's enthusiastic Platonism. Professor Penrose sees in the beauty of mathematics the evidence that there is a mysteriously non-material and yet radically physical realm (no place for immortal souls in this book) in which (here the author is less specific) mathematical formulas float as if having an "etherial" and eternal existence (p. 97). This view has far less to do with mathematics than with philosophy, indeed with metaphysics.

From chapter to chapter Professor Penrose ends (at times he even begins) with conjuring up, though unintentionally, the specter of a genuinely realist metaphysics. After looking at it briefly, perhaps because disturbed by what he sees, he passes on to the next chapter as if the moment of truth could forever be postponed.

Professor Penrose's starting point is a discussion of the strong AI position. The latter rests on two assumptions. One is that all the brain's operations can be accurately modeled by digital calculations. The other is connected with Turing's universal machine which, on the face of it, can simulate all mental operations so specified as to be computable.

Yet the core of Turing's claim belongs not to physics (computability) but to metaphysics. The latter is at play if one claims that a computably complete similarity between two sets of data proves that both embody one and the same nature. Consequently, if one knows about one of the sets that it thinks (as any human can know this by mere introspection), the same property should be attributed to the other set, a mere agglomerate of electronic circuits.

Professor Penrose seems to sense the gravity as well as the arbitrariness of that brash inference from computational similarity to ontological nature. But he omits probing into it, perhaps because he recognizes a consequence ominous for his purposes: While one can write a physiognomy of the mind insofar as it has a nature (*physis*), one cannot write a physics of the mind, for the simple reason that it is not physical. For if it is, no objection can be raised against the strong AI position.

Not wishing to see this conundrum, Professor Penrose proceeds to ch. 2, a discussion of algorithms (or any form of computability) and Turing machines. He concludes that computability has a "fundamentally objective character" and that therefore it "seems to have a kind of Platonic reality of its own" (p. 70).

There is nothing new in Professor Penrose's claim that to do good mathematics demands more than machine-like operations. He himself refers to the intuitionist school initiated by Dutch mathematician Brouwer in 1924. Not much is new in Penrose's characterization of those intuitive elements as "God-given." Only five years after Brouwer, Sir James Jeans, a self-declared pantheist, graciously granted "God" the exalted role of a mathematician in the production of the universe, though certainly not its creation out of nothing. Since then poorly metaphorical references to a God, who really cannot *give* anything, have become a commonplace in the writings of leading mathematical physicists. They merely give away their not too crude materialism.

Their effort is fraught with pitfalls. Thus at the end of ch. 2, Penrose admits that "the possibility of an etherial type of existence for mental phenomena" may lend credence to the strong (that is, unabashedly materialistic) AI position, namely, that minds are machines and machines (sufficiently complex) are minds. One more evidence that idealism (Platonist or Kantian-Hegelian) is not so distant from materialism as it appears to be. This is why mathematics (abused as idealism) provides no prompting (and certainly not for Penrose in ch. 3 on mathematics and reality) to confront material reality regardless of mathematics. It is at this point that Penrose lets mind as well as body irrevocably slip through his fingers. To anyone willing to ponder this consequence it will become a foregone conclusion that in the end the proverbial emperor's fate will be in store for Penrose himself. Even more so is this the case for Martin

Gardner, who wrote the Foreword to the book, as if it needed one, and who, I suspect, might be responsible for its main title.

Instead of pondering the decisive question whether mathematical properties give rise to things or whether things come first and mathematical properties afterwards, at least in the logical sequence, Penrose further explores the meaning of "truth, proof and insight" (ch. 4) in terms of *his* Platonism. The real Plato would hardly feel at home in that chapter. For Plato, who frowned on material reality, did not take it for non-existent. Penrose, as will be seen, is most ambivalent about the existence of matter. As to the mind, he is interested in it only insofar as it can do physics, although physics must have matter on hand if its conclusions are to be taken for experimental verities.

Professor Penrose thinks that it is possible to get around the thorny problem of the flesh and blood reality of matter. Tellingly, ch. 4 comes to an end with the suggestion that "quantum effects might be used beneficially in the solving of problems or the forming of judgments" (p. 146). Once quantum mechanics, let alone a future form of it, is brought to the scene, it is impossible not to discuss its background. The latter is the continuum postulate of classical physics which robustly survives in Einstein's theory of relativity. Einstein always held that quantum theory (which he never carefully distinguished from its Copenhagen misinterpretation) is but a transitional phase in physics. Clearly then a big roadblock (Einstein's authority as a physicist) is to be removed.

Einstein's authority as a philosopher poses no problem, a point which might have come in handy for Penrose's purposes. He fails to recall Einstein's admission to Carnap, a chief physicalist, that the experience of the *now* and the sense of the continuity of personal identity based on it escape the nets of physics. Einstein added, in proof of the subtle worshiper of physics he was, that only if those experiences are explained in the terms of physics can they be taken for objectively valid realities.[1] Einstein, who never came so close to the heart of the matter as when he approvingly recalled the saying that the man of science is a poor philosopher, would have therefore wholly agreed with Penrose's transparently physicalist declaration. It is given in the beginning of ch. 5 dealing with the classical world: "While it is undoubtedly the case that the brain is exceptionally complicated as a physical system, and a vast amount about its detailed structure and relevant operation is not yet known, few would claim that it is in the *physical* principles underlying its behavior that there is any significant lack of understanding" (p. 149).

Of course, this would not be physicalism if one investigated the brain as such and not as a carrier, though not the creator, of mental processes. But this difference cannot exist for one, who like Penrose claims that matter has no unequivocal reality. His basis for this most momentous claim is, of course, that quantum mechanics has deprived matter of place. Since we cannot locate matter exactly, it cannot have an unambigous existence.

This inference is but a version of the fallacy which Heisenberg grafted on quantum mechanics at the very moment, 1927, when he unfolded its best known consequence, which he called the principle of indeterminacy. Had he called it the principle of operational inexactitude (which it really is), he might have, unwittingly, put a brake on the rapid spread of that most pernicious scientistic ideology, the Copenhagen misinterpretation of quantum mechanics. The root of that misinterpretation (parading as its most genuine, scientifically hallowed meaning) is a fallacious rush from the operational to the ontological. It can easily be spotted if Heisenberg's principle is given as follows: A physical interaction that cannot (with the actual or future tools of physics) be measured exactly, cannot take place exactly. The fallacy is that the same word, *exactly*, is first taken in an operational, and then in an ontological sense. There is no law or principle of physics, theoretical or experimental, that would justify such a somersault in logic. The only way of justifying it is to declare the questions of ontology to be so many phantoms.

However, once that fallacy is granted the road is fully open to cheating with matter, a cheating which within two generations reached literally cosmic proportions. Around 1950 steady-state theorists failed to be taken to task by physicists for their conjuring up vast amounts of hydrogen coming into existence every moment out of nothing and without a Creator. Nor did physicists, mostly brainwashed by the Copenhagen misinterpretation of quantum mechanics, protest when in the 1980s Professor Guth of MIT took the lead in claiming that quantum mechanics allows the production of entire universes *literally* out of nothing![2] They did not even care to note that the term "universes" is a contradiction in terms. Either two universes interact with one another, or they do not. If they do, they form one single universe; if not, a physicist in one can never know (barring a supernatural revelation) about the existence of the other. Even in that case he cannot measure anything about that other universe.

Of course, if quantum mechanics can account "ontologically" for the universe, it can perform the same trick with the mind as well. It is indeed sad that Professor Penrose sees only "mystery" that can be resolved by "quantum magic" throughout ch. 6, the longest in his book. He credits quantum mechanics with the possibility of free choices, unmindful of the now half-a-century-long admission of Eddington, the first to try that magic, that it is nonsense nonetheless.

At any rate, ontological questions either about the universe, or about the mind, or about the freedom of the will cannot be expected to come readily within view toward the end of the 20th century. It still carries the consequences of its having applauded, at its very beginning, a William James for his claim that concern for ontology is the most sinistrous aberration which orthodox Christianity had inflicted on the human mind. Such is the tacit background for an account of cosmology in ch. 7. Its sole purpose is to show that because cosmic processes are unidirectional, one has on hand the explanation of the mind's perception of an irreversible sequence from past through present to the future. Nowhere does Penrose confront puny man's stupendous ability to grasp the universe, or the totality of things, both philosophically and scientifically. Was he afraid to conjure up the consequences of Aquinas' perception of "homo capax universi"[3]?

The short ch. 8 on quantum gravity, this wishfully ultimate form of quantum theory, serves but the same physicalist explanation of the mind: "We must come back to our original question. How does all this relate to the physics which governs the actions of our brains? What could it have to do with our thoughts and with our feelings? To attempt some kind of answer, it will be necessary first to examine something of how our brains are actually constructed. I shall return afterwards to what I believe to be the fundamental question: what kind of new *physical* action is likely to be involved when we consciously think or perceive?" (p. 371).

Answers to these questions are offered in the last two chapters of which the first, "real brains and model brains" ends on the remark that "a plausible case can be made that there is an essential *non-*algorithmic ingredient to (conscious) thought processes" (p. 404). Anyone expecting at this point a turn to metaphysics will be rudely disappointed. In the last chapter, true to his original premises, Penrose looks for a super-physics (superior even to algorithms) to protect his overriding claim that physics is *the* tool whereby thought processes can and should be explained.

According to Professor Penrose's crystal ball, this super- (and obviously very superb) physics will be a super-probability theory with a radical randomness built into it. What does Professor Penrose have in mind? If he thinks of radical randomness as an absence of ontological causality, he has to come clean as a philosopher, not as a physicist. If he thinks of an ultimate chaos with no stable, that is, non-chaotic parameters, he throws overboard all statistical physics, classical and modern. Is is rather sad that it fell to an entomologist, W. R. Thompson, F. R. S., to call a spade a spade by declaring that "a world of pure chance has no positive intelligible content." He did so half a century ago in a book published in London (Longmans, Green) with a most appropriate title: *Science and Commonsense.*[4] Prominent physicists still may catch up, however belatedly. If they do they will realize that, as was stated at the outset, a radically probabilistic physical theory is absolutely improbable.

Once they realize this they may ponder why the fundamental constants of physics, that are indispensable ingredients in all statistical formalism used in physics, are so specific. Are they so because the specific categories of the mind dictate them to be so? If such is the case, physicists might simply close their laboratories and repose forever at the feet of Immanuel Kant, a hopeless bungler in science. If however the mind has no choice but to take reality as it is independently of the mind, then the only solid basis has been recovered for a sane discussion of the mind-body relationship.

But then one is in a domain which is philosophy and not physics. Disregard of philosophy can, however, be ridiculously disastrous even in physics. An example is Penrose's musing: "How can concrete reality become abstract and mathematical? This is perhaps the other side of the coin to the question of how abstract mathematical concepts can achieve an almost concrete reality in Plato's world. Perhaps in *some* sense, the two worlds are actually the *same*?" (p. 430) (Italics added).

As one may expect after already more than 400 pages full of subtle evasiveness in the face of decisive questions, Penrose fails to specify the crucial words, "in *some* sense." In speaking of "some chicken, some neck," Winston Churchill, neither a physicist nor a philosopher, succeeded much better in coming clean about what he meant by "some." Professor Penrose uses that word as an enigmatic wrapper to sell within it not a riddle but a plain mystery mongering. He has outstanding models among scientists in that most dubious game. Niels Bohr, a chief architect of the Copenhagen misinterpretation of quantum mechanics had special fondness for that most evasive of all words.

On the next page Penrose contrasts determinism with strong determinism, leaving the word "strong" in limbo. He generates no clarity as he speaks of "really random." Is it then to be expected that his future "super-physics" will make possible the trick of printing pound-notes out of nothing? Is the purpose of doing "superb" physics or mathematics to aim at proving that one can eat one's cake and still have it?

This is not to suggest that Penrose perceived the irony: His super-physics must be able to do that trick if he can also emphatically claim in way of a grand conclusion: "It is only the phenomenon of consciousness that can conjure up a putative 'theoretical' universe into actual existence" (p. 448). The conjuring up of legally valid sterling-pound notes by mere thinking about them should seem a trifle compared with coming up with the universe itself in such a "conscious" way.

No one has so far raised that universe to a higher pedestal than John Henry Newman when he declared to a university audience: "There is but one thought greater than the universe, and that is the thought of its Maker."[5] It may therefore be appropriate, in this year of the centenary of his death, to have recourse to his insights even in connection with the topic of this review essay.

After all, Newman is one of those rare divines who could talk with competence about the sciences. As an undergraduate he presented himself for a double first in mathematics and classics. He failed to acquit himself creditably not because of lack of competence but because of exhaustion. For the next dozen or so years, or up to the year (1833) when he gave his unreserved attention to a superior "kindly light," he kept buying and reading "superb" books on mechanics, calculus, and astronomy. But he never took science, or rather the almost invariably dubious philosophies tagged on science, for a guide in reasoning. And he certainly did not take such a guide in respect to the kind of reasoning that bears on the human mind's eternal individual destiny.

He was fully aware of the disastrous cultural impact of those "philosophies." About Darwinism (which he never failed to keep apart from the reality of evolution, however poorly explained by science, and with which he was ready "to go whole-hog"[6]) he wrote in 1874: "It is dreadful to think of the number of souls who will suffer while the epidemic lasts."[7] It is still raging owing to the endless pouring out of books written by first-rate biologists with not even a second-rate sensitivity to logic. As one so intent on the reality and effects of original sin, Newman would not be surprised, exceedingly pained though he would be.

Newman, of course, could not foresee the new-fangled gnosticism now marketed in superbly scientific wrappings. As one so keen on the analogies provided by earlier phases of intellectual and religious history, he would easily recognize the true physiognomy of the "gnosis" spreading from the physics and mathematics departments of leading universities. He would be pained, though not surprised, that the "gnosis" is avidly lapped up by divines who would know better, if they knew their theology, even without knowing any physics. Newman would mince no words, and would find no better words than the ones he addressed to the same university audience: "With matter it [physics] began, with matter it will end; it will never trespass into the province of mind."[8]

And if words of wisdom can nowadays be taken only if they come from the mouth of leading physicists, let me recall the statement Maxwell put in print towards the end of a most distinguished and most creative career: "One of the severest tests of the scientific mind is to discern the limits of the legitimate applications of the scientific method."[9]

In the first chapter of his book, Professor Penrose briefly recalls the problems arising for moral responsibility were the strong AI position to be found reliable. The position he offers in this book (so rich in information used for a purpose it cannot serve) as a saving of the intellect poses a far more destructive prospect for morality. The former position is an epidemic that confronts rudely the unwary, giving him thereby the opportunity to come to his senses. The latter, with its evasive sophistication, can easily numb any readiness to react, and to react vigorously to it as a pernicious threat to that human intellect which can know much more than physics, however superb, and know it, as Professor Penrose does, however superbly.

1. As recounted by Carnap himself in his "Intellectual Autobiography" written to P. A. Schilpp (ed.), *The Philosophy of Rudolf Carnap* (La Salle, Il.: The Library of Living Philosophers, 1963), pp. 37-38.

2. For documentation of this extraordinary claim made by Guth, and repeatedly, in various contexts, see my *God and the Cosmologists* (Edinburgh: Scottish Academic Press, 1989), pp. 61, 134, 138, 257-8.

3. See my article, "Thomas and the Universe," *The Thomist* 53 (1989), pp. 545-72.

4. Published in 1937; for quotation, see p. 218.

5. J. H. Newman, *The Idea of a University* (London: Longmans, Green & Co., 1888), p. 462.

6. This remark of Newman remained in manuscript until H. Johnson quoted it in his article, "The Origin of Man in the Light of Recent Research," *The Dublin Review* (July-September, 1934), p. 46.

7. See *The Letters and Diaries of John Henry Newman,* vol. 27 (Oxford: Oxford University Press, 1968), p. 43.

8. Newman, *The Idea of a University*, pp. 432-33.

9. *The Scientific Papers of J. C. Maxwell*, edited by D. W. Niven (Cambridge: University Press, 1890), vol. 2, p. 759.

12

The Last Word in Physics

Almost exactly a hundred years ago, in 1891 to be specific, the academic world witnessed the foundation of the University of Chicago, a monument to the munificence of John D. Rockefeller. The legendary millionaire would not have, however, opened his purse wide, had it not been for William Rainey Harper, himself a legend since he had obtained in 1875, at the age of nineteen, his Ph.D. from Yale with a dissertation on Indo-Iranian and Semitic languages. In Harper youthful brilliance went hand in hand with eagerness to break new academic grounds.[1] This combination could not but impress the aged Rockefeller. Less a believing Baptist than a firm advocate of social Darwinism, Rockefeller certainly believed in business enterprise pursued by a vigor[2] which demanded youth or at least the ability to think and act young well beyond typical retirement age.

The first dozen or so Annual Registers of the University of Chicago, published during Harper's presidency, exuded readiness to open up new areas in higher education. From its second year on, the University of Chicago boasted of a Department of Sociology, the first such department anywhere. The fledgling University of Chicago had on its faculty an unusual number of prominent scholars, well known for their innovative daring. Albert A.

First published in *Philosophy in Science* 5 (1993), pp. 9-32. Reprinted with permission.

Michelson, the first "head professor" of the Physics Department, had already gained world reputation through his ingenious apparatus to measure the ether drift due to the earth's motion, an experiment he began in 1884 at Case Western University.

Michelson's experiment, if successful, would have provided the first hold on that ether which no less a physicist than James Clerk Maxwell called around 1875 "the largest and probably the most uniform body of which we have any knowledge." To this rather extravagant encomium, which formed the grand conclusion of Maxwell's article, "Ether," in the famed 9th edition of the *Encyclopedia Britannica*,[3] no physicist took exception. To a man they held the ether to be real.

Yet the sole support of this unsuspecting conviction about the existence of the ether was a brave inference, though fully logical in appearance. If there were undulations, there had to be an undulating body. Being taken for the vastest physical body, the ether could loom large as the ultimate prize, the very last word in physics. The vision of such a prize could mesmerize even a Poincaré, though his commodism should have barred him from saying anything about physical reality. "The ether is all but in our grasp." So Poincaré appraised, around 1902, the latest advances in physics.[4]

Lord Kelvin, who did not wade into the philosophy of physics, felt no misgivings in speaking about the ether as if he had held it in his hands. Nor did he suspect himself to be a dubious visionary as he ascribed mutually exclusive characteristics to the ether. One was extreme rigidity, far surpassing even that of steel, to allow for the speed of light. The other was a penetrability, far exceeding that of gases at the lowest available pressure, in order to permit the rushing of celestial bodies through the ether with no perceptible loss of their kinetic energy. Kelvin felt that ether vortices, about which he kept writing highly mathematical papers, were the last word in physics. He saw the physics of his day as a clear sky with only two small clouds, soon to be dispelled.[5] Prominent professors of physics were prone to advise talented young men (nineteen year-old Max Planck was such a case) not to choose for career a field, physics, with nothing essentially new to offer.

To be sure, Michelson did not expect talented young midwestern Americans to be turned away from physics by the summary he gave in the Annual Register of the University of Chicago for 1892 of what physics was about. Yet, the summary, reprinted with no essential change in the next dozen or so Annual Registers, was a monumental echo of the conviction, widely shared among physicists at that time, that there remained not much new for them to discover. If anything was to take place in physics, it was not to be a revolution. The revolution, Michelson claimed, had just occured in the previous twenty years. He described the actual status of physics as a kind of stable state. If there were still new truths to discover they lay in the borderland of the industrial applications of physics:

> Within the last twenty years the teaching and practice of Physics have undergone a revolution more complete than in any of its sister sciences. This result may be attributed, to a very great extent, to the enormous applications to electrical industries. No other industrial application since the invention of the steam-engine has so enhanced the appreciation of the importance of exact knowledge, or given a greater impetus to the search for new truths in the unexplored regions on the borderland of science.[6]

Although the United States had just surpassed Great Britain as the world's leading industrial power and was bursting with new machines of all sorts, only a morbid technologist could have found fault with Michelson's plea for a balance between pure science and its industrial applications:

> So closely interwoven are the advances in pure science and its applications that it is difficult to say which has been of greater service to the other, but it is evident that it is as ill-advised to ignore the powerful stimulus furnished by the practical development of scientific ideas, as it is to belittle the influence which theoretical and experimental science had had on the world's material prosperity.

That Michelson bracketed theoretical science with experimental science as against their industrial application, was not, however, entirely due to the physicist's conviction about the need of proving theory through experiments. He saw a promising future for physics in its experimental branch:

> While it is never safe to affirm that the future of Physical Science has no marvels in store even more astonishing than those of the past, it seems probable that most of the grand underlying principles have been firmly established and that

further advances are to be sought chiefly in the rigorous application of these principles to all the phenomena which come under our notice.

Experimental proofs of details, minute details in fact, were left for physics as its chief objective:

It is here that the science of measurement shows its importance—where quantitative results are more to be desired than qualitative work. An eminent physicist has remarked that the future truths of Physical Science are to be looked for in the sixth decimal place.

A. Kundt, the physicist in question, was also reputed to have been so enamored of measuring as to be ready to measure even the flow of rain in the gutter.[7] Kelvin himself insisted that unless one measured a thing, one's knowledge of its reality was very meager.[8] Such a glorification, however unreflecting, of the quantitative over the ontological could easily lead to a conscious and thematic reduction of the physically real to the physicists' thinking about its quantitative aspects. In the process an ominously last word was implicitly spoken on physics itself. Such is the unintended logic of Eddington's famous claim that physics merely informed the physicist about his own footprints on the ground.[9] He did not care to consider whether by the same logic he should have considered even the ground to be the product of his mental processes. More of this dubious, if not plainly sinister, last word in physics later.

Michelson merely provided an advanced proof of Einstein's remark that "the man of science is a poor philosopher,"[10] after he had noted the need of well equipped laboratories and devotion to hard work in carrying out painstaking measurements. As a principal future target of them he specified the exploration of the world of molecules and atoms. He portrayed that world as the microscopic replica of the world of stars, a world "only one degree less complex and wonderful than the stellar universe." Then he waxed philosophical:

For the study of these almost infinitesimal systems of pigmy stars, we have no telescope nor even microscope to help us; but little by little we are constructing a powerful logical engine which is destined one day to bring the revolutions, rotations, and oscillations of these minute orbs, as clearly to

the mind's eyes, as are now the motions of worlds of the
greater visible universe.

Nothing would be more tempting than to speculate on what
Michelson meant by that "powerful logical engine." The expression (reminiscent of Francis Bacon's foolproof machine for
making discoveries with the certainty of a compass making a
circle so that even plain fools could not go wrong with it[11]) was
also self-contradictory. For if it was true that "most of the grand
underlying principles" were to be taken as "firmly established,"
it could not also be claimed that they could not assure the
eventual complete elucidation of the macro-cosmos and of the
microcosmos. But this was precisely what Michelson claimed:

> It may be said, that this in fact is our chief problem,—the
> constitution of matter; and while ultimately this is, and must
> always be, beyond the scope of our powers—it is as legit-
> imate and worthy an object to extend our knowledge step by
> step in this direction, as to increase our knowledge of the
> structure of the siderial universe even though this can never
> be completely fathomed.

There is no need to recall in detail Michelson's words on the
indispensability of a variety of good instruments to obtain "valuable information of immediate practical utility," his words of
appreciation of "the generosity of the founder of the University"
and of the "donor of the Ryerson Physical Laboratory." As a
parting shot to his general description of the courses, Michelson
added the warning about the need of being thoroughly trained in
the basics before facing up to "the vexatious annoyances encoun-
tered in entering upon an original investigation." While this was
a valuable piece of advice based on personal experience, it did
not alter the prospect of discovering anything essentially original.
Michelson's summary of the physics program in a first-rate
university constituted a pithy confession that the last word had
been uttered in physics.

No one suspected in 1892 that many new startling words
were to be soon uttered in physics. The two small clouds turned
out to be the seeds of huge storms that overturned much of the
very foundations of mechanistic or Newtonian physics. However,
those storms did not have the power to impose a most important
reconsideration. Most physicists had gone along with Whitehead
only as far as to register the undoing of the age-old idol of

Newtonian physics. From a distance of half a century there remains a classic touch to Whitehead's recall, in the company of friends, of what he had felt still another half a century earlier:

> I had a good classical education, and when I went up to Cambridge early in the 1880s my mathematical training was continued under good teachers. Now nearly everything was supposed to be known about physics that could be known— except a few spots, such as electromagnetic phenomena, which remained (or so it was thought) to be co-ordinated with Newtonian principles. But for the rest, physics was supposed to be nearly a closed subject. Those investigations to co-ordinate went on through the next dozen years. By the middle of the 1890s there were a few tremors, a slight shiver as of all not being quite secure, but no one sensed what was coming. By 1900 the Newtonian physics were demolished, done for![12]

Very few physicists, either around 1900, or for the rest of this century, drew the moral drawn by Whitehead:

> Still speaking personally, it had a profound effect on me; I have been fooled once, and I'll be damned if I'll be fooled again! Einstein is supposed to have made an epochal discovery. I am respectful and interested, but also sceptical. There is no more reason to suppose that Einstein's relativity is anything final than Newton's *Principia*. The danger is dogmatic thought; it plays the devil with religion, and science is not immune from it.[13]

Then, as if to prove how dangerous an item is the idea of final word especially when total liberation from it is proclaimed, Whitehead jumped from the frying pan into the fire where all certainty, indeed all physics, would quickly burn to ashes. On a little reflection Whitehead might have seen that his dismissal of the last word could not have any lasting meaning within the remedy he sought and recommended. The remedy consisted in being a "thoroughgoing evolutionist."

To his credit Whitehead tried to be consistent to the bitter end, an end that must have been bitter to physicists. First he declared "our notions of physical dimension" to be "absurdly arbitrary." This was followed by a parting with that greatest last word in physics, the very universe, as if it could be dispensed with without throwing all rationality to the wind. Whitehead

seemed to think that negative understatements, so dear to British
thinkers, make up for illogicality:

> It does not strike me as at all impossible that the smallest
> pebble might contain within it a universe as complex as the
> one we know, and that the universe or universes which we
> have recently begun to apprehend may be as minute in the
> scale of what lies beyond as that in the pebble to the one we
> know; or that the vastness might be as much greater in the
> opposite direction—the direction of what we consider the
> infinitely small. . .[14]

As long as one retained the least respect for logic, it was not
allowed to speak of universes. They either interacted, and in that
case they formed one single universe, or they did not interact. In
the latter case all of them, except one, remained a pure fiction of
the imagination. Whitehead did not even see that by becoming a
"thoroughgoing evolutionist" one risked ceasing to be an evolutionist at all. His next phrase, "Development, I believe, goes by
jumps," amounted to a petard ready to explode in his face. The
problem rested with the definition of jumps. Instead of giving it,
he resorted to a rhetoric resting on mere luck:

> Fifty thousand years ago, let us say, there would have been
> a lucky jump; embodied in one man, or in one family, or in
> a few families, and, after an interval another great advance
> following from that.[15]

Then, as he was forced to see the implication that the scientific
and cultural present might be one of those jumps, and might
indeed bring about our extinction, Whitehead sought refuge in
casting discredit on all scientific words insofar as they stood for
laws. For it was meaningless to speak of jumps, useful for
science, if it was also true that there were no laws of science:

> Why talk about 'the laws of nature' when what we mean is
> the characteristic behaviour of phenomena within certain
> limits at a given stage of development in a given epoch - so
> far as these can be ascertained?[16]

At this point those present should have protested in the name of
rationality. Instead, in a manner typical of many academics
ensconced in the comfort of their endowed chairs and other
amenities, they laughed.

It is not, however, a laughing matter that for the rest of the century prominent physicists have been prone to believe that they had formulated the last word in physics, or were within striking distance of it. Planck certainly looked in this way on the quantum of action. Einstein spent his last thirty years looking for that last word in physics on which even the good Lord could not improve.[17] In presenting the uncertainty principle, Heisenberg claimed that "the invalidity of the law of causality will thereby definitively be established by quantum mechanics."[18] Rutherford christened two of his great discoveries alpha and proton, names that stand for the first, and by implication, of the last thing to be found. Bohr endlessly spoke of his principle of complementarity as the final perspective about everything. Schrödinger extolled his field as "the Lord's quantum mechanics."[19] Born took the view already in the early 1930s that quantum mechanics left not much to be discovered and certainly not something really startling.

Proponents, prominent and other, of this partly smug, partly despondent feeling should have experienced a jolt in the discovery, in the early 1930s, of the positron and the neutron. Instead, those two particles that respectively revealed the realm of antimatter and opened the road toward the realm of quarks, were largely taken for the last two bricks needed to account for the construction of matter. In that smug atmosphere a quick withering was in store for those few who derived their inspiration from the vista of limitless search. Their plight received a gripping portrayal in 1935 in the novel, *The Search*, whose author, C.P. Snow, had just begun to focus his literary talents on the scientific community of which he was an insider. In that novel a physicist voices his resentment about the necessity of parting with "the tradition of limitless search" in which he had been brought up.[20]

The discovery of the first muon and the first pion in the late 1930s and the late 1940s, respectively, did not dissipate that atmosphere of smugness. A proof of this can be found in the book, *The Principles of Modern Physics*, by R. B. Leighton, professor at Caltech. Destined to be widely used as an advanced text, it had to be at least two years behind the times when first published in 1959. One wonders, however, whether a brief reference in it to the latest surprise—the overthrow of parity—would have prevented its author from claiming that "with the rapid advances that are being made in particle physics, perhaps it is not too much to expect that in a few more decades all physical phenomena will be equally well understood."[21] The many students of Leighton's book could also read there its author's confident prediction that in view of the rapid advances in quantum electrodynamics only more powerful mathematical techniques were needed to derive from first principles all the data listed in the handbooks of physics and chemistry.

Tellingly, it was about that time, and also at the California Institute of Technology, that predictions were made by Murray Gell-Mann about the omega particle, etymologically too the conceivably very last word in physics. It should seem therefore ironical that eventually Murray Gell-Mann was to make the important breakthrough toward the realm of quarks, a realm well beyond the omega particle and, what it was supposed to crown, the eightfold-way of fundamental particles. The height of the irony came, however, when in 1976 Murray Gell-Mann promised a 2000-strong audience that perhaps within a few months, but certainly within a few years, he would be able to show why the system of fundamental particles as based on quarks with color, charm, and flavor, is necessarily what it is and cannot be anything else.[22] A more radically last word in physics, and a last word more radically mistaken, could not have been offered.

Before broaching the reasons for that fundamentally mistaken character of the project of Murray Gell-Mann in particular and of similar projects in general, a word is in order about those physicists who seemingly held out an endless search in physics. The idea of such an apparently endless search could be seen contained in the musings of L. W. Alvarez that fundamental particle research is like finding another layer in an onion once a layer of it has been peeled off.[23] The same impression could be gained from Oppenheimer's remark that the only truth about fundamental particles is that none of them is fundamental. But in the same context Oppenheimer also stated as the physicist's fondest hope to find eventually a unique and necessary order in that realm of fundamental particles which is so new and so much more complicated than we thought even five years ago, or in the late 1950s. Since he looked for a necessary order, he could not also be justified in stating that the order was not to be true a priori.[24]

A similar inconsistency marked Heisenberg's hopes, voiced in 1959, that in two years he would definitely be able to say yes or no about the theory of fundamental particles based only on assumptions of symmetry.[25] More modestly, he held out the hope that in the not too distance future we shall be able to write down a single equation from which will follow the properties of matter in general.[26] No such final equation is dangled before the eyes of the readers of S. Weinberg's *Dreams of a Final Theory*.[27] On the contrary, he insists that the final theory need not have a detailed mathematical form. Nor does he expect the final theory to put an end to theoretical physics. He does not join the chorus of those who see the final word either in the standard model of fundamental particles or in any actual form of string theories. He foresees the possibility that the SSC (Superconducting Super-Collider) might reveal the existence of new strong forces and of particles with masses of the order of a trillion electron volts. Undoubtedly, such findings would revolutionize physics and make short shrift of existing theories about its final form as well. Weinberg's claim that the final form of physics should be based on symmetry considerations had been voiced by Heisenberg. That those considerations should be necessarily true has been insisted upon by Einstein and others. Physics is made to expropriate the role of a heedless metaphysics in Weinberg's claim that "the aim of physics at its most fundamental level is not just to describe the world but to explain why it is the way it is."[28] In making this claim Weinberg echoes an already old and dubious cliché. The immediately weakest point of Weinberg's dicta lies in the strong emphasis he puts on the perfectly symmetrical character of the theory. He fails to note that only a nature with built-in asymmetry can accomodate physical events. The futility of his hope about the necessarily true character of the basic postulates (even if they are not cast in mathematical form) will transpire shortly.

In spite of its reservations, Weinberg's book will hardly temper a state of mind which received its best characterization in 1964, just after the discovery of the ϕ mesons, first predicted in 1962. High-energy physicists, so stated an editorial in *The New Scientist*, will probably be in for a great shock or two if they continue "walking around with a slightly hysterical look as though they are actually witnessing the apple landing on Newton's head."[29] If not hysterical, at least supremely confident faces could be seen whenever one attended a lecture by the architects of GUT, that is, Grand Unified Theory, to say nothing of the proponents of TOE, or the Theory of Everything. The complacent attitude could strike as something unwholesome even science news reporters, who, just as reporters of general news, are not particularly sensitive to what is a healthy development or not, provided the development is something novel. It seems, however, that a long-shared complacency merely surfaced in full force at the Twentieth International Conference on High Energy Physics, held at the University of Wisconsin in September 1980. There a physicist was heard stating that he was already looking for something to do when physics was over. If Dietrick E. Thomsen, a science-news reporter of some standing, was not amused, it was partly because the physicist in question was not alone in voicing the view that physics would soon be turned over to chemists to work out details in a completed edifice:

> The views expressed here may be those of a minority. It is nevertheless significant that physicists of some reputation would express such views out loud and without demanding that they be off the record. And these attitudes are supported by a general complacency that seemed to pervade the meeting, becoming almost as deep as the Marianas Trench.[30]

Of course, the science-news reporter in question was wrong in contrasting that complacent atmosphere with the one dominating earlier decades where, according to him,

> Physicists waited expectantly to see whether experiment would confirm the theoretical predictions. They wondered where a breaking point might come that would necessitate some serious amendment. Then they passed to expecting that the experiment would confirm theory but leaving room in their minds for the possibility of an overthrow. Now they seem toweringly confident.[31]

The fact is, however, that leading physicists have not, for the most part, expected such an overthrow for much of the last hundred or so years, although that time-span has been marked by revolutions in physics.

The purpose of this essay is not, however, to speculate about the near or far future of physics in the sense in which that science-news reporter did. For it is sheer speculation to say that

> Physics may be over. Or it may be in the doldrums waiting for a new storm to blow up. We may already have seen the first catspaw winds of that new storm, but we may not know it yet. We could be in for 20 years of complacency in physics, during which all the bright young minds go into chemistry. Or a hurricane could strike next week.[32]

This is all pure speculation and, in a sense, useless for a very profound reason relating to the very nature of physics. That nature holds greater depths than the method which proved so effective in bringing about the unification of various forces in physics. The method consists in postulating exchange particles whose experimental discovery demands ever more powerful accelerators. It was in this connection that Prof. Wilczek at the Institute for Advanced Study in Princeton has recently remarked that the next step along that method would demand an accelerator as big and as powerful as a galaxy.

Clearly, such an accelerator cannot be built on earth. Conceivably a method may be found of making use of the accelerating energy of a galaxy to test the truth of the unification of gravitational force with the three other forces, or the Theory of Everything. But even then the everything will not be tested. Even then there will be no assurance that the physical universe has no more surprises in store. From the viewpoint of empirical testability, a factor decisive in physics, a final or last word in physics will forever elude the physicist. He can never have the assurance that nothing basically new could ever turn up as long as research goes on.

If not empirically, then perhaps theoretically the prospect of formulating the last word in physics might be a possibility. Indeed, it is this possibility that inspires all those physicists whom I have quoted as holding out the immediate or remote prospect about formulating such a last word. Usually they base their hope on the effectiveness of some principle of symmetry or simplicity or the combination of such principles. Heisenberg himself thought that "the future theory of matter will probably contain, as conceived in Plato's philosophy, only assumptions of symmetry. Already now these assumptions of symmetry can be stated to a large extent; they seem to show that the future theory will be very simple and concise in its fundamentals, despite all complications of its inferences."[33]

Heisenberg's invocation of Plato contains more than meets the eye. First, Plato closely tied his assumptions of symmetry to geometrical simplicity. This is why he thought that it was possible to reconstruct the physical universe in terms of the five simple, that is, perfect, geometrical bodies. Second, he took the simplicity of geometry, or mathematics, as he knew it, for an a priori truth. When more than two thousand years later mathematics suddenly grew immensely more complicated, and with branches that had been developed with no concern for the physical world, leading mathematicians felt the need to trace those branches to a common and very simple source.

The way to achieve this was the arithmetization of mathematics. Progress seemed to be so great around the end of the 19th century that Poincaré declared at the Second International Congress of Mathematics in 1900 that "absolute rigor has been attained."[34] Two decades later many followed Hilbert in looking at his infinite-dimensional space as the means that would "banish once and for all widespread doubts about the certainty of mathematical conclusions."[35]

The rest is well known, at least for mathematicians. Physicists may constitute, in this respect too, a different subclass of *homo sapiens*. By 1976 I had spent two decades studying the history of physics, a study that gradually weakened my surprise on finding this or that physicist holding rather strange views or being ignorant of something obvious. Yet I still feel keenly the surprise I felt as a participant on a panel of six (three of them Nobel laureates) who discussed the nature of the physical universe for two days before an audience of two thousand. Following Prof. Gell-Mann's lecture, in which he made the confident prediction I have recalled above, it was my turn to offer a brief comment. In it I claimed that no final theory of physics can be truly final because of Gödel's theorems of incompleteness.[36]

Gödel's theorems need not be recounted here. In sum they show that even in arithmetic, this presumably simplest form of mathematics, one cannot achieve self-consistent systematization. The proof of the consistency of the system lies of necessity in an assumption not contained within the original set of assumptions or postulates. The application of this to any sufficiently broad physical theory should be obvious. Such a theory is in part empirical and in part mathematical. That in its empirical part the theory cannot claim finality has already been shown. Because of Gödel's theorems the physical theory, however successful, cannot, insofar as it is mathematical, have its proof of consistency within itself. It is, however, the consistency of a mathematical theory that should assure its finality. The physical theory may seem at a given time to cope with all known phenomena, but it will not contain, either empirically or theoretically, the very reason for its being so successful.

Nothing is more fashionable than to use Gödel's theorems as a proof that nothing can be certain. Such a use of Gödel's theorems is, of course, self-contradictory as long as Gödel's theorems are valid. The real lesson of Gödel's theorems goes well beyond physics.[37] Of course, in this age when so much, at times almost everything, is expected from physics (and by extension from biophysics and biochemistry), it may be useful to keep in mind that physics cannot be sure of its own last word, even if it is ever formulated. In this age of quantitative preoccupations it is useful to recall that mathematics can have its proof of consistency only in what is often called meta-mathematics by mathematicians. Instead they should call that meta-mathematics what it truly is, plain metaphysics. Mathematicians rely on metaphysics whenever they utter a single word to other mathematicians. To take the external world for a reality existing independently of human words is an exercise in metaphysics. The same is true of any human word insofar as every human word is a universal, a level far above the purely sensory level.

Metaphysics has never been a subject favored by physicists and for some good reasons. The metaphysics, mostly Kantian and Hegelian, of modern times, generated that Naturphilosophie which was obscurantism from start to end. For all that, metaphysics remains indispensable even for physicists. They too, like anyone else, are subject to the logic of the first step taken. The last word they may never utter even in physics and, even if by some good luck they ever stumble upon it, they cannot be sure about its being the last. But they can always know the consequences of the first word they speak. Heisenberg took mathematical formulas for the first word and generated, within two generations, the theorizing in which the universe becomes a mere statistical formula.

A generation earlier, Ernst Mach urged, with no small success, his fellow physicists to take sensations, instead of objective external reality, for the first word. In warning against Mach, Einstein remained very much on the surface with his words that on the basis of Mach's philosophy one can at best write a telephone directory. The warning which Planck delivered in his famous lecture at the University of Leiden in 1908 against Mach and Machists (still around in the form of logical and illogical positivists of all sorts) touched real depths. No wonder. The lecture came to a close with the hallowed words: "By their fruits you shall know them."[38]

[1] As set forth by Harper himself in his *The Trend in Higher Education* (Chicago: University of Chicago Press, 1905).

[2] A vigor including an element of ruthlessness, as exemplified in Rockefeller's endorsement, in a speech given, on February 2, 1905, to the Y. M. C. A. of Brown University, of the snipping of many rosebuds (business enterprises) if the "most beautiful rose" is to be obtained. For details see my Gifford Lectures, *The Road of Science and the Ways to God* (Chicago: University of Chicago Press, 1978), pp. 300 and 447.

[3] See *The Scientific Papers of James Clerk Maxwell*, ed. W. D. Niven (Cambridge: University Press, 1890), vol. 2, p. 775. In the same context Maxwell also stated that "whatever difficulties we may have in forming a consistent idea of the constitution of the aether, there can be no doubt that the interplanetary and interstellar spaces are not empty but are occupied by a material substance or body," that is, the ether. For further instances of unconditional endorsements of the existence of the ether by classical physicists, see my *The Relevance of Physics* (Chicago: University of Chicago Press, 1966), pp. 79-85 and 169-170.

[4] H. Poincaré, *Science and Hypothesis* (New York: Dover, 1952), p. 170.

[5] W. Thomson, *Baltimore Lectures* (Baltimore: Publication Agency of Johns Hopkins University, 1904), p. 486.

[6] This and subsequent quotations are taken from *The University of Chicago. Founded by John D. Rockefeller. Annual Register. July 1, 1892 - July 1, 1893. With announcements for 1893-4.* (Chicago: University of Chicago Press, 1893), pp. 81-82. Hardly any change was made in the text as it appeared in the Registers for 1893-94 (pp. 11617), for 1894-95 (pp. 150-51), for 1895-96 (pp. 159-60), for 1896-97 (pp. 282-83), for 1897-98 (pp. 292-93), for 1898-99 (pp. 297-98), for 1899--1900 (pp. 274-75), for 1905-06 (pp. 245-46), for 1906-07 (pp. 239-40). The text was dropped almost in its entirety in the Register for 1907-08 (p. 330). Robert A. Millikan was a member of the Department from 1896 on.

[7] Kundt's remark was given wide circulation by being echoed by F. Kohlrausch.

[8] W. Thomson, "Electrical Units of Measurements" (1883), in his *Popular Lectures and Addresses* (London: Macmillan, 1891-94), vol. 1, pp. 72-73.

[9] A. Eddington, *Space, Time, and Gravitation* (Cambridge: University Press, 1920), p. 201.

[10] A. Einstein, *Out of My Later Years* (New York: Philosophical Library, 1950), p. 58.

[11] As stated by Bacon in the Preface and aphorism 61 of Book I of his *New Organon*. For further details see my *The Road of Science*, pp. 55-56.

[12] *Dialogues of Alfred North Whitehead*, as recorded by L. Price (Boston: Little Brown and Company, 1954), p. 345. (September 11, 1945).

[13] Ibid., p. 345-46. Whitehead spoke in much the same vein to L. Price on December 15, 1939 (ibid., p. 131) and June 3, 1943 (ibid., p. 215).

[14] Ibid., p. 346.

[15] Ibid.

[16] Ibid.

[17] The least facetious assertion of Einstein to that effect is in his contribution, "Über den gegenwärtigen Stand der Feldtheorie," to *Festschrift Prof. Dr. A. Stodola überreicht* (Zurich: Orell Füssli Verlag, 1929): "In all such cases the matter turns on grasping the empirical law as a logical necessity. Once one assumes the basic hypothesis of molecular kinetic theory, one realizes in a sense that God himself could not have established those connections otherwise than as they actually exist, just as it was in no way possible for him to turn the number four into a prime number" (p. 127).

[18] W. Heisenberg, "Über den anschaulichen Inhalt der quantentheoretischen Kinematik und Mechanik," *Zeitschrift für Physik*, 43 (1927), p. 197. For a detailed criticism of Heisenberg's reasoning, see my essay, "Determinism and Reality," in *Great Ideas Today 1990* (Chicago: Encyclopedia Britannica, 1990), pp. 277-302; reprinted here as ch. 6.

[19] E. Schrödinger, *What Is Life? and Other Scientific Essays* (Garden City, N.Y.: Doubleday, 1956), p. 83.

[20] C. P. Snow, *The Search* (Indianapolis: Bobbs-Merill Company, 1935), p. 179.

[21] R. B. Leighton, *Principles of Modern Physics* (New York: McGraw-Hill, 1959), pp. 678-79.

[22] At the Nobel Conference held at Gustavus Adolphus College, St Peter, Minnesota.

[23] Quoted in *Time*, Sept. 15, 1961, p. 83.

[24] R. J. Oppenheimer, *The Constitution of Matter* (Eugene: Oregon State System of Higher Education, 1956), p. 31.

[25] Quoted in *Newsweek*, (Aug 24, 1959), p. 82.

[26] W. Heisenberg, *Philosophical Problems of Nuclear Science*, tr. F. C. Hayes (London: Faber, 1952), p. 101.

[27] S. Weinberg, *Dreams of a Final Theory* (New York: Pantheon Books, 1992), see especially pp. 17-18.

[28] Ibid, p. 219. Weinberg expects the final theory to explain "everything from turbulence to thought" (p. 18). If such is the case, what explains the final theory? Something else than thought?

[29] P. T. Mathews in *The New Scientist*, Feb. 19, 1964.

[30] D. E. Thomsen, "Does the Buck Stop at the Quark?" *Science News*, 118 (Oct. 4, 1980), p. 220.

[31] Ibid.

[32] Ibid., p. 222. The complacency deplored by Thomsen does not, of course, transpire in the three hundred or so papers presented at that Conference, available in two heavy volumes, *High Energy Physics - 1980 (XX International Conference, Madison, Wisconsin)*, ed. L. Durand and L. G. Pondrom (New York: American Institute of Physics, 1981). Such a discrepancy, which is significant for the historian of science, will be implied by the published version of papers presented at the XXV High Energy Physics International Conference, Aug. 2 - 8, 1990, at Singapore National University. I base this prediction on a remark made by Professor György Marx, of the Eotvos Lorant University, Budapest, following the delivery of this paper, in Hungarian, at the Hungarian Academy of Sciences, on November 7, 1990. According to Prof. Marx, a participant at that Conference, many physicists there viewed the success of the standard model with a sort of foreboding that it may represent that very last word which greatly reduces the chances of making further discoveries.

[33] Quoted in *Time* May 5, 1958, p. 53.

[34] H. Poincaré, "Du rôle de l'intuition et de la logique en ma-thématiques," in *Compte rendu du deuxième congrès internationale des mathématiciens*, ed. E. Duporcq (Paris: Gauthier-Villars, 1902), p. 122.

[35] D. Hilbert, "Die logischen Grundlagen der Mathematik," *Gesammelte Abhandlungen*, III (Berlin: Springer, 1935), p. 178.

[36] As I have argued in various contexts, beginning with the publication of my *The Relevance of Physics*, see especially pp. 127-30.

[37] For further details, see ch. 4. "Gödel's Shadow" in my *God and the Cosmologists* (Edinburgh: Scottish Academic Press; Washington DC: Regnery Gateway, 1989).

[38] M. Planck, "The Unity of the Physical Universe," in *A Survey of Physics: A Collection ot Lectures and Essays*, tr. R. Jones and D. H. Williams (London: Methuen, 1925), p. 26.

Index of Names

(continued from p. ii)

By the same author

The Physicist as Artist: The Landscapes of Pierre Duhem

The Absolute beneath the Relative and Other Essays

The Savior of Science
(Wethersfield Institute Lectures, 1987)

Miracles and Physics

God and the Cosmologists
(Farmington Institute Lectures, Oxford, 1988)

The Only Chaos and Other Essays

The Purpose of It All
(Farmington Institute Lectures, Oxford, 1989)

Catholic Essays

Cosmos in Transition: Studies in the History of Cosmology

Olbers Studies

Scientist and Catholic: Pierre Duhem

Universe and Creed

Genesis 1 through the Ages

Is There a Universe?

* * *

Translations with introduction and notes:

The Ash Wednesday Supper (Giordano Bruno)

*Cosmological Letters on the Arrangement
of the World Edifice* (J.-H. Lambert)

Universal Natural History and Theory of the Heavens (I. Kant)

Note on the Author

Stanley L. Jaki, a Hungarian-born Catholic priest of the Benedictine Order, is Distinguished University Professor at Seton Hall University, South Orange, New Jersey. With doctorates in theology and physics, he has for the past thirty years specialized in the history and philosophy of science. The author of thirty books and nearly a hundred articles, he served as Gifford Lecturer at the University of Edinburgh and as Fremantle Lecturer at Balliol College, Oxford. He has lectured at major universities in the United States, Europe, and Australia. He is an honorary member of the Pontifical Academy of Sciences, *membre correspondant* of the Académie Nationale des Sciences, Belles-Lettres et Arts de Bordeaux, and the recipient of the Lecomte du Nouy Prize for 1970 and of the Templeton Prize for 1987